This, sometimes considered the greatest of the Icelandic Sagas, appears for the first time in an English version that reflects that swift dramatic terseness and vivid character-drawing which make the saga-style in prose narrative a model to the world. The introduction and notes are designed for the general reader, who will find in this book a guide on the threshold of a fascinating realm of literature and history, which, though the birthright of Englishmen, has hitherto been curiously unknown to them.

EGIL'S SAGA

*DONE INTO ENGLISH
OUT OF THE ICELANDIC WITH
AN INTRODUCTION, NOTES, AND AN
ESSAY ON SOME PRINCIPLES
OF TRANSLATION*

BY

E. R. EDDISON

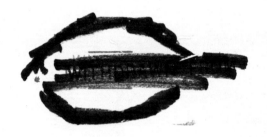

CAMBRIDGE
AT THE UNIVERSITY PRESS
1930

Cambridge University Press
Fetter Lane, London

New York
Bombay, Calcutta, Madras
Toronto
Macmillan

Tokyo
Maruzen Company, Ltd

PRINTED IN GREAT BRITAIN

To

MY DAUGHTER
JEAN
AND TO A NOBLE ICELANDIC LADY,
SVAVA ÞÓRHALLSDÓTTIR
OF *Hvanneyri*

I DEDICATE THIS BOOK

CONTENTS

viii **Contents**

Contents ix

PREFACE

EGIL SKALLAGRIMSON of Burg is the main actor in this history, not its author. Who its author may have been we do not know, and probably never shall. The time is a thousand years ago: the place the northlands, generally Norway or Iceland. Certain famous scenes (the battle of Wina-heath and the great drama of the *Höfuðlausn* in Eric's hall at York) are staged in England, and this in itself may be thought to give this saga a special interest to English readers. But quite apart from such accidents of staging, no Englishman, I think, can read the book attentively without becoming aware that this is not a foreign book but curiously his own, curiously English. The accent and manner of the story, the characters in it, their instincts and reactions and, in a subtle and fundamental way, their whole outlook on life, seem native to us; and if this is surprising it is only because we have grown accustomed to regard as distinctively English many qualities that have come down to us through the Norse strain in our ancestry.

The present edition is meant first for the man in the street, and only secondarily for the expert or scholar. The Icelandic sagas, of which *Egil's Saga* is one of the most important, are documents of interest to inquirers in many fields, history, anthropology, comparative law and custom, philology. That interest they hold in common with a thousand musty chronicles. But the sagas have another quality which they share only with a few of the great literary masterpieces of the world: the quality of vivid, unstaled and undauntable life. If they are to-day, after so many hundred years, still read and re-read in every farmhouse in Iceland, it is from no obsession with the bones of a dead past, but because the sagas are replete with individual character and action; because they are swift, direct, dramatic; because on their pages real men and women play out their everyday existence on the stage of the world uninterrupted by extraneous judgement or comment, and disguised by no specious but false lightings of romance.

The general reader, then, I have had mainly in mind. For his sake I have kept the pages of the translation free from the distraction of footnotes: I have confined the Notes at the end largely to points the elucidation of which is helpful towards the fullest enjoyment of the story and (a very different and much more troublesome matter) an understanding of the verses which occur here and there: I have included in the Introduction such general facts about the settlement of Iceland by the Northmen, the state of society in the North in the heroic age, and the nature of the classic literature as such a reader may be interested to know of if he takes up the book with no previous knowledge of the subject. Further I have, by the addition of genealogical trees, chapter-headings, and a carefully framed index, done all I could to smooth away what is the only serious obstacle met with on a first acquaintance with the sagas: the difficulty on a first reading of carrying in one's mind the many different persons, and sorting out the major from the minor characters.

Egil's Saga has not hitherto been available to English readers. A previous attempt to translate it was made, some thirty-five years ago, by the Rev. W. C. Green. It is to be feared that the translator little understood the qualities of his original or the difficulties of his task. His version (now out of print) in its flaccid paraphrasing, its lack of all sense of style, its latinized constructions, and (a comparatively venial offence) its foolish and unavowed expurgations, conveys no single note or touch of the masterpiece with which he was dealing.

I have based my translation on Dr Finnur Jónsson's text in his latest edition published at Copenhagen, 1924.

I wish to place on record my obligations to the many people who have helped me in this work. First, to Mr Bogi Ólafsson, teacher of English in the Grammar School at Reykjavík, who has given me the inestimable assistance of his criticisms of my renderings after reading the whole of my manuscript through in its first draft. Thanks to his generous help, I can at least be sure that my text is free from the grosser mistakes which must otherwise have crept into it. Secondly, to Professor Sigurður Nordal, whose own new annotated edition of the original was unfortunately not available in time for me to make use of it in preparing my Notes. He has however kindly read in MS both the Introduction and the Terminal Essay, in both of which, and in the Notes, there is much that owes its existence to his inspiration and learning. Among others to whom I am indebted are Dame Bertha Phillpotts, for her constant interest and encouragement; Sir Henry Newbolt; Professor Haakon Shetelig; and Mr Gerald Hayes for the beautiful maps he has designed and given me. I also thank Dr Finnur Jónsson, for courteously authorizing me to make use of the valuable material embodied in his editions of *Egils Saga*; Messrs Bernard Quaritch, for giving me full authority to quote from their *Saga Library*, which, besides containing Morris's magnificent (indeed, the only readable) translations of such important sagas as the *Ere-Dwellers* (*Eyrbyggja*) and the *Heimskringla*, affords in its concluding volume a mine of useful historical and critical information; Messrs Longmans Green and Co. and the Trustees of the late William Morris, for allowing me to quote from *Grettir the Strong* and *Three Northern Love Stories*; Professor E. V. Gordon and the Clarendon Press for permission to quote a passage from his *Introduction to Old Norse*; Messrs Longmans (again), the Syndics of the Cambridge University Press, and Count Hermann Keyserling together with his publisher, Mr Jonathan Cape, as regards quotations from R. L. Stevenson, the *Cambridge Medieval History*, and the *Travel Diary of a Philosopher* respectively. To Mr Cape I am also obliged for his agreement to my including in the Introduction my version of part of the *Völospá*, originally printed in my historical novel *Styrbiorn the Strong*. Finally, I am grateful to Mr Walter de la Mare for letting me use on a fly-leaf (see p. xvi) words of his which, though written in another context, sum up far better than could any words of mine the peculiar genius of the sagas.

Of Egil's personal character the saga and the specimens of his own poetry which it preserves can speak more eloquently than any latter-day translator. I will only say that the school of criticism which questions the veracity of the saga on the ground that (for example) the gouger out of Armod's eye could not in nature be also the tender and sublime poet of the *Sonatorrek*, is a school that knows little of humanity. In his pride, his reckless violence, his selfishness, as well as in his love of his art and in his simple faith that God is on his side and that those who disagree with him are therefore patently *hostes humani generis*, he stands side by side with Benvenuto Cellini. It is never to be said of Egil, whatever his faults, that he was a little man; or a liar; or a man without "kinship with the stars".

E. R. E.

71, BEDFORD GARDENS

CAMPDEN HILL, W.

September 1930

Μνάσεσθαί τινά φαμι καὶ ὕστερον ἄμμεων.

SAPPHO

"Not one overt word of horror or of warning or of admonishment, only the bare clear record; but beyond it the poising of scales so delicate and so sure that the secrets of every heart are revealed and the judgement never in doubt."

WALTER DE LA MARE

(from *Desert Islands*: on the romance enshrined in the Old Testament)

INTRODUCTION

THE HEROIC AGE AND THE SAGAS

OF the five major *Íslendinga Sögur* (*Njála, Egla, Laxdæla, Eyrbyggja,* and *Grettla*) Egil's is at once the most aristocratic in spirit, the most pagan, and (with the single exception of *Njála*) the most perfect as a work of art. That is as much as to say that it is, of all five, the most typically Icelandic. For Iceland means three things: first, on the political field—aristocratic individualism of an uncompromising kind; secondly, in its broad outlook on human life and destiny—paganism; and thirdly, in art—a peculiar and in itself highly perfected form of prose narrative. When we consider that the growing time, the flowering and the decay of this Iceland were comprised within a period beginning in the ninth century in the reign of Alfred the Great, and ending in the thirteenth, it is clear that the whole thing was only made possible by the accident of the physical isolation of Iceland from the rest of Europe. For there was no room in mediaeval Europe for an aristocracy not feudal but anarchical, or for a paganism so deep and so tolerant that it lived on, essentially unchanged, for generations after it had adopted as its own the formulas and practices of christianity. These things could not have developed in a society exposed at close quarters to the huge impersonal ideals of Empire and Papacy and to the all-embracing system of dogma and ethic of the mediaeval church; while the dead weight of Latin culture made it impossible for an original literature, owing nothing to Greece or Rome, to spring up and attain to classic perfection in the vulgar tongue.

It is as a background to *Egil's Saga*, which is the main figure in our picture, that I propose now to sketch roughly what seem to me the essential features of this profoundly interesting piece of landscape which, in the country of the mind, we may call Iceland. The sketch must be meagre and inadequate; it contains, I am afraid, nothing that is new; but I shall do my best to see that it contains nothing that is not true.

THE REPUBLIC

Politically, we may say that it was King Harald Hairfair who created the Icelandic commonwealth; not by his will, indeed, but by his act. He broke down by conquest the old order in Norway, and raised up in its place a central and autocratic power wielded by himself as sole King through subordinates, his own creatures and instruments. To the old nobility this change was the greatest of evils: in every folkland instead of their old folk-king, not much beyond themselves in power and honour, to whom they owed a loose allegiance and upholding in war, they were now faced with Harald's earl and tax-gatherer. Most hateful of all was the King's claiming of the odal rights, the freehold land-rights by which the land followed the family from generation to generation. He took away these odal rights, and gave them back only in return for taxes and other services. The great men (including small kings, earls, hersirs, and landowners of lesser rank) had therefore the choice of three things: to withstand the King in battle, to renounce their freedom and become his men, or to flee the land. The first was shown by repeated experience, extending over some twelve years and ending with the great sea-fight at Hafrsfirth, to be impossible. The second was accepted by many. But there were large numbers who preferred the third choice, to leave the country. "Because of that unpeace many noble men fled from their lands out of Norway; some east over the Keel, some West-over-the-sea. Some there were withal who in winter kept themselves in the South-isles* or the Orkneys, but in summer harried in Norway and wrought much scathe in the kingdom of Harald the King" (Eb. 1)[†]. But after Hafrsfirth, Harald cleared out the vikings in their western lairs and set his own earls in the Orkneys. Men had then to turn their eyes to more distant lands, and it was at this time, about 874, that Iceland was discovered. To that hard and lonely island in the high Atlantic there was for the next two generations an almost continuous stream of settlement from Norway, both direct and by way of the western lands. By the end of that time the country was stocked with a population of perhaps 50,000.

---

* I.e. the Hebrides.   † For List of Abbreviations see p. 227.

A small population: but so was Athens small, and the Greek cities of Ionia. Eugenically, it may be doubted whether any country in history has possessed a population of a higher quality. For the men who settled Iceland were precisely the pick and flower of the Norse race; precisely those whose fierce spirit of independence and freedom could not abide the new 'enslavement' in Norway, and who chose loss of lands and goods, and banishment in an unknown country, rather than go under King Harald's hand. To match the circumstances we must picture the sailing of a *Mayflower* not in Stuart but in Elizabethan times, and give her for passengers not William Penn and his Pilgrim Fathers, but, driven from England by some strange tyranny till then unheard of, men of the mind and temper of Raleigh and Drake, Sidney and Marlowe.

Thus Harald Hairfair, intent on consolidating his kingdom in Norway, had laid the foundations, far across the seas, of the Ionia of the North. The process is described, not in general terms but vividly in the actions and clashes of individual persons, in the first twenty-seven chapters of our saga. In the tragedy of Thorolf Kveldulfson (Egil's father's brother) and in the events leading to the decision of old Kveldulf and his family to leave Norway and start again in Iceland, is gathered up the whole history of the quarrel between the King and the great houses. The new land was apt by nature for the strange republic it was destined to nurture. Habitable enough and generally of a temperate climate in the dales and open country towards the coast, it rose inland to a high central region of dreadful wolds of lava and black sand and stone and fog and snow, where sometimes a traveller must carry every handful of fodder for his horses; for that desert of many days' journey supports neither man nor beast. There were thus great distances within the land, and great physical barriers, so that each man might in a manner be king in his own countryside: and so, in a manner, he was.

The first settlers (landnámamenn) took land far and wide in the districts where they put in with their ships, if they liked the look of it; afterwards they portioned it out in estates among their friends and dependents, as Skallagrim did with his great land-takings in Burgfirth, chs. xxviii–xxx. The settler himself was by general acceptance lord of the countryside, and temple-priest. *Goði*, which is commonly and properly translated 'priest', had under the old faith no sacerdotal connotation: the 'priest' was squire and parson in one. The position is well illustrated by the account of the settlement of the Thorsness country in Snaefellsness by Thorolf Mostbeard, the great-grandfather of Snorri the Priest. Thorolf was lord of the island of Most in the west of Norway, and "had the ward of Thor's temple there in the island, and was a great friend of Thor". He gave aid to Biorn, an outlaw of King Harald's, and so came under the wrath of the King. He "made a great sacrifice, and asked of Thor his well-beloved friend whether he should make peace with the King or get him gone from out the land and seek other fortunes. But the Word showed Thorolf to Iceland." He followed that Word: and when he came in his ship off Iceland, he "cast overboard the pillars of his high-seat, which had been in the temple, and on one of them was Thor carven; withal he spake over them, that there he would abide in Iceland, whereas Thor should let those pillars come aland". The wooden pillars came aland on the outermost point of a ness in Broadfirth, that has ever since been called Thorsness. "Thereafter Thorolf fared with fire through his land* out from Staff-river in the west, and east to that river which is now called Thors-river, and settled his shipmates there. But he set up for himself a great house at Templewick which he called Templestead. There he let build a temple, and a mighty house it was....To that temple must all men pay toll, and be bound to follow the temple-priest in all farings, even as are now the thingmen of chiefs. But the chief must uphold the temple at his own charges, so that it should not go to waste, and hold therein feasts of sacrifice" (Eb. 4).

The priest's neighbours and dependants were called his 'thingmen', because they followed him to the Thing or parliament, where laws were made and suits tried. The Thorsness Thing was the first of these assemblies. Later, in 930, the Althing was established in the south-west beyond Mossfellsheath, as the annual meeting-place for all Iceland. It is said that a man named Grim Goatshoe travelled all over Iceland to find the

---

* A ceremony to show that henceforth the land belonged to him.

best place for the Althing, "and every man in the land here brought him a penny for it; but he gave that fee afterward to the temple". The place was chosen, no doubt, for its accessibility, but it was fitted too by its grandeur to be the seat of the hallowed Thing: the quiet lake, the three-mile black lava rampart of the Almannagjá, or Great Rift, over which the little river Axewater falls and thunders, the level water-meadows and green slopes where the chiefs had their booths, set about with lava-fields torn with profound rifts and chasms, the circling mountains. It is a remarkable evidence of the political and legal instinct which co-existed in the Icelandic mind along with its intense individualism, that for hundreds of years every man of any account in Iceland rode to this place yearly; a journey, from some parts of the country, not of days but of weeks.

This, then, was the Icelandic commonwealth: scattered communities, each owing a loose allegiance to its chief or temple-priest, held together by the bond of race and the yearly meetings of the Althing. The Icelanders had come from Norway because they were minded to be their own masters, and in no other civilized community has there been greater freedom of the individual. There was no executive government: the enforcement of the law rested, in the last resort, on private vengeance. Nor (in theory, at any rate) was the bond of priest and thingman more than a matter of honourable contract between free men, which could be terminated at will by either party. The safety of the republic lay in its physical conditions: in the absence of external aggression, and the great distances within the land. This anarchy succeeded, it is to be noted, only so long as it was not put to the strain; only so long as great men were content to be great each in his own countryside, so long as the ties of kinship remained sacred, and so long as there was wide room for all.

When these conditions were broken, the whole polity went to wreck. In the thirteenth century powerful men began to collect priesthoods, to stretch out grasping hands beyond their own confines, and aspire, like the brilliant young Sturla Sig-hvatson, to political supremacy and dominion. The house of the Sturlungs shadowed half the country with their power; then split and quarrelled among themselves: marched with armies to pitched battles on a scale that was not dreamed of in the old days. Those battles were ruinous out of all proportion to their casualty lists, for it was the great men who fought to the death while their followers were given peace. The life-blood of the land was thus let out in the bitterness of civil war. Norway, that had long in these later years watched and intrigued and waited, stepped in at last. If a moment should be fixed for the passing away of the Icelandic republic, it might fitly be the night of the 22nd September, 1241, when Snorri Sturlason, historian and politician, youngest and most famous of the three Sturlung brothers, was stabbed to death in his house at Reykholt by murderers hired by his own son-in-law at the setting on of the King of Norway.

THE GODS

The reader who wishes to inform himself more closely of the character of the old Northern religion, the faith brought by the settlers to Iceland, cannot do better than turn to the ancient mythical and didactic poems of the *Elder Edda* such as the *Völospá*, the *Hávamál*, *Grímnismál*, etc., in Vigfusson and York Powell's translations, *C.P.B.* vol. I, and to the chapter by Dame Bertha Phillpotts on 'Germanic Heathenism' in vol. II of the *Cambridge Medieval History*, and Professor Chadwick's chapter on the old religion in his *Heroic Age* (Cambridge University Press). I would also refer him, were it available in English, to the brilliant monograph lately published by Professor Nordal on *The faith of Egil Skallagrimson* based on the evidence of the *Sonatorrek*.

Explicitly, there is very little about religion in the sagas. What there is, seems to show that in Iceland Thor was more widely worshipped than any other God, and after Him, Frey. Out of every five settlers, one has a name beginning with 'Þór'. It is recorded that when the Northmen came to Iceland they found there some Irish hermits who "afterwards went away because they would not be here with heathen men".*

There was among the settlers a small leaven of christianity:

* Ari, *Libellus Islandorum*, ch. I. Cf. Landn.

e.g. Queen Aud, who settled Laxriverdale, was a christian. But this quickly died out. Taking all the evidence into account, it is fair to conclude that even among its avowed adherents christianity had as yet struck no deep roots. Of such adherents the famous settler Helgi the Lean is probably a fair example: "He was much mixed in his faith: he trowed on Christ and named his homestead after Him; and yet called he upon Thor on sea voyages and in hard occasions, and in all things whereso he thought most rested on it" (Landn). This independence of attitude is, indeed, characteristic. We see it in Egil himself, in the *Sonatorrek*, where he not only expresses a desire to be given a chance of punishing Aegir, the God of the sea, for the destruction of his son, but says he has a mind to give over worshipping Odin Himself because He has broken faith with him and cast him off. The same mind is shown in Hrafnkel Frey's-priest, a mighty lord in the east country, who let build a great temple and loved no other God more than Frey, and gave "his friend Frey" a half share in his horse Freyfaxi, that he thought better than any other treasure he had; but, fallen on evil days and reft of horse and honour, said: "I account that foolery, to trow in Gods"; and kept his word, and made no more blood-offerings, but in due time had vengeance on his foes and won back all his lordship (*Hrafnkel's Saga*). Also, in Sigmund Brestison of the Faereys, who, when the great Earl Hakon asked him in what God did he most trust, answered and said, "I put my trust in my own might and main" (*Færeyinga Saga*, ch. 23). In the same way Thorolf Mostbeard, in a passage already quoted (Eb. 4), is "a great friend" of Thor.

Of a future life the conceptions do not appear to have been settled. The trend of opinion is in favour of the view that the Eddic religion of Odin and Valhalla was by no means universally entertained in the North: it may have been as ancient, probably more ancient, than the cult of Thor, but it was pre-eminently a religion of kings and vikings. That Egil himself worshipped Odin is clear from the *Sonatorrek*: but there are reasons for thinking that it may have been an acquired religion in his case, not the religion to which he was brought up from birth. That Bodvar had, as Egil believed, gone to Valhalla, seems clear from the references to "the way of bliss" and "the bee's path" in the 10th and 18th staves of the *Sonatorrek*. Odin and His Hall of the Slain, where the lordly dead carouse after fight, having for cup-maids the Valkyries of the Lord of Hosts: these things are far off, away from "middle-earth" (Miðgarðr). But Thorolf Mostbeard believed that when he died he should fare into Holyfell, the little steep basaltic hill that stands abruptly up in the midst of the Thorsness peninsula, "and all his kindred from the ness" (Eb. 4); and the night that his son, Thorstein Codbiter, was drowned in Broadfirth fishing, his shepherd saw how Holyfell "was opened in the north side, and in the fell he saw mighty fires, and heard huge clamour therein, and the clank of drinking-horns; and when he hearkened if perchance he might hear any words clear of others, he heard that there was welcomed Thorstein Codbiter and his crew, and he was bidden to sit in the high-seat over against his father" (*ibid.* 11). In the same way, Gunnar of Lithend was thought to have 'died into' his howe. The neat-herd and the serving maid were driving cattle, and "they thought that he (Gunnar) was merry, and that he was singing inside the cairn". Another night, Skarphedinn and Hogni "were out of doors one evening by Gunnar's cairn on the south side. The moon and stars were shining clear and bright, but every now and then the clouds drove over them. Then all at once they thought they saw the cairn standing open, and lo, Gunnar had turned himself in the cairn and looked at the moon. They thought they saw four lights burning in the cairn, and none of them threw a shadow. They saw that Gunnar was merry, and he wore a joyful face. He sang a song...After that the cairn was shut up again" (Nj. 77). There are many other instances of this belief of 'dying into howes'. There are also cases, throughout the old literature, of 'howe-dwellers': ghosts, but of no thin astral substance: rather, solid, strong and violent ghosts, 'undead' like the mediaeval vampire, who walk abroad, ride the roofs, and slay men and cattle. A *locus classicus* is the dead shepherd Glam, in *Grettla*. It was against such walkings that precautions were taken such as those described in ch. LVIII of our saga (see note *ad loc.*), and in Eb. 33, 34.

Christianity was 'brought into the law' in the year A.D. 1000

It is clear from the accounts given in the sagas (and this is confirmed by more general considerations referred to below) that the change of faith was primarily and in substance a political proceeding based on considerations of expediency rather than on any religious movement among the people. As soon as it became plain, at the famous meeting of the Althing in the year 1000, that religious controversy was about to split the commonwealth from top to bottom, men turned to seek an expedient that should avoid the evil of two laws in the land. Snorri the Priest was the main actor here, and by his persuasion both sides were brought to lay the matter in the hands of Thorgeir the Priest of Lightwater, who was then Speaker of the Law. Thorgeir's award made christianity the law, and forbade (on pain of outlawry) heathen rites and the exposure of children: but the old worship, though forbidden in public, was to be allowed in private. It is characteristic that this statesmanlike compromise, which brought christianity into the law and preserved the cohesion of the state, was dictated by a heathen. Henceforth, though the letter of the law was christian, the pagan spirit lived on. Its persistence, many generations after the 'change of faith', is seen in the persistence of the old ways of life. Christian bishops practised polygamy and rode on raiding expeditions in the Sturlung days as freely as the great men of old. Hallfred the Troublous-skald wore his new faith so lightly that his readiest threat was to cast it off and be a heathen again if the King would not listen to his poem. But perhaps the most striking evidence of the abiding life of the pagan spirit is the impartiality and lack of christian colouring in the sagas themselves; for in no country has christianity been a tolerant religion. In *Egla*, which was probably written down in final form about the middle of the thirteenth century, it is hard to find a phrase or turn of speech which betrays the point of view of a christian telling a story of old heathen times, or which is out of tune with the mind and temper of Egil's own generation and the heroic age.

The two essential facts about the old faith which stand out clearly amid much that is doubtful and obscure are, first, its fatalism, and secondly, the relation of fellowship between men and the Gods.

Fatalism is in the deep foundations of the old Northern mythology. Beyond death, beyond the joys of Valhalla, looms the shadow of Ragnarok—of that *Dies Iræ*, when the Wolf shall be loosed and Midgard's Worm shall come, and heaven and earth and the blessed Gods themselves shall pass away in catastrophic ruin. The terrors of that Day are foretold in one of the grandest of the Eddic poems, the *Völospá*, from which, to show the spirit of doom and desolation that informs the ultimate things in this creed, I will quote some verses, beginning with the crowing of the cocks in the three worlds to usher in the "One fight more—the best and the last":

> Sate on the howe there and strake harp-string
> The Grim Wife's herdsman, glad Eggthér.
> Crow'd mid the cocks in Cackle-spinney
> A fair-red cock who Fialar hight.
> Crowéd in Asgarth Comb-o'-Gold,
> Fighters to wake for the Father of Hosts.
> But another croweth to Earth from under:
> A soot-red cock from the courts of Hell.—
> > *Garm bayeth ghastful at Gnipa's cave:*
> > *The fast must be loos'd and the Wolf fare free.*
> Things forgot know I, yea, and far things to come:
> The Twilight of the Gods; the grave of Them that conquer'd.
> Brother shall fight with brother, and to bane be turnéd:
> Sisters' offspring shall spill the bands of kin.
> Hard 'tis with the world: of whoredom mickle:
> An axe age, a sword age: shields shall be cloven;
> A wind age, a wolf age, ere the world's age founder.
> Mimir's children are astir: the Judge up standeth,
> Even with the roar of the Horn of Roaring.
> High bloweth Heimdall: the Horn is aloft;
> And Odin muttereth with Mimir's head.
> Shuddereth Yggdrasill's Ash on high,
> The old Tree groaneth, and the Titans are unchain'd.—
> > *Garm bayeth ghastful at Gnipa's cave:*
> > *The fast must be loos'd and the Wolf fare free.*
> What aileth the Aesir? What aileth the Elves?
> Thundereth all Jotunheim: the Aesir go to Thing.
> The Dwarf-kind wail afore their doors of stone,
> The rock-walls' warders.—*Wist ye yet, or what?*
> Hrym driveth from the east, holdeth shield on high.

Jormungand twisteth in Titan fury.
The Worm heaveth up the seas: screameth the Eagle:
Slitteth corpses Neb-pale: Nail-fare saileth.
A Keel fareth from the west: come must Muspell's
Legions aboard of her, and Loki steereth.
Fare the evil wights with the Wolf all;
Amidst them is Byleist's brother in their faring.
Surt from the south cometh, switch-bane in hand;
Blazeth the sun from the sword of the Death-God:
The granite cliffs clash, and the great gulfs sunder;
The Hell-dead walk the way of Hell, and the Heavens are riven.

It is against this gloomy background of fatalism and foredoom that the men and women of the sagas play out their lives. This, like a thick black shadow of darkness, shadows their every word and deed, yet leaves them proud, and practical, and unafraid. Count Hermann Keyserling has said, with profound insight, that the belief in predestination is always grandiose in effect where its disciples possess proud souls. And he speaks of the fatalism of Islam in words that might have been spoken of the Northmen: "The fatalism of the Moslem, like that of the original Calvinist, and in contradiction to that of the Russian, is the expression not of weakness but of strength. He neither trembles before the terrible God in whom he believes, nor does he hope for His particular benevolence, nor does he suffer himself to be driven at will by fate: he stands there, proud and inwardly free, opposite to the Superior Power, facing eternity with the same equanimity as he faces death".* Such a mind we see everywhere in the sagas: in the terrible Skarphedinn when, before the burning of Bergthorsknoll, he chooses the hazard of defending the house rather than fight in the open in disobedience to his aged father: "I may well humour my father in this, by being burnt indoors along with him, for I am not afraid of my death" (Nj. 127); in Kiartan, sending back his company and riding with but two followers on his last ride southward towards Laxriverdale (Ld. 48); and, in our own saga, in old Kveldulf watching the fate he from the first foreboded step by step draw nearer to his son.

* *The Travel Diary of a Philosopher*, Part III, ch. 26 (Jonathan Cape).

Of the sense of fellowship with the Gods I have already quoted instances. The nobility of this attitude of mind is well caught by Stevenson in one of his little fables, of the priest, the virtuous person, and the old rover with his axe: "At last one came running, and told them all was lost: that the powers of darkness had besieged the Heavenly Mansions, that Odin was to die, and evil triumph.

"'I have been grossly deceived', cried the virtuous person.

"'All is lost now', said the priest.

"'I wonder if it is too late to make it up with the devil?' said the virtuous person.

"'O, I hope not', said the priest. 'And at any rate we can but try.—But what are you doing with your axe?' says he to the rover.

"'I am off to die with Odin', said the rover."*

This proud pagan spirit of fatalism and fellowship with, not subservience to, the ultimate Power, is implicit throughout the saga literature. It is, in my judgement, the deep underlying rock on which the greatness of that literature, as an expression of much that is finest and noblest in the human spirit, is founded and built.

THE SAGA

So much for the foundations. The building itself is before our eyes in one of its most characteristic elevations, in the shape of *Egil's Saga*. Here I will not waste time on trying to say more briefly what has been said, rightly and once and for all, by the late W. P. Ker in his masterpiece of inspired criticism, *Epic and Romance*. To complete our background, however, it may be useful to note a few of the salient features of that peculiar form of prose narrative which is Iceland's contribution to the creative literature of the world.

A saga may be roughly defined as a prose narrative which deals dramatically with historical material, and in which the interest is concentrated upon individual persons, their characters, actions, and destinies. Rough as it is, this definition will serve to

* *The Works of Robert Louis Stevenson: Tales and Fantasies*, vol. IV, p. 372, Edinburgh, 1897.

indicate distinctions between the Icelandic prose epic and the products of other countries and other ages. A glance at some of these distinctions may be the readiest way towards an appreciation of what a saga essentially is.

The saga is like Homer in that it is heroic in matter and in spirit: it is unlike, in that it is prose, not poetry; that its interest is more purely individual (the epic opposition of Trojan and Greek has no counterpart in the sagas: how far removed are the two attitudes is seen if we contrast the treatment of that opposition by Homer with the treatment in *Egla* of the opposition of the King and the great houses); that it eschews the supernatural and the marvellous, whereas the Gods in the *Iliad* are ever present, often as protagonists in the action, and the *Odyssey* is packed with magic, monsters, portents, and supernatural beings. Moreover, swift as is the movement of Homer, the action pauses continually for the introduction of poetic ornament, simile or description. The action of the saga never pauses except for the introduction of genealogical information.

The historical books of the Old Testament are, save in the single circumstance of their being prose and not poetry, still further removed from the saga. Their outlook is national and theocratic in a far higher degree than Homer's. French Romance, again, is epically national (Christendom against the Paynim), and abounds in miracles and marvels; besides this, it presents other qualities which distinguish it sharply from the saga: its historical basis is generally flimsy, and, which is more important, history is to it not an end in itself but a framework for fancy's most rich and unrestrained embroidery; its characters are types, not individuals; its main interest, wild and strange adventure in a dreamland of chivalry and romantic love; its method, formless and luxuriantly meandering. The heroic tales of Keltic tradition, apart from the varying but always large part played in them by the mythical element, differ from the sagas more fundamentally than do even the Romances of chivalry. This is because the old Keltic heroic story is in its processes the direct opposite of the Icelandic; the instinctive idiom and figure of the one is rhetoric and hyperbole; of the other restraint and meiosis. Thus words and phrases to the Kelt, in his great scenes, are material to be poured out in a spate of eloquent emotion; in the saga, on the contrary, the expression becomes more tense and curbed as the situation heightens, until words and phrases have effect individually and apocalyptically like lightning flashes, each trailing behind it (for in this method the effect often depends less on what is said than on what is left unsaid) a turmoil of associations like rolling thunders.

There are two more masterpieces of prose narrative which we may profitably contrast with the sagas: the *Arabian Nights*, in which the action is slowed down to give leisure for the luxurious contemplation of every form of sensuous beauty; and Boccaccio's *Decameron*, in which, on the whole, plot and situation outweigh character. By the beauty of nature* the Northman (if we may judge from the sagas) set little store: by physical beauty in man and woman he set much, but was content to note it in his terse objective way, "the fairest of men to look on", seldom going into detail and never permitting it to interrupt the stride of his story. The sagas abound in dramatic situations, but they rarely excel in plot. But the briefest consideration of, for example, *Njála* or the little saga of Hrafnkel Frey's-priest, both of which are masterpieces of plot-construction, is enough to show that the plot depends for its whole life and power upon the personalities of its actors: upon Njal, Skarphedinn, Flosi and Kari and a host of living, if minor, characters in the one case, and upon Hrafnkel and Sam in the other. And we need but call to mind any great scene, such as Njal's burning or (in our own saga) the *Höfuðlausn* scene in York, to see how the whole art of dramatic situation, suspension, irony, clash of motives and of wills, and every circumstance of tragic grandeur is bent to the single-purpose of conjuring up in living reality individual men and women without whom the situation would be left meaningless or commonplace: Eric and Arinbiorn, Egil and Gunnhild.

We have not yet looked at the modern novel, nor, for that

---

* "The leaves were all gemmed with tears the clouds had dight....Earth was carpeted with flowers tinctured infinite; for Spring was come brightening the place with joy and delight; and the streams ran ringing, to the birds' gay singing, while the rustling breeze upspringing attempered the air to temperance exquisite." (*The Book of A Thousand Nights and a Night*: Story of Nur al-Din Ali and the damsel Anis al-Jalis, Burton's transl. vol. II.)

matter, at the Elizabethan drama. Here at least is to be found that preoccupation with individual character for which we have so far found no parallel outside the sagas: Squire Western, Becky Sharp, Victor Radnor, Diana of the Crossways, Nevil Beauchamp; Beatrice in *Much Ado*, Falstaff, Othello, Hamlet, Cleopatra, Vittoria Corombona, Bosola, Flamineo, Brachiano. On the whole, Shakespeare and Webster are closer to the saga in their treatment of character than are the novelists. The novel, through its protean variations from Proust to the detective story, is almost always analytic: it would be truer perhaps to say that it nearly always employs analytic processes from time to time. But the saga is never analytic. The novelist is often introspective: the saga never. Drama, on the other hand, lends itself naturally to the revelation of character by direct word and action. So that we shall more readily find in *Antony and Cleopatra* and *The White Devil* than in the pages of the novelists passages to remind us of the peculiar architectonic of the sagas, where the living characters of the persons are built up for us as in the experience of actual life, by the cumulative effect of revealing action or word; and, as in life, events that at first seem unrelated are built together to a climax, and we look back and see, only when the drama is done, the significance of things and persons that till then we may have thought irrelevant. The working out of the tragedy of King Harald Hairfair and Thorolf Kveldulfson in the first twenty-two chapters of *Egla* is a notable instance of this architectural method of narrative.

We noticed just now that physical beauty plays but a small part in the sagas. But there is a beauty too of human action, and the part assigned to this is a very great one. Professor Gordon well says: " Probably in no other literature is conduct so carefully examined and appraised; and the basis of the valuation is not moral, but aesthetic. In no other literature is there such a sense of the beauty of human conduct; indeed, the authors of Icelandic prose, with the exception of Snorri, do not seem to have cared for beauty in anything else than conduct and character. The heroes and heroines themselves had the aesthetic view of conduct; it was their chief guide, for they had a very

undeveloped conception of morality, and none at all of sin".*
We may well rub our eyes, and wonder whether we have not
dreamed ourselves back to Hellas, and the old Greek ideal of
καλὸς κἀγαθός. There is indeed a kinship between the Greek
spirit and the spirit of the sagas. Σωφροσύνη, for which we
have no word in English, is the governing law of Northern
aesthetic as it is of the Greek. It is not 'temperance', or
'moderation', drab virtues of little men negatively withholding
them from this and that. It is rather the power by which a man
may, in spirit, ride whirlwinds, but control them; may be
passionate, but not slave to passion; may (as Webster in his
Italian dramas) tread, safe and triumphantly, the perilous knife-
edge of high tragedy where it leads across gulfs of sentimentality
and melodrama which lesser poets do not dare to approach. So
it is that, just as there is a Greek restraint and perfection about
the practical actions which enthral the saga-man's mind with
their beauty, so is the speech in which he records those actions
informed with the like qualities. The best Icelandic prose is
deliberate, simple, and laconic, using the rough, salt speech of
men of their hands: direct, unselfconscious, farmer's talk,
unsophisticated, yet classic and noble, because it is the talk of a
people born with a natural instinct for language and for dramatic
narrative.

If the question is asked why Iceland, and not Norway, Sweden
or Denmark, was the home of the classic literature, it is not easy
to find any certain answer. The likeliest explanation that I am
aware of was given me in conversation by Professor Nordal. The
Norsemen, he says, were a conquering race. They came to
Iceland meaning to conquer, but found nothing to be conquered:
only barren earth and stones. They were thus in a manner
checked in mid stride. But they were not merely rough,
violent men, adventurers on wide seas, great strikers: they were
also men of great pride of birth. Balked of temporal empire,
they turned their minds to history, and, employing those gifts
of intellect and character which we have already noticed, carved
out for themselves in the country of the mind a more perdurable
kingdom, not made with hands. This seems a reasonable account

* *Old Norse,* by E. V. Gordon, p. xxxii, Clarendon Press, 1927.

of the matter, and is at least free from the folly of those who would magnify the small Keltic admixture in the blood of the early settlers in order to pray in aid Keltic ancestry as an explanation of a phenomenon which, whatever other affinities it may have, is the antithesis of anything Keltic.

And now, before we leave this brief survey of the saga and its place in literature, let us listen for a minute more especially for its underlying note. We shall hear in it, ever and again, like a great ground-bass droning always beneath the swift play of strife and the busy affairs of men, the deep consciousness of the transience of human things. Listen to it in *Egla*: Kveldulf; Thorolf in his strength and promise; old Biorgolf and his 'loose bridal' of December and May, and its unwholesome fruit; Biorgolf dead and gone; Thorolf unjustly done to death by the King he deserved well of; Kveldulf dead on his exiled voyage to the new country; his coffin cast adrift to choose a landing for his son, since life lasted not long enough for him to choose it living; Egil's birth and violent childhood, prophetic of his after life with its skaldship and its manslayings; his time in Norway, with the old tyrant dead and a new raised up; the blood-feud lulled but not ended betwixt the house of Harald Hairfair and the house of Kveldulf; a new generation where new faces appear in the old houses; Athelstane and England, and the fall of the younger Thorolf; strife again in Norway; the noble friendship of Egil and Arinbiorn, calling to mind that friendship of an earlier generation, of Thorolf Kveldulfson and Bard, that was cut short by Bard's death after Hafrsfirth; the fresh breach with Eric and Gunnhild; Iceland again, and Skallagrim's end; Egil's new journey east, and his falling into his enemies' hand at York; the great scene with the King and Queen and Arinbiorn, and the poem *Höfuðlausn*; Arinbiorn's fall, fighting for Harald Greycloak at the Neck; Egil's last great adventure on the Vermland expedition; his latter years in Iceland; his affection for his pet daughter, Thorgerd, and the skilful, humorous, loving touch with which she brought him safe out of the shadow of death after the bitter loss of his best-loved sons; his old age, "after a great life, with eyes waxing dim", with all its masterfulness, and loneliness, and hard justness, lighted like an Indian summer by his friendship with the younger poet, Einar Jingle-scale; later on, blind and helpless, ordered about by kitchen-wenches and bondwomen; the last pitiful flicker of his cunning, his greed, and his indomitable will, when he buried his treasure and covered all traces by killing with his bare hands the thralls he took to do the work; his soft natural death after fourscore years, strange in a man whose life from his youth up was all battles and dangers; and, for a farewell, Egil's bones dug up years afterwards and wondered at for their bigness, beyond the wont of men.

We may think of that old saying: *Tout passe, tout casse, tout lasse*. The passing away of all human things both good and bad, the breaking at length of all we care for here on earth; it is this that the deep ground-bass of the saga drones of, ceaselessly, like the ceaseless rumour of the sea. But of that last cry, *tout lasse!* there is no note, listen we never so closely. The strong Northern spirit, looking with clear eyes upon the shifting pageant of death and birth, has not, it would seem, been able so much as to imagine this last betrayal of life, this whimper of little men defeated by destiny.

NOTE

The small figures in the text refer to the Miscellaneous Notes at the end, pp. 252 to 311.

As regards proper names, it may be noted that in Icelandic

(1) G is never soft as in English *gaol*;

(2) the diphthongs EI and EY are pronounced as in English *rein*, *they*, not as in German.

EGIL'S SAGA

CHAPTER I. OF KVELDULF AND HIS SONS.

THERE was a man named Wolf, the son of Bialfi and of
Hallbera, daughter of Wolf the Fearless; she was sister
to Hallbiorn Half-troll in Hrafnista, the father of Ketil
Haeng.

Wolf was a man so big and strong that there were none to
match him. And when he was in his youthful age he lay out
a-viking[1] and harried. With him was in fellowship that man that
was called Berdla-Kari: a worshipful man and the greatest man
of prowess both for doing and daring. He was a berserk.[2] He
and Wolf had but one purse, and there was betwixt them the
lovingest friendship. But when they gave over their harrying,
then went Kari to his own place in Berdla. He was a man exceeding wealthy. Kari had three children: his sons were named
Eyvind Lambi, the one, and the other Oliver Hnufa;[3] his
daughter's name was Salbiorg. She was the most beautiful of
women and a great lady,[4] and her Wolf won to wife. Thereafter
went he likewise to his own place.

Wolf was a man wealthy both in lands and loose goods. He
took style and state of a landed man,[5] like as had his father done
before him, and became a man of might. So is it said, that Wolf
was a great man in his housekeeping. That was his wont, to rise
up betimes and so go among his men at their tasks or where his
smiths were and overlook his stock and his tillage; and at whiles
would he be talking with men, those who needed his counsel.
Well he knew how to lay good counsel to every need, for he was
very wise. But every day when it drew toward evening, then
would he begin to be sulky, so that few men might come to
speech with him. He was evening-sleepy; and that was the talk
of men, that he was exceeding shape-strong.[6] He was called
Kveldulf.[7]

Kveldulf and his wife had two sons: the elder was named
Thorolf, and the younger, Grim.[8] And when they were waxen
up, then were they both men big and strong, like as their father

was. Thorolf was the comeliest of men and the ablest. He was like his mother's kinsfolk, a very glad man, open-handed and a man swift and eager in all things, and the most masterful of men; beloved was he of all men. Grim was a black man and an ugly, like to his father both in outward seeming and in bent of mind. He grew to be a great workman: he was a handy man with timber and iron and became the greatest of smiths. He fared besides oft in winter a-herring-fishing with his fishing boat, and many housecarles[9] along with him.

But when Thorolf was about twenty year old, then would he betake him to harrying. Kveldulf found him a long-ship.[10] To that faring set forth those sons of Berdla-Kari, Eyvind and Oliver: they had a big company and another long-ship, and fared that summer a-viking and won them fee,[11] and a great booty they had to share. That was certain summers that they lay out a-viking, but were at home in winter-time with their fathers. Thorolf had away home with him many costly treasures, and brought them to his father and mother. That was a time both good for gain and renown among men.

Kveldulf was then much in his declining age, but his sons were full grown.

CHAPTER II.   OF OLIVER AND SOLVEIG.

AUDBIORN was in that time king over the Firthfolk: Hroald was his earl[1] named, and the earl's son Thorir.[2] Then too was Atli the Slender[3] an earl: he dwelt at Gaular. His children were these: Hallstein, Holmstein, Herstein, and Solveig the Fair. That was on a time in autumn, that there was much folk in Gaular for the autumn-sacrifice.[4] Oliver Hnufa saw Solveig there, and dearly set his heart upon her. Thereafter he asked her in marriage, but the earl thought the match uneven and would not give her. Thereafter made Oliver many love-song ditties. So mightily had Oliver set his heart on Solveig that he left off his war-faring, and there were now in war-faring but Thorolf and Eyvind Lambi.

CHAPTER III. THE UPRISING OF KING HARALD HAIRFAIR.

HARALD the son of Halfdan the Black had taken heritage after his father east in the Wick. He had this oath sworn: to let not shear his hair neither comb it until he should be sole King over all Norway. He was called Harald Shockhead.[1]

And now he fought against those kings that were nighest at hand, and conquered them: and of that are long stories told. Thereafter gat he unto him the Uplands. Thence fared he north into Thrandheim,[2] and had there many battles ere he made himself sole lord over all the Thrand-lay. Thereafter he was minded to fare north into Naumdale to deal with those brethren, Herlaug and Hrollaug, who were then kings over Naumdale. But when those brethren heard tell of his faring, then went Herlaug with eleven men into that howe they had before let be a-making through three winters, and thereafter was the howe shut up again. But King Hrollaug tumbled himself out of kingdom[3] and took on him earl's estate, and went therewith under the might of Harald the King and gave up his own realm. So gat King Harald unto him the Naumdale folk and Halogaland. There set he men over his realm.

After that, King Harald set forth out of Thrandheim with a host of ships and fared south to Mere: had there a battle with King Hunthiof and had the victory. There fell Hunthiof. Then gat King Harald unto him Northmere and Raumsdale. But Solvi Klofi, the son of Hunthiof, had escaped away, and he fared into Southmere to King Arnvid, and bade his help, and said as thus: "Though this trouble have now lighted on our hand, 'twill not be long ere the same trouble shall come upon you; for Harald, I ween, will shortly hither come, soon as he hath all men thralled and enslaved, according to his will, in Northmere and in Raumsdale. You will have that same choice too before your hands that we had: either to defend your fee and freedom, and hazard thereon every man's ye have hope of aid from; and for this will I proffer myself, with mine aid, against this overweening and unjustness. But for your other choice, you must be content to take to that rede, as did the Naumdalers, to go of your own free

will into bondage and be made thralls4 of Harald. To my father
that seemed glory, to die in kingdom with honour, rather than
be made in his old age under-man unto another king. I think that
to thee, too, it so shall seem, and to others, them that show somewhat of free-board in their sailing,5 and will be men of valour".

With such-like talk was the king brought to this set resolve,
to raise forces and defend his land. He and Solvi bound them
now in league together, and sent word to King Audbiorn that
ruled over the Firthfolk, that he should come and help them.
But when the messengers came to King Audbiorn and bare him
this word-sending, then took he rede with his own friends, and
that rede they gave him all, to raise forces and go join with Mere,
even as word was sent him.

King Audbiorn let shear up the war-arrow6 and fare a host-
bidding through all his realm. He sent men to all the great men
to bid them to him. But when the king's messengers came to
Kveldulf and said unto him their errand, and this, too, that the
king will that Kveldulf come to him with all his housecarles,
then answereth Kveldulf as thus: "That may the king think
binding on me, that I fare with him if he must defend his own
land and be harried in the Firthfolk: but this count I all outside
my bond, to fare north to Mere and do battle there and defend
land of theirs. That is your swiftest to say, that Kveldulf will sit
at home through this war-rush, and he will summon no war-host,
and not make his this faring abroad to do battle against Harald
Shockhead. For I ween that Harald hath weight enough of luck7
there, where our king hath not so much as a good fistful".

The messengers fared home to the king and said unto him
their errand's speeding. But Kveldulf sat at home in his own
place.

CHAPTER IV. OF THE BATTLE OFF SOLSKEL.

KING AUDBIORN fared, with that force that followed
him, north into Mere, and fell in there with King Arnvid
and Solvi Klofi, and they had all together a mighty war-
host. King Harald was then too come from the north with his

host, and their meeting was on the inner side of Solskel. There was there a great battle, and great man-fall in either host. There fell out of Harald's host two earls, Asgaut and Asbiorn, and two sons of Hakon the Earl of Hladir,[1] Griotgard and Herlaug, and much else of men of might; but of the host of Mere fell King Arnvid and King Audbiorn. But Solvi Klofi came off by fleeing, and became thereafter a great viking, and did oft great scathe to the realm of Harald the King, and was called Solvi Klofi.

After that, Harald the King laid under him Southmere. Vemund, brother of King Audbiorn, held the Firthfolk, and made himself king thereover.

These things befell late in autumn, and men counselled King Harald that he should not fare south about Stad these autumn-days. Then set King Harald Earl Rognvald[2] over either Mere, and over Raumsdale. King Harald turned back north then into Thrandheim, and had about him great strength of men.

That same autumn the sons of Atli made an onset upon Oliver Hnufa in his house, and would slay him. They had a company so great that Oliver had no means to withstand them, but ran away and so came off. He fared then north into Mere, and there found Harald the King, and Oliver went under the hand of him and fared north to Thrandheim with the King that autumn; and he grew into the greatest loving-kindness with the King, and was with him long time afterward, and became a skald[3] of his.

That winter fared Earl Rognvald by the inland road across the Eid south to the Firths, and had espial of the goings of King Vemund, and came by night to that place that is named Naust-dale, and there was Vemund a-feasting. There Earl Rognvald took the house over their heads, and burnt the king within door with ninety men. After that, came Berdla-Kari to Earl Rognvald with a long-ship all manned, and they fared both north into Mere. Rognvald took those ships that King Vemund had had, and all those loose goods that he found. Berdla-Kari fared then north to Thrandheim to find Harald the King, and became his man.

That next spring fared King Harald south along the land with a host of ships, and laid under him the Firths and Fialir and placed in power there men of his own. He set Earl Hroald over the Firthfolk. King Harald was much heedful, when he had gotten to him those folk-lands that were new-come under his dominion, of the landed men and powerful bonders and of all those that he had doubt of, that some uprising was to be looked for from them. Then let he every one of them do one of two things: become his servants, or get them gone out of the land; and, for a third choice, suffer hard conditions, or lose their lives else; and some were maimed either of hand or foot. King Harald gat to him in every folk-land all odal rights4 and all land, dwelt and undwelt, as well as the sea and the waters; and all dwellers therein should be his tenants, be it they that worked in the forests, or salt-carles, or all manner of hunters or fishers, both by sea and by land, these were all now made tributary unto him. But from this enslavement fled many men away out of the land, and then began to be settled many waste parts far and wide, both east in Jamtaland and Helsingland and in the west countries: the South-isles, Dublin's shire in Ireland, Normandy in Valland, Caithness in Scotland, the Orkneys and Shetland, the Faereys. And in that time was found Iceland.5

CHAPTER V. OF KING HARALD'S SENDING TO KVELDULF.

HARALD the King lay with his war-host in the Firths. He sent men up and down the land there to seek out those men that had not come to him, that it seemed to him he had an errand with. The King's messengers came to Kveldulf, and found there good welcome. They bare up their errand: said that the King would that Kveldulf should come and see him. "He hath", said they, "heard tell that thou art a worshipful man and of great family: thou wilt have choice at his hand of great honours: great store setteth the King by this, to have with him those men that he heareth are men of prowess in strength and in hardihood."

Kveldulf answered and said that he was now an old man, so that he was now nought fit to be out in war-ships. "I will now sit at home, and give over serving of kings."

Then spake the messenger: "Let then thy son fare to the King. He is a big man and a soldierly.[1] The King will make thee a landed man, if thou wilt serve him".

"I will not", said Grim, "be made a landed man, while my father liveth, because he only shall be my over-man while he liveth."

The messengers went away; and when they were come to the King, they said to him all that which Kveldulf had spoken before them. The King became sulky with that, and spake but a word or two: said that these must be men of a haughty make, or what then were they minded for?

Oliver Hnufa was then stood near, and prayed the King be not wroth. "I will go and see Kveldulf and he will be willing to come and see you,[2] the instant he knoweth that you think aught lieth on it."

And now fared Oliver to see Kveldulf, and said to him that the King was wroth, and nought would do but one or other of them, father or son, must go to the King; and said that they should get great honour of the King, if they would but serve him. He spake much too of this (as true it was), that the King was good to his own men both as for fee and meeds of honour.

Kveldulf said that that was his mind's foreboding, "That we, father and sons, will get no luck with this King,[3] and I will not go to see him. But if Thorolf come home this summer, then will he be easily 'ticed to this faring, and so to become the King's man. So say unto the King, that I will be friend of his, and all men that obey my words I will hold to friendship with him. I will, too, hold that same meed of rule and stewardship under his hand as before I had of our former king, if the King will that so it be. And later on 'twill be seen what way things shape 'twixt us and the King".

And now fared Oliver back to the King and said to him that Kveldulf would send him a son of his, and said that one was of nature apter thereto who was then not at home. The King let it rest then. He fared now for the summer into Sogn, but when it began to be autumn he made ready to fare north to Thrandheim.

CHAPTER VI. HOW THOROLF KVELDULFSON WENT TO
KING HARALD.

THOROLF KVELDULFSON and Eyvind Lambi
came in the autumn home from their viking. Thorolf
went to his father. Then fall they, father and son, to
talk one to another. Thorolf asketh what hath been the errand
of those men that Harald sent thither. Kveldulf said that the
King had sent word to this intent, that Kveldulf should become
his man, he or one or other of his sons.

"What way answeredst thou?" quoth Thorolf.

"So said I, as was in my mind, that never would I go under
the hand of Harald the King, nor yet should either of you two,
if I should have the say. Methinks in the end 'twill so come
about that there shall betide us nought but ruin from that
King."

"Then shapeth it all another way," said Thorolf, "than my
mind saith of it; because methinks there shall betide me from
him the greatest furtherance. And on this am I fast resolved, to
go see the King and become his man. And that have I heard for
true, that his bodyguard¹ is manned but with men of derring-do
only. That seemeth to me a thing much to be longed for to come
into their fellowship if they will take to me. Those men are
holden far better than all others in this land. So is it said to me
of the King, that he is most free-handed of money-gifts to his
men, and no less swift to give them advancement and award
them lordship, them that seem to him apt thereto. But that way
am I told, of all those who will turn their backs on him and not
serve him friendly, that all those are become men of nought:
some fly out of the land abroad, but some are made his hirelings.
That seems to me wonderful, father, in so wise a man as thou
beest and such a seeker after high things, that thou wouldst not
with thanks take this honourable using that the King bade thee.
But if thou think thyself foresighted as to this, that there will
betide us but unhap from this King, and that he will wish to be
our unfriend: why wentest thou not then into battle against him
with that king under whose hand thou wast aforetime? Now,

methinks, is that of all things unseemliest: to be neither friend of his nor unfriend."

"So came it about," said Kveldulf, "even as my mind foreboded me, that they would fare on no victorious journey who did battle against Harald Shockhead north in Mere. And in such same wise will that be true, that Harald will be for a great scathe unto my kindred. But thou, Thorolf, wilt have thine own way belike, to do as thou wilt. Of this have I no dread: lest, and thou be come into the company of the men of Harald's bodyguard, thou shouldst be thought not of a measure with thy lot, yea, and a match for the foremost in all that trieth a man. Beware thou of this, lest thou hold not thyself well in hand nor bring to strife with thee greater men; and yet wilt thou not give back before them neither."

But when Thorolf made ready to be gone, then Kveldulf led him down to the ship, kissed him, and bade him farewell and a safe return.

CHAPTER VII. OF BIORGOLF AND BRYNIOLF, AND OF THE BEGINNINGS OF THE SONS OF HILDIRID.

BIORGOLF was named a man of Halogaland.[1] He dwelt in Torgar. He was a landed man, rich and powerful: also he was half mountain-giant in strength and in growth and by birth withal. He had a son that was named Bryniolf: he was like his father.

Biorgolf was then old, and his wife dead, and he had made over into his son's hand all his affairs and looked about for a wife for him; and Bryniolf gat to wife Helga, a daughter of Ketil Haeng of Hrafnista. The son of those twain is named Bard: he was early big and comely of look, and became the most skilled of men in all feats.

That was of an autumn, that in that place was a banquet[2] well-thronged, and those two, Biorgolf and his son, were the worshipfullest men at that banquet. There was lots cast for men to sit two and two[3] for the afternoon, as was then the wont to do.

Now there at the banquet was that man that was named Hogni. He had his dwelling in Leka. He was a man of great wealth; of all men the comeliest of look, a wise man, withal of lowly kindred, and had made his own way. He had a daughter right comely, that is named Hildirid. To her it was allotted to sit beside Biorgolf. Much they talked on that evening, and in his sight the maid was fair. A little while after, brake up that banquet.

That same autumn old Biorgolf made him a journey from home, and took a cutter[4] that he had and aboard of her thirty men. He came his ways to Leka and went up to the house twenty in company, but ten minded the ship. But when they came to the farmstead then went Hogni to meet him and welcomed him kindly: bade him be there with his company; so he took that offer and they went in to the hall.[5] But when they had doffed their clothes and done on their mantles, then let Hogni bear in a mixing-bowl and strong beer.[6] Hildirid, the bonder's daughter, bare ale to the guests.[7]

Biorgolf calleth to him goodman Hogni and saith unto him that "This is mine errand hither, that I will that thy daughter fare home with me, and now will I make her a loose bridal".[8] But Hogni saw no other choice but to let all be so, as Biorgolf would have it. Biorgolf bought her with an ounce of gold,[9] and they went both into one bed together. Hildirid fared home with Biorgolf into Torgar.

Bryniolf accounted ill of these redes.

Biorgolf and Hildirid had two sons: the one was named Harek and the other Hraerek. Thereafter died Biorgolf; but as soon as he was carried out, then let Bryniolf fare away Hildirid, and her sons along with her. She fared then to Leka to her father, and there were they bred up, those sons of Hildirid. They were men comely of look, little of growth, well witted, like to their mother's kinsfolk. They were called the sons of Hildirid.[10] Little account made Bryniolf of them, and suffered them not to have aught of their father's heritage. Hildirid was Hogni's heiress, and she and her sons took heritage after him and dwelt now in Leka and had wealth enow. They were much of an age, Bard Bryniolfson and the sons of Hildirid.

That father and son, Biorgolf and Bryniolf, had long time had the Finn-fare and the Finn-scat.[11]

North in Halogaland is a firth named Vefsnir. There lieth an isle in the firth, and is named Alost, a great isle and a good. In it is a farmstead, Sandness by name: there dwelt a man that was named Sigurd. He was wealthiest of all in the north there. He was a landed man, and cunning of wisdom. Sigrid was his daughter named, and was thought the best match in Halogaland. She was his only child, and had the heritage to take after Sigurd her father.

Bard Bryniolfson made him a journey from home: had a cutter and aboard of her thirty men. He fared north to Alost and came to Sandness to Sigurd's. Bard took up the word and bade Sigrid to wife. That suit was well answered and in likely wise, and so came it that troth was plighted betwixt Bard and the maiden, and the wedding should be next summer. Then should Bard betake him thither north again for the wedding.

CHAPTER VIII. OF THOROLF AND BARD BRYNIOLFSON.

HARALD the King had that summer sent word unto the great men, them that were in Halogaland, and summoned to him those that had aforetime not been to see him. Bryniolf was minded for that journey, and with him Bard his son. They fared at autumn-tide south to Thrandheim and there met the King. He took to them exceeding kindly. Bryniolf became then the King's landed man. The King bestowed on him great revenues beside those that he had aforetime had: he bestowed on him withal the Finn-fare: the King's stewardship on the fell,[1] and the Finn-cheaping. After that, fared Bryniolf away and home to his own place; but Bard abode behind, and became of the King's bodyguard.

Of all the men of his bodyguard the King set most store by his skalds.[2] They had place on the lower bench. Inmost of them sat Audun Ill-skald: he was their eldest, and he had been skald to Halfdan the Black, the father of Harald the King. Next after

sat Thorbiorn Hornklofi,3 and next after sat Oliver Hnufa, but
next to him was place made for Bard. He was called there
Bard the White, or Bard the Strong. He was well esteemed
there of every man. Betwixt him and Oliver Hnufa there was
great good-fellowship.

That same autumn came to King Harald those two, Thorolf
Kveldulfson and Eyvind Lambi, the son of Berdla-Kari. They
found there a good welcome. They had thither a snake-ship,4 of
twenty benches well manned, that they had before had a-viking.
Place was made for them in the guest-hall with their following.
When they had tarried there until it seemed to them time to go
and see the King, there went with them Berdla-Kari and Oliver
Hnufa. They greet the King. Then saith Oliver Hnufa5 that here
is come the son of Kveldulf, "Whom I said to you last summer
that Kveldulf would send to you. You will find his promises
fast kept. You may now see sure tokens that he will be your full
and perfect friend, sith he hath sent his own son hither to service with you: so gallant a man, as you now may see. And that
is our boon, of Kveldulf and all of us, that thou take to Thorolf
honourably and make him a great man with you".

The King answereth well his suit, and said he should so do,
"If Thorolf approve himself to me as good a man as he hath the
look of a full manly one".

And now Thorolf gat himself under the hand of the King and
went there into the lay of the bodyguard; but Berdla-Kari and
Eyvind Lambi, his son, fared south with that ship which Thorolf
had had north. Then fared Kari home to his own place, he and
Eyvind both. Thorolf was with the King, and the King appointed him to sit between Oliver Hnufa and Bard, and there
grew to be amongst all three of them the greatest good-fellowship. That was men's talk of Thorolf and Bard, that they were
even-matched for comeliness and in growth and might and all
feats of skill. Now is Thorolf there in exceeding great loving-
kindness with the King, both he and Bard.

But when winter wore and summer came, then Bard bade
leave of the King to go look to that marriage that had been
promised him the summer before. And when the King knew
that Bard had an errand of moment, then gave he him leave for

homeward-faring. But when he had gotten leave, then bade he Thorolf fare with him northaway. He said (as was true) that he would there likely be able to meet many noble kinsfolk of his[6] that he would not have seen before or had acquaintance with them. To Thorolf that seemed much to be longed for, and for this they get them leave from the King.

So now they make ready: had a good ship and ship's company: fared then on their way as soon as they were ready. But when they come to Torgar, then send they men to Sigurd and let say to him that Bard will now look to that marriage which they had bound themselves to, the summer before. Sigurd saith that he will hold by all that which they had spoken: they fix, then, the wedding-feast, and Bard and his folk must seek north thither to Sandness. But when the time was come, then fare they, Bryniolf and Bard, and had with them a mort of great men, kinsmen of theirs by blood and affinity.[7] It was as Bard had said, that Thorolf met there many kinsfolk of his that he had not before had acquaintance with. They fared until they came to Sandness, and there was there the stateliest of feasts. But when the feast was ended, Bard fared home with his wife and tarried at home that summer, he and Thorolf both. But in the autumn come they south to the King, and were with him another winter.

That winter died Bryniolf. But when Bard learneth of this, that his heritage was there fallen in, then bade he leave for faring home; and the King granted him that. And before they parted, Bard was made a landed man, like as his father had been, and had of the King all revenues, the like that Bryniolf had had. Bard fared home to his own place, and in short while became a mighty lord.[8] But Hildirid's sons gat nought of the heritage then no more than aforetime.

Bard had a son with his wife, and that was named Grim. Thorolf was with the King, and had there great esteem.

CHAPTER IX. OF THE BATTLE OF HAFRSFIRTH.

HARALD the King bade out a great war-gathering, and drew together a host of ships. He summoned to him the folk wide about the lands. He fared out from Thrandheim and stood south along the land. These tidings had he heard, that a great war-host was drawn together about Agdir and Rogaland and Hordaland, gathered from near and far, both down from the land and from eastaway out of the Wick, and there was there a mort of great men come together, and minded to defend the land against Harald the King.

King Harald held his way from the north with his folk. Himself he had a great ship and manned with his bodyguard. There, in the stem,[1] was Thorolf Kveldulfson, and Bard the White, and those sons of Berdla-Kari, Oliver Hnufa and Eyvind Lambi; but the berserks of the King were twelve together in the bows. Their meeting was south off Rogaland, in Hafrsfirth.[2] There was there the greatest battle of any that King Harald had had, and great man-fall of either host. The King laid his ship well forward, and there was the battle strongest; but so ended it, that King Harald gat the victory. And there fell Thorir Longchin, King of Agdir; but Kiotvi the Wealthy fled, and all his host that yet stood up, save those that went under the King's hand after the battle.

Now when the host was kenned of Harald the King there was much people fallen and many were sore wounded. Thorolf was wounded sore, but Bard worse, and not one was unwounded in the King's ship forward of the sail, save those that iron bit not[3] (and that was his berserks). Then let the King bind the wounds of his men, and thanked men for their forwardness, and bestowed gifts, and laid most praise on them that seemed to him worthiest of it, and promised them to swell their honour: named for this his skippers, and next to them his stem-men and other forecastle-men.

This was the latest battle that Harald the King had within the land, and after that found he no withstanding, and gat to himself thenceforth all the land.

The King let leech his men, them that there was yet hope of

life for, and let give lyke-help⁵ unto the dead men, in such sort
as was then the wont to do. Thorolf and Bard lay in their wounds.
Thorolf's wounds took to healing, but Bard's wounds grew like
to be banesome. Then let he call the King to him and said to
him thus: "If so betide, that I die of these wounds, then will
I crave this of you, that you let me rule mine inheritance after
me".

But when the King had yea-said that, then said he: "All mine
inheritance after me will I that Thorolf, my fellow and kinsman,
take: both lands and loose goods; to him will I give my wife,⁴
too, and my son for uprearing, because I do trust him for this,
best of all men". He settleth these matters, as was the law
thereto, with the King's leave. And now dieth Bard, and there
was given him lyke-help, and it was thought much harm of his
death.

Thorolf gat well of his wounds, and followed the King that
summer, and had gotten exceeding great renown. The King
fared in the autumn north to Thrandheim. Then prayeth
Thorolf leave to fare north to Halogaland to look to those gifts
which he had received that summer of Bard his kinsman. The
King giveth leave for that, and sendeth word therewith and
tokens that Thorolf shall have all that which Bard gave him: let
that follow, that that gift was made with rede of the King, and
that his will it is so to let it be. The King maketh now Thorolf a
landed man, and bestoweth on him now all those revenues the
same which before Bard had had: granteth him the Finn-fare
with like conditions, even as Bard had had it before. The King
gave Thorolf a good long-ship with all her gear and let make
ready his journey thence as best might be. And now fared
Thorolf thence on his journey, and he and the King parted
with the greatest loving-kindness.

But when Thorolf came north to Torgar, then was there
joyful welcoming of him. He said to them then of Bard's death,
and that withal, that Bard had given him to take after him lands
and loose goods, and his wife too that had before been his: and
now set forth the word of the King and the tokens. But when
Sigrid heard these tidings, then thought she that great scathe
she had to lose her man. But Thorolf was before well known to

her, and well she wist that he was the greatest man of mark and that that match was exceeding good; and, seeing it was the King's bidding, she counted it good rede (and her friends were with her in this) to plight troth with Thorolf, if that were not against her father's liking. Therewith took Thorolf unto him the management of all things there, and withal the King's stewardship.

Thorolf made him a journey from home, and had a long-ship and nigh sixty men and fared now when he was ready, north along the land. And on a day at evening came he into Alost, to Sandness: laid their ship in harbour; and when they had tilted[6] her and made all snug, Thorolf went up to the farmstead with twenty men. Sigurd welcomed him joyfully, and bade him be there, for well known was each to other before, since first Sigurd and Bard had become father and son-in-law.[7] And now went Thorolf and his folk into the hall and took there guesting. Sigurd sat him down to talk with Thorolf, and asked for tidings. Thorolf told of that battle that had been last summer south in the land, and the fall of many men that were well known to Sigurd; Thorolf said that Bard, his son-in-law, had died of those wounds that he gat in the battle. That seemed to them both the greatest man-scathe. Then saith Thorolf unto Sigurd what had been in the privy talk betwixt him and Bard, before he died, and so he bare forward the word-sending of the King, that the King would let all that hold: and therewith he showed the tokens. And now Thorolf took up his wooing with Sigurd, and bade to wife Sigrid his daughter. Sigurd took that suit well: said that many things held for this: first, that the King's will it is so to let it be; that too, that Bard had asked for this, and that withal, that Thorolf was known to him and he thought his daughter well given so. That suit was easy-sped with Sigurd. Then went forward the betrothals and appointing of the bridal feast, to be in Torgar that autumn. Thorolf fared home then to his own place, he and his company, and made ready there a great feast and bade thither great throng of men. There was there a mort of Thorolf's noble kinsmen. Sigurd too set out from the north, and had a great long-ship and good choice of men. There was at that feast the greatest throng of men.

Soon was that found, that Thorolf was an openhanded man, and a great man of account. He had about him a great following, and soon became that exceeding costly and needed great provision. Then was the year good and an easy stroke to get that whereof need was.

The same winter, died Sigurd at Sandness, and Thorolf took all his heritage after him. That was exceeding great fee. Those sons of Hildirid came to see Thorolf and brought up that claim which they would be thought to have there, to that fee which had belonged to Biorgolf their father. Thorolf answereth as thus: "That was known to me of Bryniolf, and yet better known as to Bard, that they were men of so great manliness that they would sure have dealt out unto you two so much of Biorgolf's heritage as they wist you had a right to. I was by, when ye raised these same claims with Bard; and so it sounded to me as though he should think there was no true claim there, sith he called you bastard-born".[8]

Harek said that they would bring witness to this, that their mother was dower-boughten, "And yet true it was that we followed not at first this suit with Bryniolf our brother. For there 'twas dealing 'twixt kin and kin; but of Bard we looked to get our due every whit, but it came about that no long dealings might we have with him. But now is this heritage come to men nought of kin with us twain, and we may not now altogether hold our peace over this loss of ours. And yet, it may hap that there shall yet be, as afore, that stress of power, that we get not our right in this suit 'cause of thee: if thou wilt hear no witness, such as we have to put forward, that we be men odal-born".

Thorolf answereth then moodily: "So far from me is it to deem you heirship-born, that 'tis said to me that the mother of you two was with violence taken and was had home as spoil of war".

After that, they brake off this talk.

CHAPTER X. OF THOROLF'S FINN-FARING.

THOROLF made him that winter his journey up into
the fell,[1] and had with him a great force, not less than
ninety men. But before had the wont of it been that the
King's bailiffs had had thirty men, and whiles fewer. He had
with him great store of cheaping. He set him speedily a tryst
with the Finns and took of them scat[2] and had with them a
cheaping-fair. All went in kindness betwixt them and in friendly
wise, albeit some deal 'twas awe made them willing.

Thorolf fared wide about the Mark: but when he set his face
east toward the fell, he had word that the Kylfings[3] were come
from the east and fared there a-Finn-cheaping, but some part
they fared a-robbing. Thorolf set on the Finns to hold espial of
the faring of the Kylfings; but he came after a-seeking for them,
and hit upon thirty men of them in one lair and slew all, so as
not one came off, and after that he hit upon fifteen together or
twenty.   In all, they slew nigh a hundred men and took there
fee past all telling, and came back about spring-time, their affair
thus sped.

Thorolf fared then to his own place at Sandness and sat there
long through the spring. He let make a long-ship, great, and a
drake's head thereto: let dight her like the best: had her along
with him from the north. Thorolf swept much into his own net
of those takings that then were in Halogaland: had men of his in
the herring-fisheries and so too in the cod-fisheries.[4] There were
seal-takings too enow, and egg-takings. He let flit all that home
to him. He had never fewer freedmen at home than a hundred.[5]
He was an openhanded man and a bountiful and made friends
much with the great men, all those men that were in his neighbourhood. He became a mighty man, and laid much thought to
his ships' arraying and his weapons.

CHAPTER XI. OF THE FARING OF KING HARALD INTO HALOGALAND AND HIS GUESTING WITH THOROLF KVEL-DULFSON.

HARALD the King fared that summer into Halogaland and there were made feasts against his coming, both there where were houses of his, and so too did the landed men make feasts and the powerful bonders. Thorolf made ready a feast against the King's coming and laid out great charges thereon: that was appointed for when the King should come there. Thorolf bade thither a throng of men, and had there the best pick of men that was to choose from. The King had near three hundred men when he came to the feast, but Thorolf had to meet him five hundred men.

Thorolf had let make ready a great corn-barn that was there, and let lay benches in it, and let drink there; because there was there no hall so great as that that throng of men might all be within it. There were shields withal fastened to the walls all round about inside the house.

The King sate him in the high seat. But when all was arrayed both withinward and to doorward, then the King gazed about him and turned red, and spake not; and men thought they knew that he was wroth.

The feast was of the stateliest and all the fare of the best. The King was something unmerry, and was there three nights, as he had meant to be.

That day when the King should fare away, came Thorolf to him and prayed that they should go down to the strand together. The King did so. There lay afloat by the land there that drake which Thorolf had let build, with her tilts and all her gear. Thorolf gave the King the ship, and prayed that the King should so esteem it (even as it had gone in his own mind), as that he had only for this sake had so great throng of men, that he might do the King honour, and not at all for a matching of strength with him. The King took well with Thorolf's words, and made himself now blithe and merry. And now many laid good words thereto, saying (as true it was) that the feast was of the honour-ablest and the parting-gift of the splendidest, and that there was great strength to the King of such-like men. Then parted they with great loving-kindness.

The King fared north in Halogaland as he had had the mind to do, and turned again south as summer wore. He fared then still to feasts, where they were made ready before him.

CHAPTER XII. OF THE EVIL SPEECH OF THOSE SONS OF HILDIRID.

HILDIRID'S sons went to see the King and bade him home to a three nights' feast. The King said yea to their bidding, and told them whenabouts he should come there. But when the appointed time was come, then came the King there with his folk, and there was there no throng of men to meet him, yet the feast went forward at the best. The King was all merry.

Harek fell a-talking with the King, and it came to this in his talk that he asketh of the King's farings which had been that summer. The King answered so much as he asked him: said all men had made him good cheer, and each much according to his means.

"Great odds," said Harek,[1] "will there have been in this, that in Torgar will your feast have been most thronged with men?"

The King said that so it was.

Harek saith, "That was to be looked for, sure, for as much as for that feast was the most provision made. And you did bear, King, the mightiest good luck therein, that so it turned out that you came into no danger of your life. It fared, as indeed was likely, that thou wast both wisest and best gifted with luck, in that thou didst misdoubt thee straightway that all should not be wholesome, when thou sawest that great throng of men which was there drawn to a head. Ay, and it was said to me that thou didst let all thy folk be ever all-weaponed, or didst have watch and ward kept alway both night and day".

The King looked on him and spake: "Why speakest thou such-like things, Harek, or what canst thou thereof to say?"

He saith, "Whether shall I speak with your leave, King, even as likes me?"

"Speak," saith the King.

"That is my thought," saith Harek: "if thou, King, mightest hear the word of each man, when men speak at home after their own heart and mind, what slavery that seemeth to them that you do put upon all men-folk, methinks thou shouldst think it not well. And that is truest to say unto you, King, that there wanteth no other thing to the common sort that they should rise up against you, save only hardihood and a captain. And that is nought wondrous," saith he, "in such-like men as Thorolf is, that he think himself far above every man else. He wanteth not might, nor goodly seeming neither. He hath, too, his bodyguard about him, like a king. He hath a mort of money, were it he had that only which himself had a right to. But, more than this, he maketh free to do as he list with other men's fee as of his own. You have granted him withal great revenues; and 'twas now all gotten ready so as he should pay you back nowise well for that. Because that is truest to tell you, that, soon as 'twas heard that you were a-faring north to Halogaland with no more folk than you had, three hundred men, then was that the rede of men hereabout that here should a host come together and take thy life, King, of thee and all thy folk; and 'twas Thorolf was leader in these counsels, because that offer was made him that he should be king over the folk of Halogaland and over the Naumdale folk. Fared he then both out and in by every firth and about all the isles and gathered every man that he found and every weapon, and that went nowise hidden, that that host-gathering was for the going against Harald the King in battle. Yea, but that is true, King, that, albeit you had a host something lesser than theirs when you met them, there shot terror into the breasts of these bonder-lads,[2] soon as they saw your sailing. Then was the other rede taken, to go and meet you with blitheness and bid you to feasting. But then were they minded, if you should be drunken and be laid a-sleeping, to make an onslaught on you with fire and weapons: whereof this for a token, if I have heard tell aright, that you were bidden in to some corn-barn, because Thorolf would nowise burn up his own hall, new and well bedight. And that withal was for a token, that every house was full of weapons and war-harness. But when they found no good way to work their wiles on you, they took that rede that seemed best to hand: cut all adrift of these former plottings. Methinks all know well how to dissemble these redes, for few I ween may know themselves sackless if the truth come up. Now this is my rede, King, that thou take Thorolf to thee and let him be in thy bodyguard, bear thy banner, and be in the forecastle aboard thy ship: unto this is he by nature apt beyond all men else. But if thou wilt that he be a landed man, then find him revenues south in the Firths. There is all of his blood and kin. You may there have oversight of him, that he wax not over big. But give thy stewardship here in Halogaland into the hand of those men that be men of temperate mind and will with trueness serve you, and have their kin here, and their kinsmen have here before had such-like business. We brethren shall be found both bidden and boun³ for such things as you may have the will to use us for. Our father had here long time the King's stewardship. Well went that in his hands. 'Tis hard for you, King, to find right men to set over your affairs here, sith here may you but seldom come yourself. Here is little main of land, that you should fare here with your host; and scarce will you do thus again, to fare hither with few folk, seeing that here is much untrustworthy people."

The King waxed exceeding wroth with this talk, and spake yet quietly, as was ever the wont of him whenso he heard such tidings as were of great matter. He asked then, whether was Thorolf at home in Torgar.

Harek said that there was no hope of this. "Thorolf is so well knowing, that he would have the wit to be out of the way of your host, King; for he would look for this, that they should not all hold their tongues so well as that thou, King, shouldst not be made ware of these tidings. Fared he north to Alost straightway when he heard tell that you were on your way from the north."

The King spake little of these tidings before men; yet was that found, that he would put fast trust in those words that had been spoke to him.

And now fared the King on his journey. Hildirid's sons led him forth in worthy wise with gifts, but he promised them his friendship. Those brethren gave out that they had an errand into Naumdale, and fared so in a round with the King that they fell in with him at every other while. Alway he took well with their talk.

CHAPTER XIII. OF THOROLF'S SENDING OF THE SCAT TO KING HARALD AND GIFTS THEREWITH.

THERE was a man named Thorgils the Yeller. He was a homeman of Thorolf's and was had of him in the most esteem of all his housecarles. He had followed Thorolf then when he was a-viking. Then was he his forecastle-man and his banner-bearer. Thorgils had been at Hafrsfirth in the host of King Harald, and was skipper there of that ship which Thorolf had, the same he had had a-viking. Thorgils was a mighty man of his hands and the greatest man of valour. The King had bestowed on him gifts of friendship after the battle and promised him his friendship. Thorgils was overseer of the household at Torgar when Thorolf was not at home. Thorgils had then the ruling there. But when Thorolf had fared from home, then had he gotten together the Finn-scat, even all that which he had had from the fell and which was the King's, and made it over into the hands of Thorgils, and bade him bring it to the King, if himself came not home afore that the King should fare from the north and southaway.

Thorgils arrayed a ship of burden,[1] a great and a good, that Thorolf had, and bare aboard of her the scat, and had near twenty men: sailed south after the King and found him in Naumdale. But when Thorgils came to see the King, then bare he to the King Thorolf's greetings, and said that he fared there with the Finn-scat, that Thorolf sent unto the King. The King looked upon him and answereth nought, and men saw that he was wroth.

Then Thorgils gat him gone, and thought to find a better

season to have speech with the King. He came to see Oliver
Hnufa and said unto him all as it had befallen, and asked if he
knew aught of what was toward.

"I know not that," said he. "But this have I found, that the
King falleth silent every while that Thorolf is spoke of, ever
since we were in Leka; and I misdoubt me therefore lest he be
slandered. That know I of Hildirid's sons, that they be in long
privy talkings with the King, and that is easy-found in the words
of them, that they be unfriends of Thorolf's. But I will shortly
find out all this from the King."

Thereafter fared Oliver to see the King, and spake: "Thorgils
the Yeller is hither come, your friend, with that scat that is come
out of Finnmark and is yours; and the scat is far greater than
hath aforetime been, and of far better wares. There is haste upon
him of his journey. Do so well, King, as go and see, for sure
none shall ever have seen such good grey-wares".[2]

The King answereth him not, and yet went thither where the
ship was laid. Thorgils brake bulk straightway of the wares and
showed them to the King. But when the King saw that it was
true that the scat was far greater and better than had aforetime
been, then smoothed was his brow somewhat, and then might
Thorgils hold speech with him. He brought the King some
beaver-skins[3] that Thorolf sent him, and more costly treasures
besides that he had gotten on the fell. The King was then glad
of himself and asked what had befallen to tell of in the farings of
Thorolf and his men. Thorgils told him clearly of all that. Then
spake the King: "Great scathe is that, whereas Thorolf will not
be true to me, but will fain be my banesman".

Then many that were by, and all with one accord, answered
and said that here must be some slander of ill men, if such-like
things were said to the King, but Thorolf must be held guiltless
of such things. It came to this, that the King said he would
liever trow it to be as they now said. Then was the King light in
all his talk with Thorgils, and they parted well agreed.

But when Thorgils saw Thorolf he said unto him all this,
even as it had fared.

CHAPTER XIV. OF THOROLF'S SECOND FARING INTO
FINNMARK.

THOROLF fared that winter yet again to the Mark, and
had with him near a hundred men. And now fared he
like as in that former winter: had a cheaping-fair with
the Finns and fared wide about the Mark. But when he sought
farther east, and news spread there of his farings, then came
Kvens[1] to him and said that they were sent unto him, and that
that was done of Faravid, the king of Kvenland: said that
Kirials[2] harried in his land, and he sent word to this intent,
that Thorolf should fare thither and give him help. There was
this too in his word-sending, that Thorolf should have even
shares with the king, and every man of his should have as much
as three Kvens. Now that was their law of the Kvens, that the
king should have of the booty shared with the men of his host
one-third part, and, over and above that, to his own sole use, all
beaver-skins and sables and miniveres. Thorolf laid this before
the men of his host and bade them choose which it should be, go
or no: but that was the choice of most, to take that hazard
wherein lay so great fee to be gained, and the end of their rede-
taking was that they fared east with the messengers.

Finnmark is wide exceedingly. The main sea goeth by the west
thereof, and from it big firths; so likewise by the north and all
east-about; but south thereof is Norway, and the Mark taketh
well nigh all the inland region southaway, even as Halogaland
the coast-lands. Now east from Naumdale is Jamtaland, and
then Helsingland, then Kvenland, then Finnland, then Kirialaland: but Finnmark lieth back beyond all these lands, and there
be wide fell-settlements up in the Mark, some in the dales, and
some by the waters' side. In Finnmark be waters wondrous big,
and there by the waters' side big mark-lands, but high fells lie
aback from end to end of the Mark, and that is called the Keel.[3]

Now when Thorolf came east to Kvenland and was met with
King Faravid, then make they ready for their journey and had
three hundred men, and the Northmen the fourth hundred, and
fared the upper way about Finnmark and came forth there where

the Kirials were on the fell, the same which had aforetime harried the Kvens. But when these were ware of unpeace toward, they gathered together and fared forth to meet it: they looked for victory, like as before. But when they fell to battle, the Northmen went hard forward. They had shields withal trustier than had the Kvens. And now turned it to man-fall in the host of the Kirials: much people fell of them but some fled. King Faravid and Thorolf took fee there past all telling: turned back to Kvenland, and after that fared Thorolf and his folk to the Mark. He and King Faravid parted with friendship.

Thorolf came down from the fell into Vefsnir: fared then first to his own place, to Sandness: there tarried awhile: fared from the north about spring-time with his folk to Torgar. But when he came there it was said to him how Hildirid's sons had been that winter in Thrandheim with King Harald, and this withal, that they had not spared to slander Thorolf to the King. There was much said to Thorolf hereof, what manner of stuff they had to their slander. Thorolf answered thus: "The King will not believe it, though such lies be borne up before him (seeing that there is no matter in it), that I should bewray him: for he hath in many a thing done great good to me, and in no thing done me ill. And so far is it from me, that I should will to do him a hurt, though I had the choice, that I had much rather be landed man of his than be called king, when there might be another, mine own countryman, one that might make me his thrall if he would".

CHAPTER XV. OF MORE LIES AND SLANDERS OF THOSE SONS OF HILDIRID.

HILDIRID'S sons had been that winter with Harald the King and had with them homemen of theirs and neighbours. Those brethren were oft a-talking with the King, and drave still o' the same road with Thorolf's case.

Harek asked: "Liked you well of the Finn-scat, King, that Thorolf sent you?"

"Well," said the King.

"Then should you have found matter indeed," saith Harek, "if you had had all that which was yours of right: but now it fares far otherwise. Much the greatest part it was that Thorolf kept for himself. He sent you for a gift three beaver-skins; yet I know for a truth that he kept back thirty of them, that were yours of right, and well I think it must have fared on such wise with other things. Sooth it is, King, if thou give the stewardship into the hand of us brethren, we shall fetch you more fee."

Now unto all this they said against Thorolf did the men of their company bear witness with them. And so it came about that the King was of the wrathfullest.

CHAPTER XVI. OF THOROLF KVELDULFSON AND THE KING.

THOROLF fared that summer south to Thrandheim to see Harald the King, and had there along with him all the scat and much fee beside and ninety men and all well arrayed. But when he came to the King then was place made for them in the guest-hall and entertainment done them of the noblest. Afterward the same day goeth Oliver Hnufa to Thorolf his kinsman. They talked together. Oliver said that Thorolf was then much evil spoke of, and that the King gave ear to such stories. Thorolf bade Oliver take up his case for him with the King; "Because I", said he, "am like to be short-spoken before the King, if he will rather believe slander of wicked men than true things and singleness such as he may approve in me".

Another day came Oliver to find Thorolf and said that he had talked of his case with the King. "I know not now," said he, "no whit better than afore, what he hath in his mind."

"Then shall I myself go to him," saith Thorolf.

He did so: went to the King when he sat at meat; and when he came in he hailed the King. The King took his greeting and bade give Thorolf to drink. Thorolf said that he had there the scat which was the King's, which was come from Finnmark; "And yet more things have I for gifts of remembrance[1] unto you, King, that I have to bring to you. I know that all will best betide me in these things that I have done to do you pleasure ".

The King saith that nought might he look for from Thorolf save good only, "Seeing that nought else ", saith he, "am I deserving of. And yet men's speech goeth somewhat two ways about this, how far thou art apt to give heed to what shall like me ".

"I am not truly spoke of ", saith Thorolf, "if any say that, that I have shown me untrue to you, King. Well I think that they must be thy friends less than I, they that have borne up such tales before thee. But this much is clear, that they must mean to be unfriends unto me-ward, full and perfect: and that is likeliest, too, that they shall get that they came to market for,[2] if we shall have the settling of it, I and they."

Therewith Thorolf gat him gone.

Another day after this Thorolf paid the scat out of hand, and the King was stood by; and when all was paid over, Thorolf bare forth certain beaver-skins and sables: said that he will give these to the King. Many that were standing by spake and said that that was well done, and was a thing worthy of friendship: the King said Thorolf had himself portioned out his own reward. Thorolf said that he had with truth and honesty done all that he knew to pleasure the King, "And if yet it like him not, then must I find all my doing brought to naught. It was known to the King, when I was with him and in his following, what way I carried me; and that meseemeth wonderful if the King will think me now another man than the man he did then approve me for ".

The King saith, "Well didst thou fare, Thorolf, of thine haviour, when thou wast with us. And now I am minded that the best way to do of it is that thou go into my bodyguard. Take ward of my banner, and be over the other men of my bodyguard. Then may no man slander thee if I may overlook thee night and day, what way thou carriest thee ".

Thorolf looked to either hand of him. There stood his house-carles. He spake: "Loth must I be to let go from mine hand this following of mine. Thou must do as thou wilt, King, with the titles of dignity you gave me and these thy revenues, but these followers of mine may I not let go from mine hand for so long as there remaineth to me the means to keep them, though 'twere at mine own private cost. This is my boon and my wish, that you, King, should come and see me at home and hear the words of those men that thou trustest, what witness they bear me in this matter. And after that, do according as you shall find to be true".

The King answereth and saith that he will not be feasted a second time by Thorolf.

Then Thorolf gat him gone, and therewith made ready for his journey home. But when he was gone away, then gave the King into the hand of Hildirid's sons those stewardships in Halogaland which till now Thorolf had had, and so too the Finn-fare. The King seized to himself the house at Torgar and all the possessions that Bryniolf had owned: gave all this into the keeping of Hildirid's sons.

The King sent men with tokens to find Thorolf and tell him of these dispositions that the King had made. And now Thorolf took those ships that were his own and bare aboard them all the loose fee that he might away with him, and had with him all his men, both freedmen and thralls. And now fared he north to Sandness to his own place. There had Thorolf no smaller throng of men and no smaller largesse.

CHAPTER XVII. OF HILDIRID'S SONS AND THEIR GATHERING OF THE FINN-SCAT, AND OF THEIR NEW LIES AND SLANDERS.

HILDIRID'S sons took up the stewardship in Halogaland. No man spake against it, because of the might of the King. But to many this change seemed much against their liking, to such as were kinsmen of Thorolf's or friends of his.

They fared that winter to the fell, and had with them thirty men. The Finns made much less account of those bailiffs than when Thorolf fared thither. Altogether in much worse wise was that gild paid which the Finns should yield.

That same winter fared Thorolf up into the fell with a hundred men: fared straightway east to Kvenland and met with King Faravid. They took rede together, and this was their rede, to fare on the fell even as last winter; they had four hundred men, and came down into Kirialaland; fell upon the settled parts whereso they deemed it fit for the strength of men they had: harried there and gat them fee. Then fared they back, as winter wore, up into the Mark.

Thorolf fared home about spring-time to his own place. He had then men in the cod-fishing in Vagar,[1] and some in the herring-fishing, and sought all manner of provision for his household. Thorolf had a great ship: she was built for the main sea. She was wrought in all ways of the best, well painted down to the water-line; there went with her a sail streaked with stripes blue and red: all the gear was well wrought in the ship. That ship Thorolf let make ready and appointed thereto housecarles of his to fare with her: let bear aboard of her dried fish and hides and white-wares. He let go therewith much grey-wares withal, and other skin-wares that he had gotten off the fell, and that was exceeding great fee. That ship he let Thorgils the Yeller sail west to England, to buy him clothes and other provision whereof he stood in need. They held their course south along the land and after that out on the main sea and came their ways to England, found good cheaping there, loaded the ship with wheat and honey, wine and clothes, and set sail home again in the autumn. They had wind at will, and came to Hordaland.

That same autumn fared Hildirid's sons with the scat and brought it to the King. But when they paid the scat out of hand, the King himself was by and saw it. He spake: "Is now all the scat paid out of hand, the same which ye took up in Finnmark?"

"So it is", said they.

"Both is it now", said the King, "that the scat yielded out of hand is much smaller and worser than when Thorolf fetched it, and ye did say that he dealt ill with the stewardship."

"Well is that, King," saith Harek, "that thou hast considered how great is the scat that is to be looked for to come from Finn-

mark; for then knowest thou more clearly how much you missed
if Thorolf squandered all the Finn-scat for you. We were last
winter thirty men in the Mark, even as hath aforetime been the
wont of your bailiffs. Then came Thorolf there with a hundred
men.² We heard that this was his word, that he was minded to
take the life of us brethren and of all those men which followed
us; and this the cause he found thereto, that thou, King, hadst
given into our hand that stewardship which he would have. We
saw that this was our best choice, to keep out of the way of him
and save ourselves, and for that sake came we but a short way
forth of the settled parts on the fell. But Thorolf fared through
all the Mark with a host of men. He had all the cheaping: the
Finns yielded unto him the scat: yea, and to this had he
bounden himself, that your bailiffs should nowise come into the
Mark. He hath the mind to make himself king over them in the
north there both over the Mark and Halogaland; and that is a
wonder, that you suffer him to gad it howsome'er he will. And
here may sure witness be found of that good catch of wealth
which Thorolf hath out of the Mark, inasmuch as the greatest
cheaping-ship that was in Halogaland was laden last spring at
Sandness, and Thorolf avowed him only owner of all the cargo
that was aboard of her. Well I do think, she was near full laden
with grey-wares, and there I well think should be found of
beaver and sable more than that which Thorolf brought unto
thee; and there fared aboard of her Thorgils the Yeller. Methinks he hath sailed west to England. But if thou wilt know the
truth of this, then do you hold espial of Thorgils's faring when
he fareth east, for well I think that on no cheaping-ship hath
come so great fee in our days. I deem that truest to say: that
you, King, are right owner of every penny there was aboard
of her."

These things they of his company affirmed for true, every
whit that Harek said. And here were none knew how to speak
against it.

CHAPTER XVIII. OF THE KING'S SENDING OF TWO
BRETHREN AND THEIR ROBBING OF THOROLF'S SHIP.

SIGTRYGG SHARP-FARER[1] and Hallvard Hard-farer
hight two brethren. They were with King Harald, men of
the Wick. Their mother's kin came of Westfold,[2] and they
had ties of kinship with Harald the King. Their father had his
kindred on both sides of the Gaut-Elf: he had had his dwelling
in Hising and was a man exceeding wealthy, and now had they
taken the heritage after their father. They were four brethren, all
told. One was named Thord, another Thorgeir, and these were
younger: they were at home and had charge of the household.

Sigtrygg and Hallvard had the King's errands[3] of all kind,
both inland and outland; and on many errands had they fared
that were of perilous kind, both for the taking off of men or else
for fee to be taken up from those men that the King let set upon
at home. They had a great following. No good friends were they
with the common sort, but the King set great store by them,
and they were of all men the best goers both afoot and on snow-
shoes; so too in ship-faring were they swifter than other men.
Mighty men of valour were they withal, and foreseeing in most
things. They were then with the King, when these tidings came
about.

In the autumn the King fared a-feasting about Hordaland.
That was on a day, that he let call to him those brethren, Hallvard and Sigtrygg, and when they came to him he said to them
that they should fare with their following and hold espial of that
ship which Thorgils the Yeller fared with, "And he had her
this summer west in England. Fetch me the ship and all that is
aboard of her, except men; them let ye go their ways in peace, if
they will not defend the ship".

Those brethren were all ready for this, and took his long-ship
each of them; and now they fare a-looking for Thorgils and his,
and had word that he was come from the west and had sailed
north along the land. They fare north after them and come upon
them in Firsound: speedily they knew the ship, and laid aboard
of her another ship on the outer side, but some went up aland

and out on to the ship by the gangways. Thorgils and his men wist not of any danger toward and kept no guard. They found out nought afore a throng of men were up aboard of the ship all weaponed, and themselves were all laid hand on and therewith led up aland weaponless, and had nought else but the clothes they stood in. But Hallvard and his cast off the gangways and let go the cable and dragged out the ship; and now turn they back the way they came, and sailed south until they found the King. They brought him the ship and all that was aboard. But when the lading was borne off the ship, then the King saw that here was great wealth, and that that was no lie4 that Harek had said.

But Thorgils and his fellows found them convoy, and they seek now to Kveldulf and his son, and told him of their journey, nowise smooth: yet found they there a good welcome. Kveldulf said that now would it draw toward this, even as his foreboding had been aforetime, that Thorolf would not, when all came to all, bear good hap of his friendship with Harald the King: "And it should seem to me no great matter of this loss of fee that Thorolf hath now the miss of, if now there were not a greater to come after. It misdoubts me even as before, that Thorolf will not clearly know how to see his own power, what it is beside such overmastery as he hath now to deal with"; and he bade Thorgils so say unto Thorolf "that my rede it is", saith he, "that he fare abroad out of the land; because it may be that he shall come in better case if he seek to England's King or to the Dane-King or to the Swede-King".

With that, he gave Thorgils a rowing-cutter and therewith all her gear, and tilt and victual and all that they needed for their journey. Therewith fared they and ceased not from their faring till they were come north to Thorolf, and said unto him this that was befallen to tell of.

Thorolf bare well with his scathe. So said he, that he should not lack for fee: "Good it is, to lay out fee with the King for partner".

Thereafter Thorolf bought meal and malt and what else he had need of for maintaining of his folk. He said that his housecarles would not be so showily dressed as he awhile ago had meant they should be. Thorolf sold his lands, but some he set to wed;5 but

he held on with all his expense like as heretofore. Moreover he
had then no fewer folk about him than in the former winter:
rather had he somewhat more of men. And so as for feasts and
home-biddings with friends of his: then had he more of all these
things even than heretofore. He was at home all that winter.

CHAPTER XIX. OF THOROLF'S HARRYING IN THE WICK,
AND OF COUNSEL GIVEN HIM BY KVELDULF.

NOW when spring was come and the snow began to break
up and the ice, Thorolf let set forth a great long-ship
that he had, and let array her and manned her with his
housecarles, and had with him more than a hundred men; that
was a host of the gallantest, and weaponed exceeding well. So
when they had wind at will, Thorolf held south along the land
with his ship, and as soon as he was come south beside Byrda
then held they the outer course outside all the islands, and at
whiles so as only the hill-tops showed over the sea's bourne.[1]
So they let their going be still southward off the land: they had
no tidings of men till they were come east into the Wick. There
they heard tell that King Harald was in the Wick, and that he
was minded that summer to fare to the Uplands. Nought wist
the landsmen of the faring of Thorolf.

He had a fair wind, and held south to Denmark, and thence
eastaway[2] and harried there summer-long and had no good gain
there. In the autumn he held his course from the east to Denmark at that time when is the breaking up of the Ere-fleet;[3] and
there had been that summer, as the wont was, a throng of ships
from Norway. Thorolf let all that host sail before him, and made
none ware of him. He sailed one day at evening to Most-sound,
and there in the haven before him was a great round-ship come
from Ere. Thorir Thruma was named the man that steered her.
He was a bailiff[4] of King Harald's: he had rule over his house
in Thruma. That was a great house: the King sat there long
whiles, at such times as he was in the Wick. There needed great
provision for that house. Now for this sake had Thorir fared

to Ere, to buy cargo there, of malt and wheat and honey, and had laid out thereon much fee that was the King's. They set on against the round-ship, and bade Thorir and his men choose whether to defend themselves; but, seeing that Thorir had no force to hold out against that strength of men that Thorolf had, they gave themselves up. Thorolf took that ship with all her lading, and put Thorir up aland on the island.

Thorolf held his way then with both those ships north along the land: but when he was come off the Elf, then lay they there and waited for night; but when it was dark they rowed the long-ship up into the river and set on against that house that belonged to Hallvard and Sigtrygg. They come there before day and threw a ring of men about it: therewith they whooped the war-whoop, and those waked thereat that were within and straight-way leaped up and to their weapons. Thorgeir fled out straight-way out of the sleeping-bower. There was a high wood fence about the dwelling: Thorgeir leapt at the fence and grabbed hold with his hand high up on a stake of it and cast himself forth of the garth. There was stood a-nigh Thorgils the Yeller. He slashed after Thorgeir with his sword, and it came on the hand of him and took it off against the fence-stake. After that, Thorgeir ran to the woods, but Thord, his brother, was felled there, and more than twenty men.

After that, they robbed all the goods and burnt the house, and so went back again down the river to the main sea. They had a fair wind, and sailed north to the Wick. There they found fair before them a great cheaping-ship that belonged to the men of the Wick, laden with malt and meal. Thorolf and his set on against that ship, but they that were on board thought they had no means to hold out against them, and gave themselves up. They went up aland weaponless. But Thorolf and his took the ship with her cargo, and went their ways.

Thorolf had then three ships when he sailed from the east about the Fold. So sailed they by the highway to Lidandisness; fared then at their speediest, but lifted ness-liftings whereso they came and hewed them strand-hewings. But when they sailed north from Lidandisness they fared more on the outer course. Still, wheresoever they came nigh land then robbed they.

But when Thorolf was come north off the Firths, then turned
he in from his way and went to see Kveldulf his father and found
there a good welcome. Thorolf said to his father what tidings
had befallen in his faring that summer. Thorolf tarried there a
little while, and Kveldulf and Grim led him down to his ship.
But before they parted they talked together. Said Kveldulf:
"Not far from that hath it fared, Thorolf, even that which I said
to thee then when thou wentest into the bodyguard of Harald
the King: that it should so turn out for thee as that neither unto
thee nor unto us thy kinsfolk should good luck betide from it.
Thou hast now taken to that rede that I warned thee most
against, to pit thyself against Harald the King; and for all thou
be well furnished of valour and of all prowess yet hast thou not
the gift for this, to hold thine own against Harald the King: a
thing that hath been given in the end to no man here in the land,
had he never so great power aforetime and throng of men. And
now my mind forebodeth me that this may fall to be our last
meeting together. That were the right way of it (for our ages'
sake), that of us twain thou shouldst live the longer. But another
way I am apt to think it shall come about".

Now stepped Thorolf aboard of his ship and departed on his
ways. Nought is said of his journey to tell of until he came home
to Sandness, and let flit to his house all that spoil of war that he
had had home with him, and let lay up the ships. He had then
no scant of provision to feed his folk through the winter.
Thorolf sat at home all this while, and had a throng of men no
smaller than the winters before.

CHAPTER XX.   OF SKALLAGRIM'S WEDDING.

THERE was a man named Yngvar, powerful and wealthy.
He had been landed man unto the former kings, but
since Harald was come into kingdom, Yngvar sat at
home and served not the King. Yngvar was a married man and
had a daughter that was named Bera. Yngvar dwelt in the Firths.
Bera was his only child,[1] and stood to take the heritage after him.

Grim Kveldulfson sought the hand of Bera, and that matter was settled betwixt them. Grim gat Bera to wife that same winter after their parting with Thorolf the summer before. Grim was then twenty-five years of age, and was bald-headed:² from thenceforth was he called Skallagrim. He had then the overseeing over all the household of him and his father and all the supply thereof; howbeit Kveldulf was a hale man and a well able. A mort of freedmen had they about them, and many men withal that had grown up at home there and were nigh of an age with Skallagrim. They were mostly men of great prowess and strength, because Kveldulf and his sons carefully picked out men of strength to follow them, and broke them in to their own bent of mind.

Skallagrim was like his father in growth and strength, and so too in outward seeming and in bent of mind.

CHAPTER XXI. OF REDE TAKEN FOR AN ONSET AGAINST THOROLF.

HARALD the King was in the Wick when Thorolf was a-harrying. He fared in the autumn to the Uplands and thence north to Thrandheim, and sat there for the winter and had great throng of men.

Then were Sigtrygg and Hallvard with the King, and had heard tell what way Thorolf had put in order their abode in Hising, and what man-scathe and fee-scathe he had there wrought them. They minded the King oft of that, and moreover of this too, that Thorolf had robbed the King and his thanes, and had fared with harrying there within the land. They prayed leave of the King that they two brethren should fare with that band which was wont to follow them and set upon Thorolf in his home.

The King answereth thus: "Well may ye think ye have cause thereto, though ye should rid Thorolf of his life; and yet methinks ye come greatly short of the luck to carry this work. Thorolf is no make of yours, albeit ye think you to be men of valour and of doughty deeds".

Those brethren said that this would soon be proven, if the King will give them leave therefor: they say, withal, that they have oft put themselves in great hazard with men in whose affairs they had less to avenge them of, and oftenest had they gotten the victory.

Now when it began to be spring, then men made them ready for their farings. Then was it even as aforesaid, that Hallvard and his brother held yet by their prayer, that they may go to Thorolf and take his life. He said he would give them leave for this, to take Thorolf's life, "And I wot, ye may bring me his head when ye come back again, and many costly treasures besides. And yet 'tis the guess of some men," saith the King, "if ye sail north, that from the north ye are like both to sail and to row".

Now they make them ready at their swiftest, and had two ships and a hundred and eighty men, and when they were ready they stood out down the firth with a north-east wind. But that is a head-wind going north along the land.

CHAPTER XXII. THE FALL OF THOROLF KVELDULFSON.

HARALD the King sate then at Hladir when Hallvard and his folk set forth. And straightway, with a like speed the King made him ready at his swiftest and went ashipboard, and they rowed in along the firth by Skarnsound, and so by Beitsea inland to Elda-eid.[1] He left the ship behind there, and fared north across the neck to Naumdale; there took he long-ships that the bonders had and gat him ashipboard with his folk: he had his bodyguard and nigh three hundred men. He had five ships or six, and all big.

They had a sharp head-wind and rowed night and day as fast as they might go. Night was then light for travelling. They came at eventide to Sandness after sundown, and saw there before the house a great long-ship a-floating, with her tilt rigged. They knew her for that ship which Thorolf owned; he had let array her, and was minded to fare abroad out of the land; and even then had he let brew his parting-ale.

The King bade his men go ashore from the ships, every man of them. He let set up his banner. It was but a short way to go to the house; moreover Thorolf's watchmen sat within-door a-drinking and were not gone to set the watch, and there was not any man without: all the folk sat within-door a-drinking. The King let throw a ring of men about the hall. Then set they up the war-whoop, and in the King's trumpet was blown the war-blast. But when Thorolf and his hear that, they leapt to their weapons, for every man's weapons hung all at hand over his seat.

The King let call to them in the hall and bade go out[2] women and young men and old men and thralls and bondmen. And now went out Sigrid the housewife, and with her those women that were within-door and those other men that were given leave to go out.

Sigrid asked if they were there, those sons of Berdla-Kari. They stood forth both, and asked what she would have of them. "Bring me to the King," said she.

They did so. But when she was come to the King, then asked she, "Shall it aught avail to seek for atonement, Lord, betwixt you and Thorolf?"

The King answereth: "So Thorolf will give himself up into my power to be forgiven, he shall hold by life and limb. But his men must abide punishment for whatso things they shall be found guilty of".

After that, went Oliver Hnufa to the hall and let call Thorolf to speech with him. He said unto him that choice which the King gave him. Thorolf answereth: "Nought of forced atonement will I take of the King. Bid thou the King to give us way out: then let things shake out as fate hath shapen".

Oliver gat him to the King and said what Thorolf bade for himself.

The King said, "Bear fire to the hall. I will not fight with them and have hurt of my folk. I wot that Thorolf will do us great man-scathe if we shall go seek him there, where it must be slow work to win in at him, albeit he hath fewer folk than we".

Therewith was fire borne to the hall, and that took swiftly, for the timber was dry and the woodwork tarred, and it was thatched with birch-bark about the roof. Thorolf bade his men break up the wainscot that was betwixt hall and fore-hall, and that was swiftly gotten done; but when they gat the beam, then took hold on the one beam as many men as might fasten a hold on it, and drave with the other end against the corner so hard that the nave-rings burst off of the outer side and the walls sprang asunder, so as there was a great way out.

There gat Thorolf out the first, and then Thorgils the Yeller, and so each after other. Then it came to battle; and so it was for a while, that the hall guarded the backs of Thorolf and his folk; but when that took to burning, then came the fire against them. There fell then much of their folk.

Then leapt Thorolf forth and hewed on either hand: set on thitherward where the King's banner was. Then fell Thorgils the Yeller. But when Thorolf came forth so far as the shield-burg,3 he laid his sword through that man that bare the banner. Then spake Thorolf: "Now come I three feet short". There stood in him then both sword and spear, but the King himself dealt him his bane-wound, and Thorolf fell forward at the feet of the King.

Then called out the King and bade give over slaying of more men; and it was so done. And now the King bade his men go down to the ships. He spake with Oliver and his brother: "Take now Thorolf your kinsman and do him lyke-help, and so with the other men that here be fallen, and give them burial; and let bind the wounds of men, of them that have hope of life. And there shall be no robbing here, sith all this fee is mine".

Therewith the King gat him down to the ships and the most of his people along with him, but when they were come aship-board then took men to binding of their wounds. The King walked about the ship and looked to the wounds of men. He saw where a man was a-binding of a wound that was gotten of a glancing blow. The King said that 'twas not Thorolf dealt that wound: "All another way did weapons bite for him. Few, I think, might bind up those wounds that he gave. And great scathe it is, the loss of such men as he".

Now forthwith at morning of day the King let draw up his sail and sailed south with all speed. But as day drew on, the King and his folk found many rowing-ships in every island-sound;

and those folk had been minded to join with Thorolf, for he had had espial holden all southaway in Naumdale and wide about the isles. It had been made known to them that Hallvard and his brother were come from the south with a great force, and meant to set upon Thorolf. Hallvard and his had ever a head-wind, and they had tarried in every haven, until news of them had fared up about the land; and of this had Thorolf's espiers been made ware, and for this cause had that war-rush come about.

The King sailed before a strong fair wind until he was come to Naumdale: left there his ships behind him, but he fared the overland way to Thrandheim. He took there his ships that he had left behind there, and so held his course with his folk out to Hladir.

These tidings were soon noised abroad, and came to the ears of Hallvard and his where they lay. They turned back then to join the King, and their journey was thought somewhat to be laughed at.

Those brethren, Oliver Hnufa and Eyvind Lambi, tarried awhile at Sandness. They let deal with the slain that there were fallen. They did with Thorolf's body after the accustomed way, like as it was fit to do with the bodies of men of worship; set up standing stones for him. They let heal the sick men. They set in order the household, too, with Sigrid. There was left all the stock, but the household furniture and table-array and the clothes of men had for the most part been burnt up.

Now when those brethren were ready, they fared from the north and came to find Harald the King, in Thrandheim where he was, and were with him awhile. They were silent and spake little with men. So it was, upon a day, that those brethren went before the King. Then spake Oliver: "This leave will we two brethren ask of you, King, that you give us leave to fare home to our own place, sith here hath such things betided as we have not the heart to drink and sit at board with those men which bore weapon against Thorolf our kinsman".

The King looked at him and answereth somewhat short: "I shall not give you leave for this. Here shall you bide, with me".

Those brethren gat them gone and back to their seats.

The next day after, the King sate in his council-hall: let call thither Oliver and his brother. "Now shall ye two know," saith the King, "touching that errand ye had with me, and prayed to go home. You have been here awhile with me and been well behaved. Ye have done well always. In all things I have been well pleased with you. Now it is my will, Eyvind, that thou fare north to Halogaland. I will give thee Sigrid in Sandness, that woman whom Thorolf had to wife. I will give thee all that fee that Thorolf owned. Thou shalt have therewith my friendship, if thou knowest how to keep it. But Oliver shall follow me. I will not let him go, for the sake of the skill that is his."

Those brethren thanked the King for that honour that he did them: said they would take that right gladly. Then Eyvind made ready for his journey: gat him a good ship that served his turn. The King gave him his tokens for this business. Well sped Eyvind of his journey, and came up north to Sandness in Alost. Sigrid took well with them. And now Eyvind bare forward the tokens of the King and his errand unto Sigrid, and began his wooing of her: said that this was the King's word-sending, that Eyvind should gain that suit. But Sigrid saw she had but this only choice, as it was now come about, to let the King rule herein. So went that rede forward, that Eyvind gat Sigrid to wife. He took to him then the household at Sandness and all that fee that Thorolf had had.

Eyvind was a worshipful man. The children of him and Sigrid were Finn Skialg, the father of Eyvind Skaldspiller,[4] and Geirlaug that Sighvat the Red had to wife. Finn Skialg had to wife Gunnhild, the daughter of Earl Halfdan: her mother was named Ingibiorg, daughter of King Harald Hairfair.

Eyvind Lambi held himself in friendship with King Harald whiles they both were alive.

CHAPTER XXIII. THE SLAYING OF HILDIRID'S SONS.

THERE was a man named Ketil Haeng, son of Thorkel the Naumdale Earl and of Hrafnhild, daughter of Ketil Haeng of Hrafnista. Haeng was a worshipful man and a man of mark. He had been the greatest friend of Thorolf Kveldulfson and his near kinsman. He was then in that rush to arms when the host-gathering was in Halogaland and men were minded to give aid to Thorolf, as was afore-writ. But when King Harald fared from the north and men were made aware of Thorolf's taking off, then broke they up their gathering.

Haeng had with him sixty men, and he turned toward Torgar. And there were Hildirid's sons, and had few in their following. And when Haeng came to the house, he made an onslaught upon them. There fell Hildirid's sons[1] and most of their men that were there, but Haeng and his took all the fee they might lay hand on.

After that, Haeng took two round-ships, the biggest he might find: let bear aboard of them all the fee he owned and might come away with. He had with him his wife and children, besides all those men who had been at this work with him. There was a man named Baug, Haeng's fosterbrother, a high-born man and a wealthy. He steered one of the round-ships. So when they were ready and a fair breeze blew, then sailed they out into the main.

A few winters before had Ingolf and Hiorleif[2] gone to settle Iceland, and that journey was then much in the talk of men: men said there was right good choice of land there. Haeng sailed west into the main and sought toward Iceland. Now when they were ware of land they were come upon it from the south; and because the gale was fierce, and surf along the land, and nought harbour-like, they sailed west along the land off the sands. But when the gale began to fall and the surf to abate, then was a great river-mouth before them, and they held on there with their ships up into the river and laid them aland on the eastern bank. That river is named now Thursowater: ran then much narrower and was deeper than now it is.[3]

They unladed the ships: took then and kenned the land from the east along the river and flitted after them their livestock. Haeng was, for the first winter, in the country out beyond the outer Rangriver; but in the spring he kenned the land eastward, and took then land between Thursowater and Markfleet, between fell and foreshore, and dwelt at Hof beside the eastern Rangriver. Ingunn his wife bare a child in the spring, after they had been there their first winter, and the boy was named Hrafn. And when the houses there were pulled down, then was the place called thereafter Hrafntofts.

Haeng gave Baug land in Fleetlithe down from Markriver to the river out beyond Broadlairstead, and he dwelt at Lithend;4 and from Baug is come a great line of kindred in that countryside.

Haeng gave land to his shipmates, but sold to some for a little price, and they are called land-take men.5

Storolf was named a son of Haeng: he had the Knoll and Storolfsfield. His son was Worm the Strong.

Heriolf was named the second son of Haeng: he had land in Fleetlithe marching with Baug, and out as far as Knollslech. He lived under the Brents. His son was Summerlid, father of Weatherlid the skald.6

Helgi was the third son of Haeng. He dwelt at the Field, and had land as far as the upper Rangriver and down to march with his brethren's.

Vestar was named the fourth son of Haeng. He had land to the east of Rangriver, betwixt that and Thwartwater, and the lower part of Storolfsfield. He had to wife Moeid, daughter of Hildir of Hildisey. Their daughter was Asny, whom Ofeig Grettir had to wife. Vestar dwelt at Moeidsknoll.

Hrafn was the fifth of Haeng's sons. He was the first Speaker of the Law7 in Iceland. He dwelt at Hof after his father. Thorlaug was Hrafn's daughter, whom Jorund the Priest had to wife. Their son was Valgard of Hof. Hrafn was the worshipfullest of the sons of Haeng.

CHAPTER XXIV. THE SORROW OF KVELDULF.

KVELDULF heard tell of the fall of Thorolf his son. He became sorrowful with these tidings, so that he laid him in his bed, for grief and old age. Skallagrim came often to him and talked to him: bade him arouse himself: said that all things else were fitter than this, to come to utter worthlessness and lie bed-ridden: "That rather should be our rede, to look for vengeance after Thorolf. May be, that we may come at some of those men that have been at Thorolf's fall. And if not that, then will there be men, whom we may catch, that the King shall think it much against his liking".

Kveldulf quoth a stave:[1]

> News from a northern island:
> (The Norns are grim!) too early
> The Thunder-Lord hath chose him:
> Thorolf lieth low now.
> Nought swift, for all I strive for't,
> Nought swift will be the 'venging:
> By thowless eld enthralled I'm bann'd
> From Thing of Odin's shield-mays.

Harald the King fared that summer to the Uplands, and fared in the autumn west to Valdres and all up to Vors. Oliver Hnufa was with the King, and came oft to speech with the King, if he would be willing to pay boot[2] for Thorolf: bestow on Kveldulf and Skallagrim money-boot or some such manly gift as they might be content with. The King did not wholly warn him off from this, if that father and son would come and see him.

And now Oliver started on his journey north into the Firths: stayed not till he came at fall of day to that father and son. They took to him in thankful wise: tarried he there some while.

Kveldulf asked Oliver carefully about those doings that had come about at Sandness when Thorolf fell, of this too, what Thorolf had framed to do before he fell; and this, who bare weapons upon him, and where he had the greatest wounds, and what way his fall was. Oliver said to him all that he asked; this too, that King Harald dealt him that wound that should alone have been enough and more to be the bane of him, and that Thorolf fell nigh upon the feet of the King face downward. Then answereth Kveldulf: "Well hast thou said. For that have men spoken of old, that of that man will be vengeance who fell face downward, and nigh to him will the vengeance come who was in the way of him when he fell. But unlikely it is that unto us should that good luck be fated".

Oliver said to that father and son that he had hope if they would go and see the King, and seek atonement, that that might turn out an honourable journey, and bade them make hazard of this, and laid many words thereto.

Kveldulf said that he was nought fit for that, for eld's sake. "I will bide at home," said he.

"Wilt thou go, Grim?" said Oliver.

"I think this is no errand of mine," said Grim. "I shall seem to the King nought ready of word. I think I should not stand long bidding atonement of him."

Oliver said that he should have no need of that: "We shall speak all on thy behalf, so well as we know how".

And what with Oliver's much pressing of his suit, Grim promised that he would go on this journey soon as he should deem him ready. He and Oliver fixed a time between them when Grim should come to meet with the King. Fared then Oliver first away, and to the King.

CHAPTER XXV. OF SKALLAGRIM'S GOING TO THE KING.

SKALLAGRIM made him ready for that journey that was aforesaid. He picked him men of his homemen and neighbours, them that were strongest of might bodily and doughtiest of those that were to hand. One man was named Ani, a wealthy bonder: another named Grani: the third Grimolf, and Grim, his brother, homemen of Skallagrim's, and those brethren Thorbiorn Krumm and Thord Beigaldi. They were called Thorarna's sons. She dwelt a short way from Skallagrim's and was learned in wizardry:[1] Beigaldi was a sit-by-the-fire.[2] One man was named Thorir the Giant and his brother Thorgeir Jardlang: a man named Odd Live-alone; Griss the Freedman. Twelve were they for that journey, and all the strongest men, and many shape-strong.

They had a rowing-ferry that belonged to Skallagrim: fared south along the land: laid their course in into Osterfirth: fared then the land-way up to Vors, to that water which is there, and their road so lay that they must fare over it. They got them a rowing-ship, such as served their turn; and so rowed over the water. And then was it no long way to that farmstead where the King was a-feasting.

Grim and his came there at that hour when the King was gone to table. Grim and his found men to speak to out in the garth,³ and asked what tidings were there; and when that was told them, then Grim bade call to speak with him Oliver Hnufa. That man went into the hall and thither where Oliver sat, and said to him: "Men be here come, outside, twelve together, if men you shall call them. But liker be they to giants in growth and seeming, than to mortal men".

Oliver stood up straightway and went out. He thought he knew who would be come. Welcomed he well Grim his kinsman, and bade him go in into the hall with him. Grim said to his fellows: "That will here be the way of it, that men go weaponless before the King. We shall go in, six, but other six shall be without and mind our weapons".

And now go they in. Oliver went before the King. Skallagrim stood at the back of him. Oliver took up the word: "Now is Grim hither come, the son of Kveldulf. We shall now take great joy of it, King, if you make his journey hither a good one, even as we hope it will be. Many be they that have of you great honour that are less fit for it than he, and that are nought near so well gifted in all feats of mastery as he will be. And thou mayest so do this, King, which is a thing I myself set most store by, if that is aught to thee".

Oliver spake long and readily, for he was a man apt of word. Many other friends of Oliver's went before the King and pushed this suit.

The King looked about him. He saw that a man stood at the

back of Oliver and was by a head taller than other men, and bald.
"Is that he, Skallagrim?" said the King: "The big man?"

Grim said that he guessed aright.

"I will, then," said the King, "if thou biddest boot for
Thorolf, that thou become my man, and go here into the lay of
my bodyguard, and serve me. May be it shall like me so well of
thy service, that I shall bestow on thee atonement after thy
brother, or other honour, no smaller than I bestowed on him,
on Thorolf thy brother; and thou must know better how to keep
it than he did, if I make thee so great a man as he was become."

Skallagrim answereth: "That was known, how greatly Thorolf
was beyond what I am in all that belonged to him, and no good
hap bare he of his serving thee, King. Now will I not take that
rede. I will not serve thee; for I know that I shall not bear that
good hap in doing thee service, that I should wish for and
worthy were. I think that in more things should I be found
wanting than was Thorolf".

The King was silent, and was set blood-red to look upon.

Oliver turned straight away and bade Grim and his go out.
They did so: went out, and took their weapons. Oliver bade
them fare away at their swiftest. Oliver went on their way with
them as far as the water, and a many men with him. Before he
and Skallagrim parted, Oliver spake: "Another way turned out
thy faring to the King, kinsman Grim, than I would choose.
Much I urged thy coming hither, and now will I pray this, that
thou fare home at thy speediest: and this withal, that thou come
not to see King Harald unless there be better agreement betwixt
you than meseemeth now things turn toward. And guard thee
well against the King, and against his men".

And now fared Grim and his over the water, but Oliver and
his folk went where those ships were that were drawn up aland
by the water-side, and hewed them so that they were not sea-
worthy: because they saw faring of men down from the King's
house: they were many men together, and much weaponed, and
fared hastily. Those men had King Harald sent after them for
this, to slay Grim.

The King had taken up the word a little after Grim and his
had gone out: said as thus: "That see I in that great bald-head,

that he is choke-full of wolfishness, and needs must he do a hurt
to some of those men that we should feel the loss of, if he catch
them. You may make up your minds for this, you men whom he
may reckon he hath some quarrel against, that that bald-head
will spare no single man of you if he but come across you. Fare
then now after him, and slay him ".

Therewith fared they, and came to the water and found there
not a ship that was sea-worthy. So now fared they back again,
and said to the King of their journey, and that too, that Grim
and his should by then be gotten over the water.

Skallagrim went his ways with his company till he came home.
Skallagrim said unto Kveldulf of their journey. Kveldulf deemed
well of it that Grim had not fared on this errand to the King to
go under the hand of him; said too, as aforetime, that there would
befall them from the King scathe only and no upholding.

Kveldulf and Skallagrim talked oft of what counsel they
should take, and that came always to an agreement betwixt them:
so said, that they might in no wise be there in the land, no more
than other men, such as were out of atonement with the King;
and that this should be their rede, to fare abroad out of the land.
And they thought that a thing to be desired, to seek to Iceland,
because it was then well spoken of for the choice of land there.
Thither were by then come friends of theirs and folk of their
knowing, Ingolf Arnarson and his fellows, and had taken choice
of land there and taken up their dwelling in Iceland. Men might
there take to themselves land unboughten, and pick their
dwelling-place. That was firmest set in their rede-taking, that
they would break up their household and fare abroad out of the
land.

Thorir Hroaldson[4] had been in his childhood's days at
fostering with Kveldulf, and he and Skallagrim were much of
an age: there was dear love there in that fosterbrotherhood.
Thorir was become landed man unto the King when these things
betided: but the friendship betwixt him and Skallagrim held
fast always.

Early in the spring Kveldulf and his folk made ready their
ships. They had great choice of ships, and good: made ready

two great round-ships5 and had aboard each thirty men, of them that were fit for fighting, and, over and above these, women and young folk. They had with them all their loose goods that they might come away with. But their lands durst no man buy, because of the King's might. So when they were ready, then sailed they away. They sailed to those islands that are named the Solunds:6 these be many islands and big, and so much shorn with bays that it is said that there will few men know all the havens.

CHAPTER XXVI. OF THE CHILDREN OF DUKE GUTTHORM.

GUTTHORM1 was the name of a man, son of Sigurd Hart. He was mother's brother of Harald the King. He was fosterfather of the King and governor over his land, for the King was then in his childhood when first he came to power. Gutthorm was war-duke of the host of Harald the King then when he won the land under him; and he was in all the battles that the King had when he gat unto him the land of Norway. But when Harald was become sole King over all the land, and sat him down in quiet, then gave he unto Gutthorm his kinsman Westfold and East Agdir and Ring-realm and all that land that had belonged to Halfdan the Black, his father.

Gutthorm had two sons and two daughters. His sons were named Sigurd and Ragnar, and his daughters Ragnhild and Aslaug.

Gutthorm took a sickness, and when it grew heavy on him, then sent he men to find Harald the King and prayed him see to his children and his realm. A little after, he died. But when the King heard of his death, then let he call to him Hallvard Hardfarer, him and his brother: said that they must fare on a sending of his east into the Wick. The King was then stopping in Thrandheim.

Those brethren made them ready for their journey in stateliest wise: picked their host and had the best ship they might get. That ship they had which had been Thorolf Kveldulfson's, and they had taken from Thorgils the Yeller. But when they were ready for their journey, then said the King unto them their errand, that they must fare east to Tunsberg.[2] There was then a cheaping-stead: there had Gutthorm had his seat.

"You shall", said the King, "fetch me the sons of Gutthorm, but his daughters shall be bred up there until I give them in marriage. I shall find men to take ward of the realm and to give fostering to the maidens."

So when those brethren were ready, then fare they on their way, and had wind at will. They came in the spring-time into the Wick, east to Tunsberg, and there bare forward their errand. Hallvard and his take up the sons of Gutthorm and much of loose goods. Fare they then, when they are ready, on their way back. They were somewhat later then in getting a fair wind, but there befell nought to tell of in their journey until they were a-sailing north of the Sogn-sea, with a good breeze and bright weather, and were then all merry.

CHAPTER XXVII. THE SLAYING OF HALLVARD AND SIGTRYGG: AND HOW KVELDULF AND SKALLAGRIM FARED TO ICELAND.

KVELDULF and Skallagrim and their folk held espial all the summer in along the highway of the sea. Skallagrim was of all men the keenest sighted: he saw the sailing of Hallvard and his and knew the ship, for he had seen that ship before, when Thorgils fared with her. Skallagrim kept watch on their faring, where they laid her in haven at eventide; and now fareth he back to his folk and saith to Kveldulf that which he had seen, and that, too, that he had known the ship for that which Hallvard and his men had taken from Thorgils, and had been Thorolf's, and that there would be some of those men along with her who should make them good hunting.

So now make they ready, and make ready both the boats, and had twenty men aboard of each: Kveldulf steered one, and the other Skallagrim. Row they now, and look for the ship; but when they come there where the ship lay, then put they in to land.

Hallvard and his had tilted their ship and had then laid them down to sleep; but when Kveldulf and his came at them, then leapt up the watchmen that sat by the gangway head, and called out to the ship: bade men stand up: said that unpeace was come upon them. Hallvard and his leapt to their weapons. But when Kveldulf and his came to the gangway head,[1] then went he out on the stern gangway, but Skallagrim went on the fore gangway. Kveldulf had in his hand a byrny-troll.[2] But when he was come aboard the ship then bade he his men go on the outer side along the gunwale and hew the tilt out of its props, but himself raged aft towards the poop; and so it is said, that there he ran berserk, and many were they of his company that then ran berserk. They slew all those men that came in the way of them; in like same manner wrought Skallagrim, whereso he went upon the ship. That father and son slacked not until the ship was cleared.

But when Kveldulf came aft to the poop, he swung aloft the byrny-troll and hewed at Hallvard through helm and head, and it sank all in to the shaft: wrenched he it then so hard towards him that he bare Hallvard up in the air and slung him overboard.

Skallagrim cleared the fore-stem and slew Sigtrygg: a mort of men leapt into the water, but Skallagrim's men took the boat that they had thither had and rowed to them and slew all them that were swimming: there perished of Hallvard's men, in all, more than fifty men, but Skallagrim and his took the ship that Hallvard and his had had thither, and all the fee that was aboard her.

They laid hand on two or three men, them that seemed to them of least might or worth, and gave them peace and had of them tidings: learnt what men had been aboard that ship, and likewise what manner of journey they had been bound on. And when they understood all the truth, then kenned they the slain, that which lay on the ship: found they then that for sure, that a greater lot of the men had leapt overboard and had been lost than had fallen on the ship. Those sons of Gutthorm had leapt overboard and had been lost: then was one of them twelve winters old, and the other ten, and the hopefullest of men.

So now let Skallagrim go free those men that he had given peace to, and bade them go find Harald the King and say unto him carefully these tidings that were there come about, and this too, who had been in it. "You shall", said he, "bear to the King this ditty:3

> Now's hersir righted
> And King quited:
> Corpse-bird and beast
> On Yngling's bairns feast.
> Hurl'd hewn on the sea
> Floats Hallvard's bodie.
> Grey eagles tear
> Wounds of Sharp-fare."

Thereafter Grim and his folk flitted the ship with her lading out to their own ships; changed then the ships: loaded her which they had then won, and emptied that which they had before and which was smaller: bare stones aboard of her, and brake holes in her, and sank her: sailed therewithal out into the deep, soon as a fair breeze blew.

So is it said of those men that were shape-strong or of them on whom was the berserk-gang, that for so long as that held, they were so strong that there was no holding against them, but forthwith when that was passed over, then were they unmightier than of wont. And it was so with Kveldulf that, as soon as the berserk rage was gone from him, then knew he his weariness after those onslaughts he had made, and then was he altogether without might, so that he laid him down in his bed.

Now the breeze bare them out into the deep. Kveldulf captained that ship which they had taken from Hallvard and his men. They had a fair breeze and held much together in their voyage, so that they had for long whiles sight each of other. But when the main deep was passed, then took Kveldulf's sickness the upper hand with him. And when it drew toward this, that he was like to die, then called he his shipmates to him and said to them that he thought that likely, that now would soon be a parting of ways for them: "I have not", said he, "been a man used to sickness, and if so it fare as methinks now likeliest, that I die, then make me a chest and let me fare overboard; and this goeth all another way than I deemed it should be, if I shall not come to Iceland and there take land. Ye shall bear my greeting unto Grim, my son, then when ye find one another, and say to him this withal: if so betide that he come to Iceland, and it so come about (though that may be thought unlikely) that I be there before you, then let him take to him his dwelling as near as may be to that place where I shall have come aland".

A little thereafter died Kveldulf. His shipmates did so, even as he before had spoken, and laid him in a chest and thereafter shot it overboard.

There was a man named Grim, the son of Thorir the son of Ketil Keelfarer, a man of great kindred and a wealthy. He was a shipmate of Kveldulf's. He had been an old friend of that father and son, and had been on journeys both with them and with Thorolf. And he had gotten the wrath of the King for that sake. He took charge of the ship after Kveldulf was dead. But when they were come off Iceland, then sailed they from the south toward the land: they sailed west along the land, because they had heard say that Ingolf had there taken up his dwelling, but when they came round Reekness4 and they saw the firth open up before them, then stood they in to the firth with both their ships. The gale blew fierce, and great rain and fog; and now the ships parted. They sailed in up Burgfirth till there was an end of all skerries; then cast anchor till the gale abated and the air cleared; then waited they for flood-tide, and therewith flitted their ship up into a certain river-mouth: that is called Gufa. They brought the ship up the river so far as they might: and now bare the lading off the ship, and made their dwelling there the first winter. They kenned the land along by the sea both up the firth and down, and when they had fared but a short way, then found they where in a certain wick was cast ashore the chest of Kveldulf. They flitted the chest to that ness that was there,5 set it down there, and piled it with stones.

CHAPTER XXVIII. OF SKALLAGRIM'S LAND-TAKING.

SKALLAGRIM came there aland where a great ness went out into the sea, and a narrow neck landward of the ness, and there bare the lading off the ship. That called they Knarrarness.

Thereafter Skallagrim kenned the land, and there was great marshlands and wide woods,[1] long betwixt fell and foreshore, seal-takings enow and great catch of fish. But when they kenned the land south along the sea, then was there before them a great firth;[2] but when they fared in along that firth then stayed they not from their faring until they found their fellows, Grim the Halogalander and those fellows of his. That was a joyful meeting: said they unto Skallagrim of his father's death, and that withal, that Kveldulf was there come aland and they had laid him in earth there. And now brought they Skallagrim to the place, and so it seemed to him as if it should be but a short way thence to where a good stead would be for building of a house.

Fared Grim then away and back to his shipmates, and they sate there, of either part, through the winter where they had come aland. Then took Skallagrim land betwixt fell and foreshore, all the Myres out as far as Selalon and inland as far as Burglava, and south to Havenfell, and all that land that is marked off by the river-waters falling to the sea. He flitted his ship next spring south to the firth and in into that inlet which was nearest to that where Kveldulf had come to land, and set his house there, and called it Burg, and the firth Burgfirth; and so too the countryside up from there they named after the firth.

To Grim the Halogalander gave he dwelling south of Burgfirth, there where it was called Hvanneyri.[3] A short way out from thence stretches inland a wick, nought great: they found there many ducks, and called it Andakil,[4] and Andakilswater that which there fell into the sea. Up from that river to the river that was called Grimswater, there between them had Grim his land.

In the spring, when Skallagrim let drive his livestock up along the sea-shore then came they to a certain little ness, and caught there some swans, and called it Alptaness.

Skallagrim gave land to his shipmates.5 To Ani gave he land betwixt Longwater and Hafslech, and he dwelt at Anisbrent: his son was Onund Sjoni,6 by whom arose the strife between Thorstein and Odd-a-Tongue.

Grani dwelt at Granistead in Digraness.

To Thorbiorn Krumm gave he land up by Gufa, and to Thord Beigaldi. Krumm dwelt at Krummsknolls and Thord at Beigaldi.

To Thorir the Giant, him and his brother, gave he land up from Einkunnir and to the outer side along Longwater. Thorir the Giant dwelt at Giantstead; his daughter was Thordis Stang that dwelt at Stangarholt thereafter. Thorgeir dwelt at Jardlangstead.

Skallagrim kenned the land up about the countryside: fared first in along Burgfirth till the firth ended, and after that along the river on the western side, that he called Whitewater7 because he and his fellows had never before seen those waters that were fallen out of the jokulls: it seemed to them that river was of a wondrous look. They fared up along Whitewater, till that river was before them that fell out of the north from the fells: that called they Northwater, and fared up along that river till there was yet again a river before them, and therein was but little fall of water. Fared they over that river and still up along North-water: saw then soon where the little river fell out of gorges, and called that Gorgewater. And now fared they over Northwater and fared back again to Whitewater and up along it; it was then but a short way to that river that was athwart their way before them and fell into Whitewater; that called they Thwartwater; they were ware of this, that there was every water full of fishes.

And now fared they out again, back to Burg.

CHAPTER XXIX. OF THE WORKS OF SKALLAGRIM.

SKALLAGRIM was a great workman. He had with him always a mort of men: let fetch in much those takings that were at hand and were needful for the keep of men: because at first had they little livestock as against that which was needed for that throng of men there was; and what there was of livestock went then every winter self-feeding in the woods.

Skallagrim was a great ship-builder, and there was no lack of driftwood west along the Myres. He let make a farmstead at Alptaness and had there a second dwelling: let work from there out-rowings and seal fisheries and egg-takings, seeing there was then enough of all those takings, and so too of driftwood to let flit home to him. Then also were there great comings of whales ashore, and a man might shoot as he would: all was then quiet in the fishing-steads, for the wild things were without knowledge of man.

A third dwelling had he by the sea-side in the westward Myres. It was there yet better for sitting for drifts, and there he let sow the land and call the place Acres. Isles lay there out from the land that whale was found in, and they called these Whale-isles.

Skallagrim had men of his also up by the salmon rivers for fishing. Odd Live-alone he set by Gorgewater to mind the salmon fisheries there. Odd dwelt under Live-alone Brents. After him is named Live-aloneness. Sigmund was a man named, whom Skallagrim set by Northwater. He dwelt there where it was called Sigmundstead: there it is now called the Howes. After him is called Sigmundness. Afterwards he moved his homestead in to Munodsness: that seemed a readier place for salmon fisheries.

But when Skallagrim's livestock was much increased, then went the cattle all up into the fells in the summer. He found there was great odds in this, that those beasts became better and fatter which went on the heaths, and this too, that the sheep throve a-winters in the mountain dales, even though they could not be driven down. So now Skallagrim let make a farmstead up by the fell and had a dwelling there: let there tend his sheep. That dwelling Griss had ward of, and it is called after him Grisartongue.

And now stood Skallagrim's estate on many feet.

Some while later than Skallagrim had come out, came a ship from the main sea into Burgfirth, and that man owned her who was called Oleif Hialti. He had with him his wife and children and a band of kinsfolk of his beside, and had been so minded of his journey that he should find him a dwelling-place in Iceland. Oleif was a man wealthy and of great family and wise of wit.

Skallagrim bade Oleif home to lodge with him, him and all his company, and Oleif took that gladly, and he was with Skallagrim the first winter that Oleif was in Iceland. But afterward in the spring Skallagrim showed Oleif choice of land along the south of Whitewater, up from Grimswater to Flokadaleswater. Oleif took that gladly, and carried thither his home and household and set up house there where it is named Varmalech. He was a worshipful man: his sons were Ragi of Laugardale and Thorarin Ragi's brother, that took the Speakership of the Law in Iceland next after Hrafn Haengson. Thorarin dwelt at Varmalech: he had to wife Thordis, daughter of Olaf Feilan and sister to Thord the Yeller.[1]

CHAPTER XXX. OF THE COMING OUT OF YNGVAR, THE FATHER-IN-LAW OF SKALLAGRIM.

KING HARALD HAIRFAIR laid his ban on all those lands which Kveldulf and Skallagrim had left behind in Norway, and on all their fee besides which he might seize upon. He sought much too after those men who had been in their redes or private counsels, or had been aught of help to Skallagrim and his in that work that they wrought before Skallagrim fared abroad out of the land: and to such a pitch came that enmity that the King bare toward that father and son, that he made himself hateful unto all kindred of theirs or other of their affinity, or such men as he wist of that they had been in dear friendship with them. Some were dealt punishment by him, and many fled away and sought their safety, some within the land, but some fled clean away out of the land abroad.

Yngvar, Skallagrim's father-in-law, was one of those men aforesaid. He took that rede, that he laid out his fee so far as he might in loose goods and gat him a sea-going ship: manned her, and made ready to fare to Iceland, because he had heard that

Skallagrim had taken there his fixed abode and that there should be no lack of choice land with Skallagrim.

Now when they were ready and had wind at will, then sailed he into the deep and it sped him well of his journey: came he to Iceland southward of the land, and held west round Reekness and sailed into Burgfirth and held in up Longwater and so all up to the force: bare there their cargo off the ship.

But when Skallagrim heard of the coming of Yngvar, then fared he straightway to meet him and bade him to him with so many men as he would. Yngvar took that gladly; the ship was laid up, and Yngvar fared to Burg with many men and was that winter with Skallagrim. But at point of spring, Skallagrim bade him choice of land: he gave Yngvar that house which he had at Alptaness, and land inland as far as Leirulech and out as far as Streamfirth. Thereafter fared he to that out-farm, and took it unto him; and he was the ablest of men, and had a wealth of fee. Skallagrim made then a dwelling in Knarrarness and had a dwelling there long thereafter.

Skallagrim was a great iron-smith and had great smelting of ore in winter time. He let make a smithy beside the sea a long way out from Burg, there where it is called Raufarness: he thought the woods lay not over far away there. But when he found there no stone that was so hard and so smooth as might seem to him good to beat iron on (because there is there no sea-worn stone: it is there small sand all beside the sea), that was of an evening, when other men went to their sleep,[1] that Skalla-grim went down to the sea and dragged down an eight-oar ship that he had, and rowed out to Midfirthisles: then let drop his anchor-stone at the stem of the ship. And now stepped he over-board, and dived, and had up with him a stone, and brought it up into the ship. And now fared he himself up into the ship, and rowed to land, and bare the stone to his smithy and laid it down before the smithy door, and thenceforward beat his iron on it. That stone lieth there yet, and much burnt slag nigh; and that is seen of the stone, that it is hammered down, and that is surf-worn rock, and nought like to that other rock which is there, and now will not four men lift a greater.

Skallagrim wrought hard with his smith-work, but his house-carles grumbled, and thought 'twas early rising. Then made he this stave:[2]

> Much betideth that iron-smith
> Early to rise, who pennies
> Will lay up. The wind's weeds
> Welcome Viddi's brother.
> Let the sledge-hammers yell on glowing
> Gold of Beam-enjoyer,
> While stirring cots that swallow
> The storm-blast whistle.

CHAPTER XXXI. OF THE CHILDREN OF SKALLAGRIM.

SKALLAGRIM and Bera had very many children, and so it was at first that all died. Then gat they a son, and was sprinkled with water[1] and named Thorolf. But when he was waxen up, then was he early great of growth and the comeliest to look upon. That was the talk of all men, that he would be the likest to Thorolf Kveldulfson, whom he was named after. Thorolf was far beyond those of like age with him in strength: and when he waxed up, he became a master-man in most of those feats that it was then the wont of men to perform, of them that were men of doughty deeds. Thorolf was a very glad man. Early was he so far come to his full strength that he was deemed fit to accompany with other men of full age. Soon was he well loved of the folk. Right fond of him too were his father and mother.

Skallagrim and his wife had two daughters: the one was named Saeunn and the other Thorunn. They too were lasses of good make in their upgrowing.

Yet again had Skallagrim and his wife a son. That one was sprinkled with water and a name given him, and was called Egil. But when he waxed up, then might it soon be seen of him that he would be exceeding ugly and like his father, black of hair. And when he was three winters old, then was he great and strong, even as those other boys that were six winters old or seven. He was soon a chatterbox, and skilled in words. Something ill to deal with he was, when he was at play with other young folk.

That spring fared Yngvar to Burg, and this was his errand, that he bade Skallagrim to a bidding, out there at his own place, and named for that journey Bera his daughter and Thorolf her son, and any men else that she and Skallagrim would have go. Skallagrim promised he would come. Fared Yngvar then home, and made ready against the feast and let brew ale then. But when it came to the day appointed, when Skallagrim should fare to the bidding and Bera with him, then Thorolf made him ready for the journey along with them, and housecarles, so that they were fifteen together.

Egil talked of this with his father, that he would go too: "I have as much to say to them there as Thorolf," saith he.

"Thou shalt not go," saith Skallagrim; "because thou knowest not how to behave thyself in a throng of folk, where there be great drinkings. They think thee not good to do with, though thou be not drunk."

Then went Skallagrim a-horseback and rode away.

But Egil was ill content with his lot. He went out of the garth and found a certain draught-horse that Skallagrim had: fared a-back of him, and rode after Skallagrim and his. It was uneasy going for him through the marshes because he knew not the way, but yet he saw very often the riding of Skallagrim and his, when neither holt nor woodland blocked his sight.

There is that to tell of his journey, that late in the evening came he to Alptaness, then when men sate there a-drinking. Went he into the hall. But when Yngvar saw Egil, he took to him kindly, and asked why he was come so late. Egil said what Skallagrim and he had talked about. Yngvar sat Egil down by his side. Sat they over against Skallagrim and Thorolf. That was their way there at ale-quaffings that men quoth staves. Then quoth Egil a stave:[2]

> Come am I hale to hearthstone
> Of Yngvar, he that giveth
> To lads the glittering ling-thong's
> Bed, (lief would I find him!)
> Scarce shalt thou, O lavisher
> Of the light-encircl'd worm-lands,
> Find a three-year-old ode-smith
> Better than me.

Yngvar made much of that stave, and thanked Egil well for the stave; and the day after, then brought Yngvar to Egil, for skaldship's guerdon, three sea-snail shells and a duck's egg. But the day after that, at their drinking, Egil quoth another stave upon his guerdon:3

> Wise herdsman of the wound-fowl,
> To wordy Egil gav'st thou
> Three ever-silent surf-dogs
> For song's rewarding.
> And, steerer of the sea-steed,
> Still a fourth thing gav'st thou:
> Bed of the beck-partridge—
> Boon to gladden Egil!

Egil laid up for himself thanks for his skaldship with many men. There was nought else to tell of in their journey; fared Egil home with Skallagrim.

CHAPTER XXXII. OF BIORN BRYNIOLFSON AND THORA JEWEL-HAND.

BIORN was named a mighty hersir in Sogn, who dwelt at Aurland. His son was Bryniolf, who took all the inheritance after his father. The sons of Bryniolf were Biorn and Thord: they were men in their youthful age when these things betided.1

Biorn was a great man in sea-faring: was whiles a-viking, and whiles in cheaping voyages. Biorn was the ablest of men. That befell one summer, that Biorn was abiding in the Firths at a certain feast thronged with men. There saw he a fair maid, and great joy he took to gaze upon her. He asked after her, of what kindred she was. That was said to him, that she was sister to Thorir the Hersir, Hroald's son, and was named Thora Jewel-hand. Biorn set forth his wooing and bade Thora in marriage, but Thorir denied him his suit, and they parted with things in such case.

But that same autumn Biorn gathered him folk and fared with

a cutter all manned north into the Firths and came to Thorir's at such time that he was not at home. Biorn took Thora away and had her home with him to Aurland. They were there winter-long, and Biorn would fain make his wedding with her.

Bryniolf his father liked ill of that, that Biorn had done this shame unto Thorir, whereas before had long friendship been betwixt Thorir and Bryniolf: "So far shalt thou be, Biorn," saith Bryniolf, "from wedding with Thora here in mine house without leave of Thorir her brother, that she shall here so well abide as if she were my very daughter, and sister of thine."

And so must needs be everything, even as Bryniolf would bespeak it there in his household, whether Biorn liked well of it or ill.

Bryniolf sent men to Thorir to bid him atonement and redress for that journey Biorn had fared upon. Thorir bade Bryniolf send home Thora: said that no atonement might there be else. But Biorn would for no sake let her fare away, albeit Bryniolf bade this.

So wore the winter. But when it began to be spring, then talked they, Bryniolf and Biorn, one day concerning what rede they should take. Bryniolf asked what he was minded for. Biorn said that was likeliest, that he would fare away out of the land: "That is nearest to my mind", said he, "that thou find me a long-ship and a following therewith, and I fare a-viking."

"It is not to be thought of", said Bryniolf, "that I should put in thine hands a war-ship and a great following, sith I know not but that thou'dst come down in that place of all places 'twould please me least to see thee in; and now, without that, stand we in more than enough unrest because of thee. A cheaping-ship will I put in thine hands, and therewith cheaping-wares. And fare thou then south to Dublin. That is now the best spoken of of voyages. I will find thee a good ship's company."

So saith Biorn, that he needs must take it as Bryniolf would. Then let Bryniolf make ready a good cheaping-ship and found men thereto. Biorn made him ready then for that journey, and was not early ready.

But when Biorn was all ready and a fair breeze set in, then stepped he aboard of a boat with twelve men and rowed in to

Aurland, and they went up to the farmstead and to that bower which was his mother's. She sat within there, and very many women. There was Thora.

Biorn said that Thora must fare with him. They led her away, but his mother bade the women be not so bold as make them ware of this within-door in the hall: said that Bryniolf would take an ill thing in hand if he wist of this, and said that then would the way be cleared for great peril 'twixt that father and son. But Thora's clothes and precious things were there all laid ready to hand, and Biorn and his had all that along with them. Fared they now by night out to their ship: hoisted sail forthwith, and sailed out down the Sogn-sea and thereafter into the main.

They had an ill wind and big seas, and wallowed long in the main, because they were fast set on this, to get them the furthest they might from Norway. That was on a day, that they sailed from the east toward Shetland in wild weather, and struck their ship coming aland on Mosey. There bare they off the cargo and fared to the burg that was there and bare thither all their wares, and laid up the ship and mended that which was broke.

CHAPTER XXXIII. OF BIORN'S FARING TO ICELAND.

A LITTLE before winter, came a ship to Shetland from the south out of the Orkneys. They said there were these tidings, that a long-ship had come in the autumn to the isles; and that was messengers from Harald the King with this errand unto Earl Sigurd,[1] that the King would let slay Biorn Bryniolfson, whereso he might be laid hand on, and the like word-sendings made he to the South-Isles, and all as far as Dublin.

Biorn heard these tidings, and this withal, that he was made outlaw in Norway. But straightway when he was come to Shetland he had made his wedding with Thora. Sat they that winter in Moseyburg.[2]

But straightway in the spring, when the sea began to abate, Biorn launched his ship and made her ready at his hastiest. But when he was ready and had wind at will, sailed he into the main. They found a strong gale and were but a little while out: came from the south to Iceland.

The gale blew now on the land, and bare them west along the land and then out into the main. But when the breeze blew fair again for them, then sailed they toward the land. There was not a man of them ashipboard that had been before to Iceland. They sailed in into a certain firth wondrous great,3 and bare toward the western strand. There was nought seen to landward save breakers only and harbourless shores. They beat about then in the teeth of the wind, east along the land, till at last a firth was before them,4 and they sailed in up the firth till there was an end of all skerries and surf. Then they lay to at a certain ness.5 An isle lay there on the outer side, and a deep sound between: made fast there the ship. A wick went up along the western side of the ness, and up from the wick stood a great burg.

Biorn gat him into a boat, and men with him. Biorn said to his companions that they must beware and say nought touching their journeys that might stand them in trouble. Biorn, he and his, rowed to the house and met with men there to talk to. Asked they this first, where they were come aland: men said to them that that was named Burgfirth, but that house, which was there, was named Burg, and the bonder Skallagrim.

Biorn knew of him at once, and went to meet Skallagrim and they talked together. Skallagrim asked what men they were. Biorn named himself and his father, and Skallagrim knew right well of Bryniolf, and bade Biorn all his furtherance, whatsoever he stood in need of. Biorn took that thankfully.

Then asked Skallagrim, what more there might be of those men in the ship that might be men of account. Biorn said that here was Thora, Hroald's daughter, sister of Thorir the Hersir. Skallagrim was all glad at this; and so he said, that it was but just and right, for the sister of Thorir his fosterbrother, that he should do her such furtherance as she stood in need of or he had the means unto, and bade both her and Biorn be with him, with all their shipmates. Biorn took that gladly.

There was then flitted the cargo off the ship up into the home-mead at Burg. There set they their booths, but the ship was dragged up into that brook which is there. And there is it called Biorn's-infields where Biorn and his people had their booths.

Biorn and all those shipmates went to lodge with Skallagrim. He had never fewer folk about him than sixty fighting men.

CHAPTER XXXIV. OF SKALLAGRIM AND BIORN.

THAT was in the autumn, when ships had come to Iceland from Norway, that that tittle-tattle came over, that Biorn should have run away with Thora (and not by the rede of her kinsfolk), and the King had made him therefore an outlaw out of Norway. But when Skallagrim was ware of this, then called he Biorn to him and asked what way it might have fared touching his marriage, whether that had been done by kinsfolk's rede. "I looked not for this", said he, "in a son of Bryniolf, that I should not know the truth from thee."

Biorn said, "Truth alone have I said unto thee, Grim, and thou canst not blame me for that, though I should tell thee no further than thou askedst. And yet, now must go with it what is true, that thou hast heard truly that these redes were not done with the good will of Thorir her brother".

Then spake Skallagrim, exceeding wroth, "Why wast thou so bold-faced as come hither to me? or knowest thou not, what friendship was 'twixt me and Thorir?"

Biorn saith, "I knew it," saith he, "that 'twixt you was foster-brotherhood and dear friendship. But for this cause sought I home to thee, that here was I borne aland; and I knew it should nought avail me to seek to escape from thee. It will now be in thy power, what my lot must be; but I look for good hereof, in that I am homeman of thine".

And now stood forth Thorolf, son of Skallagrim, and laid many words thereto, and bade his father hold not Biorn guilty in this, sith even so he had taken to Biorn. Many others there laid words thereto. So it came about, that Grim was appeased: said that Thorolf should rule in this: "And take thou to Biorn, if thou wilt, and be good to him even as thou wilt".

CHAPTER XXXV. OF THE BIRTH OF ASGERD: AND HOW
THOROLF SKALLAGRIMSON WENT WITH BIORN TO
NORWAY.

THORA bare a child that summer, and that was a little
maid: she was sprinkled with water and a name given her,
and was named Asgerd. Bera found a woman to mind the
little maid.

Biorn was that winter with Skallagrim and all his shipmates.
Thorolf made great friends with Biorn, and was ever in company
with him.

But when spring came, it befell upon a day that Thorolf went
to talk with his father and asked him this: what rede he would
lay down for Biorn, his winter-guest, or what help and overseeing he would afford him. Grim asked Thorolf what he had
in mind.

"That have I in mind," saith Thorolf, "that Biorn would
liefest fare to Norway, if he might be there in peace. Methought
that rede might lie i' the way, father, that thou send men to
Norway to bid atonement for Biorn; and Thorir will set great
account by word of thine."

So well came off Thorolf in setting forth of his case, that
Skallagrim was turned by it and found men for faring abroad
that summer. These men fared with word-sending and tokens
to Thorir Hroaldson and sought atonement betwixt him and
Biorn. But straightway when Bryniolf knew of the word-
sending, then set he all his mind on this, to bid atonement for
Biorn. So came it about then in this matter, that Thorir took
atonement for Biorn; because he saw this, that it was so come
about that Biorn need not now be afeared for himself.

Then took Bryniolf on him atonement for Biorn. But Grim's
messengers were for the winter with Thorir, and Biorn was that
winter with Skallagrim. But the summer after fared Skallagrim's messengers back, and when they came back in the
autumn then said they these tidings, that Biorn was taken into
peace in Norway.

Biorn was yet a third winter with Skallagrim; but afterward

in the spring he made ready for faring away, and that band of men that had thither followed him. But when Biorn was ready for his journey, then said Bera that she will that Asgerd, her fosterdaughter, stay behind; but Biorn and his wife took that offer, and the maid was left behind and brought up at Skallagrim's. Biorn gave good gifts to them, Grim and Bera.

Thorolf, the son of Skallagrim, took rede to fare with Biorn, and Skallagrim found him means to the journey. He fared abroad in the summer with Biorn. It sped them well of their journey, and they came in from the main deep at Sogn-sea. Sailed Biorn then into Sogn, and fared thereafter home to his father. Thorolf fared home with him. Bryniolf took to them then in joyful wise.

Thereafter was word sent to Thorir Hroaldson: Bryniolf and he appointed a meeting betwixt them. There came thither Biorn too to that meeting. He and Thorir made firm then the atonement between them. And now Thorir paid out of hand that fee which Thora owned in his garth; and now took they up, Thorir and Biorn, friendship besides their ties of affinity. Biorn was then at home at Aurland with Bryniolf. Thorolf was there too, in all good esteem with that father and son.

CHAPTER XXXVI. OF THE KING'S SON ERIC, AND THOROLF SKALLAGRIMSON.

HARALD the King had for long whiles his seat in Hordaland or Rogaland at those great houses that were his, at Outstone or Ogvaldsness or at Fitiar, at Alrekstead or at Lygra, at Seaham. But that winter, that was now told of, was the King north in the land. But when Biorn and Thorolf had been one winter in Norway and spring came, then made they ready their ship and gathered strength of men thereto: fared in the summer a-viking eastaway, and fared home at autumn and had won them great fee. But when they came home, then heard they that King Harald was then in Rogaland and would sit there through the winter. Then took King Harald to age greatly, but

his sons were then much gotten upon their legs. Eric, the son of
King Harald, that was called Bloodaxe[1] was then in his youthful
age. He was at fostering with Thorir Hroaldson the Hersir. The
King loved Eric most of all his sons. Thorir was then in the
greatest loving-kindness with the King.

Biorn and Thorolf and their folk fared first to Aurland when
they came home, and thereafter began they their journey north
into the Firths to see Thorir the Hersir at his house. They had
a caravel[2] that twelve men or thirteen rowed of each side of, and
they had near thirty men. That ship had they gotten in the
summer a-viking: she was much painted down to the water-
line, and was of the fairest. But when they came to Thorir's,
found they there good welcome and tarried there awhile; but
the ship floated under her tilt before the farmstead.

That was on a day that those two, Thorolf and Biorn, went
down to the ship. They saw that Eric, the King's son, was there:
went at whiles out aboard the ship, whiles up aland: stood then
and looked upon the ship.

Then spake Biorn to Thorolf: "Much wondereth the King's
son at the ship; and bid thou him receive it of thee. For I wot
that that shall be to us a great help with the King, if Eric is our
upholder. I have heard that said, that the King hath a heavy
mind towards thee, for thy father's sake".

Thorolf said that that would be a good rede. Therewith went
they down to the ship, and Thorolf spake: "Narrowly look'st
thou on the ship, King's son: or how seemeth she to thee?"

"Well," saith he. "'Tis the fairest of ships," saith he.

"Then will I give thee", said Thorolf, "the ship, if thou wilt
receive her."

"Receive her I will," saith Eric. "And it will seem to thee
but a little reward, though I pledge thee my friendship. But
there is hope yet in that, if I live long enough."

Thorolf saith that that reward seemed to him much more
worth than the ship. Thereafter they parted. But from that time
forth was the King's son all merry with Thorolf and his.

Those two, Biorn and Thorolf, come to talk with Thorir,
what he thinketh, whether that be true indeed, that the King
hath a heavy mind towards Thorolf. Thorir hideth it not, that

he had heard that. "Then would I this," said Biorn, "that thou fare to see the King and set forth Thorolf's case before him; because one fate shall go over us two, Thorolf and me. So did he unto me then when I was in Iceland."

So came it about, that Thorir promised to fare to the King, and bade them try if Eric, the King's son, would fare with him; but when Thorolf and Biorn came to talk of this with Eric, then promised he to take a hand in the business with his father.

So now fared they, Thorolf and Biorn, their ways into Sogn; but Thorir and Eric, the King's son, manned that caravel, the new-given, and fared south to meet the King, and fell in with him in Hordaland. He took to them joyfully. Tarried they there awhile and looked for a chance to come upon the King when he was in good mood: bare then up that matter before the King: said that that man was thither come who was named Thorolf, son of Skallagrim: "This would we bid of thee, King, that thou be mindful of this, that kinsmen of his have done well to thee; and let him not have to pay for that which his father did, albeit it was in avenging of his brother".

Thorir talked of this in gentle wise, but the King answered somewhat short: said that they had stood in much untowardness because of Kveldulf and his sons, and deemed this was to be looked for, that that Thorolf should be of like frame of mind with his kinsfolk: "They be all of them", said he, "overweening men, so that they know no measure, and care not a jot whom they have to deal with".

Therewith took Eric up the word: said that Thorolf had made friends with him and given him a noble gift, that ship which they had there: "I have pledged him my friendship full and perfect. Few will come forward to make friends with me, if this shall nought avail. Thou wilt not let that be so, father, with that man who hath been first to do this, to give me a costly treasure".

So it came about, that the King promised them this before he ended, that Thorolf should be in peace as for him: "But I will not", quoth he, "that he come and see me. But thou mayest make him, Eric, as dear to thee as thou wilt, ay, or more of those kinsmen; but one of two ways will it be, either that they will show themselves gentler unto thee than unto me they have shown them, or thou wilt repent thee of this boon, and of this too, that thou lettest them long be with thee".

After this fared they, Eric Bloodaxe and Thorir, home into the Firths: thereafter sent word and let say to Thorolf how it had turned out, their errand unto the King. Thorolf and Biorn were that winter with Bryniolf: but many summers 3 lay they a-viking, and in winters they were with Bryniolf, and at whiles with Thorir.

CHAPTER XXXVII. ERIC BLOODAXE IN BIARMALAND.

ERIC BLOODAXE now took power. He had the overseeing of Hordaland and about the Firths. Then took he and had with him bodyguardmen.

And one spring made ready Eric Bloodaxe for faring into Biarmaland,¹ and picked carefully his folk for that journey. Thorolf betook him to that journey with Eric, and was in the stem of his ship and bare his banner. Thorolf was then bigger and stronger than every man else; and like, in that, to his father.

In that journey was much to tell of. Eric had a great battle in Biarmaland beside the Dwina; there gat Eric the victory, as it saith in his songs; and in that journey gat he to wife Gunnhild,² daughter of Ozur Toti, and had her home with him. Gunnhild was of all women the comeliest and the wisest and much learned in wizardry: great loving-kindness was betwixt those two, Thorolf and Gunnhild. Thorolf was then ever a-winters with Eric, but in the summers a-viking.

That befell then next to tell of, that Thora, Biorn's wife, took a sickness and died. And a little after that, Biorn gat him another wife; she was named Alof, daughter of Erling the Wealthy out of Oster. They had a daughter, who was named Gunnhild.

There was a man named Thorgeir Thornfoot. He dwelt in Hordaland in Fenhring, at a place named Ask. He had three sons: one was named Hadd, the second Bergonund,³ the third was named Atli the Short. Bergonund was bigger and stronger than all men else, and was a stubborn man and ill to deal with.

Atli the Short was a man not tall but burly-built and was strong and powerful. Thorgeir was a man exceeding wealthy of fee; he was a great man for blood-sacrifices and learned in wizardry. Hadd lay out a-viking and was seldom at home.

CHAPTER XXXVIII. THOROLF COMETH HOME TO ICELAND.

THOROLF SKALLAGRIMSON made ready one summer for a cheaping-voyage: was minded then (and so too he did) to fare to Iceland and see his father. He had then been long abroad. He had then fee past all telling and many costly treasures.

But when he was ready for his journey, then fared he to see Eric the King: and when they parted the King put into Thorolf's hand an axe that he said he would give to Skallagrim. The axe was snag-horned and great and dight with gold and the shaft mounted with silver, and that was the most precious of treasures.

Thorolf fared on his journey as soon as he was ready, and it sped him well and he came with his ship into Burgfirth and fared straightway quickly home to his father: that was a great joyful meeting when they met. And now fared Skallagrim to the ship for Thorolf's belongings: let lay up the ship: but Thorolf fared home to Burg with eleven men. But when he was come home, bare he unto Skallagrim the greetings of King Eric, and brought him that axe that the King had sent him. Skallagrim took the axe, held it up and looked at it awhile, and spake nought about it: fastened it up near his bed.

That was in the autumn, on a day at Burg, that Skallagrim let drive home a great many oxen that he was minded to hew. He let lead two oxen together under the house-wall, and lead them with their heads each across other. He took a great slab of stone and shot it down under their necks. And now went he to it with the axe, King's-loom, and hewed the oxen both at a stroke, so that it took the heads off both of them: but the axe crashed down on the stone, so that the mouth burst all out and ripped up through the tempered steel. Skallagrim looked at the edge, and spake nought about it: therewith went in into the firehall, and climbed then up on to the wainscot-post and shot the axe up above the door-beam. There it lay through the winter.

But in the spring, Thorolf gave out that he meant to fare abroad that summer. Skallagrim letted him from this: said that "'Good it is to drive home with sound waggon.' Thou hast", said he, "fared an honourable journey and a great one, but that is a saying, 'many wendings, divers endings'. Take thou now here such share of fee as thou thinkest shall be enough to make thee a man of substance".

Thorolf said that he will yet fare one more journey, "And I have a needful errand[1] for my faring. But when I come back the second time, I will here take up my set abode. But Asgerd thy fosterdaughter shall fare abroad with me to see her father: that was his bidding to me when I fared from the east".

Skallagrim said he might have his way, "But so sayeth my mind hereof: if we two part now, we shall not meet together afterwards".[2]

And now fared Thorolf to his ship and made ready that. But when he was all ready, they brought the ship out to Digraness, and lay there for the breeze. Fared then Asgerd to the ship with him; but before Thorolf fared from Burg, then went Skallagrim and took the axe down from the door-beam, the King's gift, and went out with it. By then was the shaft black with smoke, and the axe gone to rust. Skallagrim looked at the edge of the axe; then he gave the axe to Thorolf. Skallagrim quoth a stave:[3]

> Many a flaw there lieth
> (I've a soft switch's care-bed:
> An ill cheat's in the axe-blade,)
> I' the edge of the raging wound-wolf.
> With's smoke-grim'd shaft let muck-horn
> Hie back to him that gave it.
> No need t' have sent it hither:
> That was a prince's giving.

CHAPTER XXXIX. THORUNN SKALLAGRIM'S DAUGHTER GIVEN IN MARRIAGE.

THAT befell to tell of, while Thorolf had been in the outlands and Skallagrim dwelt at Burg, that upon a summer came a cheaping-ship from Norway into Burgfirth. There was then, far and wide, berths for cheaping-ships in the river or in the mouths of brooks or in sykes. There was a man named Ketil, and was called Ketil Blund, who owned that ship: he was a Norseman, of great kin and wealthy. Geir was his son named, who then was of full age and was ashipboard with him. Ketil was minded to find himself a dwelling-place in Iceland. He came late in the summer.

Skallagrim knew every deal about him. Skallagrim bade him to lodge with him with all his ship's company. Ketil took that gladly, and he was through the winter with Skallagrim.

That winter Geir, the son of Ketil, bade to wife Thorunn, daughter of Skallagrim, and that was agreed upon. Geir gat Thorunn to wife, and afterward in the spring Skallagrim showed Ketil land up from the land of Oleif beside Whitewater from Flokadalewater's-oyce, and as far as Reekdalewater's-oyce, and all that tongue that was there in the midst, up to Raudsgill, and all Flokadale up from the brents.

Ketil dwelt at Thrandsholt, and Geir at Geirslithe: he had another dwelling in Reekdale,[1] at Upper Reeks: he was called Geir the Wealthy. His sons were Blund-Ketil[2] and Thorgeir Blund; the third was Thorodd Hrisa-Blund who was first to dwell at the Bushes.

CHAPTER XL. OF EGIL'S CHILDHOOD AND UPBRINGING.

SKALLAGRIM took great game in tests of strength and plays. Of that he thought it good to talk. Ball-plays[1] were then the fashion. There was there in the countryside good choice of strong men in that time, and yet was there none to match with Skallagrim. He was come then somewhat into the decline of years.

Thord was the name of Grani's son at Granistead, and he was the hopefullest of men and was in his youthful age. He was very fond of Egil Skallagrimson.

Egil was much a-wrastling. He was very masterful and angry tempered, and all had learnt that, to learn their sons to give way before Egil.

The ball-play was set in Whitewater-meads with great throng of men in the early winter. Men sought thither to it from far and wide about the neighbourhood: many of Skallagrim's home-men fared thither to the play: Thord Granison was mainly at the head of them. Egil bade Thord let him fare with him to the play: he was then in his seventh winter. Thord humoured him in this, and let him ride on his horse's back behind him. But when they came to the play-meeting, then were men ordered there for the play. There was come too a mort of small boys, and they made themselves another play. For that too, was order taken. Egil was allotted to play with that boy who was named Grim, the son of Hegg of Heggstead. Grim was eleven winters old, or ten, and strong for his years.

But when they fell to playing together, then was Egil over-matched for strength. Grim used his vantage all he might: then Egil became wroth, and heaved up the bat and smote Grim; but Grim laid hands on him and drave him down, a great fall, and played somewhat ill with him, and said he would lame him if he would not behave himself. But when Egil was gotten on his feet again, then went he out of the play, but the boys whooped at him.

Egil went to find Thord Granison, and said to him what had been done. Thord spake: "I shall fare with thee, and we two shall have revenge on him".

He put into his hands a beard-axe that Thord had had in his hand: those weapons were then the fashion. Go they thither where the boys' play was. Grim had then caught the ball and ran away with it, but the other boys rushed after him. Then leapt Egil at Grim and drove the axe into the head of him, so that straightway it stood in his brain. Therewith Egil and Thord went away and to their own men.

Leapt the Myresmen then to their weapons, and so on either

side. Oleif Hialti ran to those men of Burg with those men that
followed him: they were then much the stronger in numbers,
and they parted with things in such a case. From this arose that
strife betwixt Oleif and Hegg: they fought at Laxfit by Grimswater: there fell seven men, and Hegg was wounded to loss of
life, and Kvig fell, a brother of his.

Now when Egil came home, Skallagrim made as if he found
little to be pleased with in this. But Bera said that Egil was of
viking stuff, and said that that would be his lot, as soon as he had
age thereto, that they should find him warships. Egil quoth a
stave:[2]

> My mother told me
> For me they should buy
> Fleet keel and fair oars
> To fare abroad with vikings:
> To stand up in the stem there,
> Steer the good ship,
> Hold her so to harbour,
> Hew a man or twain.

When Egil was twelve winters old, he was so great of growth
that few were the men so big, and so ready of strength, as that
Egil might not get the better then of most men in the plays. That
winter (that was for him his twelfth), he was much in the plays.
Thord Granison was then upon twenty year old: he was strong
of sinew.

That was oft-times, as winter wore, that these two, Egil and
Thord, were chosen to play against Skallagrim. That was on a
time that winter, as it wore by, that the ball-play was at Burg,
south in Sandwick: then were Thord and he against Skallagrim
in the play, and he waxed weary before them and their work was
lighter. But about evening, after sunset,[3] then began it to go
worse with Egil and his fellow: Grim became then so strong
that he grabbed Thord up and drave him down so hard that he
was all to-broken, and straightway gat his bane.

Thereupon he grabbed at Egil. Thorgerd Brak was named a
bondmaid of Skallagrim's. She had fostered Egil in his childhood. She was a big woman, strong as a carle and much skilled
in wizardry. Brak spake: "Run'st thou now berserk, Skallagrim, at thine own son?"

Then Skallagrim let loose Egil, but caught at her. She doubled and ran off, but Skallagrim after her. Fared they so along the outward shore of Digraness. Then leapt she out from the cliff into the sound. Skallagrim cast after her with a great stone, and set it betwixt her shoulders, and neither it nor she came up again. There it is now called Brak's Sound.

But afterwards in the evening, when they came home to Burg, was Egil all wroth. And when Skallagrim was set down to table, and all the men of his house, then was Egil not come in to his seat. Then went he into the firehall and up to that man that there had then the overseeing of the work and the management of his fee with Skallagrim, and was most dear to him. Egil hewed him his bane-wound, and thereafter went to his own seat.

But Skallagrim spake then nought of this, and that matter lay quiet thenceforth, and that father and son spake then nought together of it, whether good or ill. And so went that winter.

Now the next summer after, came Thorolf out as was aforesaid. But when he had been one winter in Iceland, then made he ready his ship the spring after in Brak's Sound. But when he was all ready, then was that upon a day, that Egil went to find his father and bade him fetch him means to faring abroad: "I will", said he, "fare abroad with Thorolf".

Grim asked if he had spoken aught about that matter with Thorolf. Egil saith that that was not so. Grim bade him do that first. But when Egil waked that matter with Thorolf, then quoth he that this was not to be thought of, "That I should flit thee abroad with me. If thy father thinketh there is no managing thee here in his own house, then bear I no trust in this, to have thee in the outlands with me; for that will not do for thee, to show thy temper there, like as thou dost here".

"May be", said Egil, "that then neither of us will go."

The night after, was a raging gale, a southwester. And in the night, when it was mirk darkness and the tide at the flood, then came Egil there and went out aboard the ship, outside the tilt: hewed he in sunder those ropes that were on the outer side: went he straight at his swiftest up on to the gangway, and hewed those ropes that went up aland. Then the ship drove out into the firth. But when Thorolf and his were ware that the ship was adrift, leapt they into the boat: but the weather was much too wild for them to get aught done. The ship drove over to Andakil, and there up on to the eres: but Egil fared home to Burg.

But when men were ware of this trick that Egil had done, then most of them cursed it. He said that he would but for a short while let be ere he should do Thorolf more hurt and mischief, if he would not flit him abroad with him. But then took men a hand in it betwixt them, and so it came about in the end that Thorolf took to Egil, and he went abroad with him in the summer.

So soon as Thorolf was come to his ship, when he had taken that axe that Skallagrim had put in his hands he cast the axe overboard into the deep, so that it came not up again.

Thorolf fared on his journey that summer, and it sped him well on the main sea, and they came in by Hordaland. Stood Thorolf straightway north to Sogn; and there had this befallen to tell of in the winter, that Bryniolf had died of a sickness, but his sons had divided his inheritance. Thord had Aurland, that farmstead that their father had dwelt at: he had gotten himself under the hand of the King and been made a landed man. Thord's daughter was named Rannveig, the mother of Thord and of Helgi: Thord was the father of Rannveig, the mother of Ingirid, that King Olaf4 had to wife. Helgi was the father of Bryniolf, the father of Serk of Sogn, and of Svein.

CHAPTER XLI. OF BIORN AND THOROLF AND KING ERIC; AND OF EGIL AND ARINBIORN.

TO Biorn was allotted another homestead good and honourable. He gat himself not under the hand of the King, wherefore was he called Biorn the Franklin.1 He was a man wealthy in gold and a man of great largesse. Thorolf fared early to see Biorn, so soon as he came from sea, and brought home Asgerd his daughter: that was a joyful meeting. Asgerd was the comeliest of women and the most skilled, a wise woman and very well learned.

Thorolf fared to see King Eric, and when they met, Thorolf bare unto King Eric Skallagrim's greeting and said that he had taken in thankful wise[2] the King's sending: bare forward then a good long-ship's sail, that he said that Skallagrim had sent to the King: King Eric took it well of that gift, and bade Thorolf be with him for the winter. Thorolf thanked the King for his bidding: "I must now first fare to Thorir's: I have with him an errand of moment".

And now fared Thorolf to Thorir's, as he had said, and found there all good welcome. Thorir bade him be with him. Thorolf said he would take that gladly: "There is too that man with me that must have lodging there where I am: he is my brother, and he hath never before gone from home, and need he hath that I should look after him".

Thorir said it was but meet and right, though Thorolf should have yet more men with him thither: "It seemeth to us", saith he, "that that shall be bettering of our company, to have thy brother, if he is at all like thee".

Therewith fared Thorolf to his ship and let lay her up and make all snug; but he fared, and Egil, to Thorir the Hersir.

Thorir had a son that was named Arinbiorn.[3] He was somewhat older than Egil. Arinbiorn was even thus early a noble-looking man and the greatest man at feats of skill. Egil made great friends with Arinbiorn, and was ever in company with him, but there was somewhat of coldness betwixt those two brethren.

CHAPTER XLII. OF THOROLF'S WEDDING WITH ASGERD.

THOROLF SKALLAGRIMSON brought up this talk with Thorir, what way he would take that suit if Thorir should ask to wife Asgerd his kinswoman. Thorir took that lightly: said that he would be a speeder of that suit.

And now fared Thorolf north into Sogn and had with him a good company. Thorolf came to Biorn's house and found there a good welcome. Biorn bade him be with him for so long as he would. Thorolf bare quickly up his errand with Biorn: began then his wooing, and asked to wife Asgerd, Biorn's daughter. He took that suit well, and that was easy-sped with him; and that was resolved upon, so that the betrothal went forward, and a day appointed for the bridal; and that feast should be at Biorn's then in the autumn.

And now fared Thorolf back to Thorir and said to him that which had befallen to tell of in his journey. Thorir deemed well of it, that this rede should be taken. But when the appointed day was come when Thorolf should betake him to the feast, then bade he men to fare with him: bade first Thorir and Arinbiorn and housecarles of theirs and powerful bonders; and there was for that journey both throng of men and good men.

But now, when it was come near to that appointed day when Thorolf should fare from home and the bridesmen were come, then fell Egil sick, so that he was not fit to go.

Thorolf and his had a great long-ship, all manned, and fared on their journey as had been appointed.

CHAPTER XLIII. EGIL IN ATLEY.

THERE was a man named Oliver. He was a housecarle of Thorir's and was overseer and manager of his household: he had the getting in of debts and was keeper of his fee. Oliver was past his youthful age, and yet a man of the briskest.

So it befell, that Oliver had a journey from home to get in Thorir's land-rents, those that were outstanding that spring. He had a rowing-ferry, and aboard of her were twelve housecarles of Thorir's. Now began Egil to be brisk and rose up again. He thought things went somewhat deaf-like at home, now that all the men were gone away. He came to talk with Oliver, and said that he would fare with him. And Oliver thought his ship's company would not be over-great for the adding of one good man, seeing there was room in the ship. Egil betook him to that journey. Egil had his weapons: sword and halberd and buckler.

Fare they now on their journey, when they were ready, and found a hard head-wind, wild weather and unhandy; but they sought doughtily on their way, took to rowing, and shipped much sea aboard.

So betided them of their journey that they came in the afternoon to Atley, and laid her up to land there. Now there in the isle, a short way up, was a great house that belonged to King Eric, and there ruled over it that man whose name was Bard. He was called Atley-Bard, and was a great man of affairs and a good worker; he was not a man of great kindred, but very dear to King Eric and to Queen Gunnhild.

Oliver and his men drew up their ship above highwater-mark: went then to the farmstead and met Bard without and said to him of their journey, and that too, that they would fain be there for the night. Bard saw that they were much wet, and carried them to a certain firehall. That was away from the other houses. He let make a great fire for them and there were their clothes dried, and when they had taken their clothes again, then came Bard there.

"Now will we", saith he, "here set tables for you. I wot you will be ready for sleep; ye be men outwearied with storm and wet."

That liked Oliver well. Therewith were tables set and food given them, bread and butter, and set forth great bowls of curds.[1]

Bard said, "Great pity is that, now, that there is no ale within, that I might welcome you as I would. Now needs must ye put up with such fare as is to hand".

Oliver and his were exceeding thirsty, and supped the curds. After that, Bard let bear in butter-milk, and they drank that.

"Dearly would I like", quoth Bard, "to give you better drink, if it were there."

Of straw there was no lack within there. He bade them lay them down there to sleep.

CHAPTER XLIV. OF BARD'S SLAYING.

KING ERIC and Gunnhild came that same evening into Atley, and Bard had there made ready a banquet against their coming: and there should there be a blood-offering unto the Goddesses,[1] and there was a banquet of the best and great drinking within in the hall. The King asked where Bard might be, "Sith I see him nowhere".

A man saith, "Bard is without, and serveth his guests".

"Who be those guests", saith the King, "that he reckoneth that more his duty than to be in here near us?"

The man said to him that thither were come housecarles of Thorir the Hersir.

The King spake: "Go after them with all speed and call them in hither". And so it was done: said that the King will meet them. And now go they in. The King greeted Oliver well, and bade him sit over against him in the high-seat, and his fellows there out from him on either side. They did so. Egil sat next to Oliver.

And now was borne to them ale to drink. There went many health-cups, and there must a horn be drunk to every health. But as the evening wore, then it so came about that Oliver's fellows began many of them to be speechless: some spewed within there in the hall, but some found their way out before the door. Bard went hard to it, to bear them drink.[2] Then took Egil that horn that Bard had fetched for Oliver, and drank it off. Bard said that he was mighty thirsty, and brought him forthwith the horn full and bade him drink it off. Egil took the horn and quoth a stave:[3]

> Said you swig was lacking,
> Shatt'rer of helm-bane ogress?
> Where ye held feast of Goddesses?—
> Master of cheats I call thee!
> All too ill thou hiddest
> From unwitting sword-saplings,
> (An ill cheat have you cheated!)
> Bard, thine heart of evil.

Bard bade him drink, and have done with his fleering ditties. Egil drank every cup that came to him, and so too for Oliver.

Then Bard went to the Queen and said to her that that man was there who brought shame upon them, and never drank so much but that he said he was still thirsty. The Queen and Bard blended then the drink with venom, and bare it then in. Bard signed the cup: brought it therewith to the cup-maid:4 she bare it to Egil and bade him drink.

Egil drew then his knife and stuck it into the palm of his hand: he took the horn and scored runes5 thereon and did them over with the blood. He quoth:6

> Write we runes on the horn now:
> Redden the spells with life-blood:
> These be the words I'll choose for
> Root of the fierce beast's ear-tree.
> Drink we free of the draught borne
> By good gleesome bondmaids.
> Let us know how this will medicine us:
> Ale that Bard did sign.

The horn sprang asunder, and the drink spilt down into the straw.

Then it began to go ill with Oliver. Up stood Egil then, and led Oliver out to the doors, and had his sword in hand. But when they come to the doors, then came Bard after them and bade Oliver drink his parting-health. Egil took it, and drank, and quoth a stave:7

> Ale bear to me, sith ale now
> Gars Oliver turn greenish.
> Let I wild ox's bill-drops
> Drizzle through my moustachios.
> Clean miss goes thy foretelling
> What weather's toward, O spear-sky's
> Rain-boder! lo, it raineth
> Rain of Gods most High!

Egil casteth down the horn, but grabbed his sword and drew. It was dark in the fore-hall. He laid the sword through Bard's middle, so that the point leapt out at his back: he fell down dead, and the blood leapt out from the wound. Then fell Oliver, and the spew gushed out of him. Egil leapt out then forth from the

6-2

hall: then was it moonless dark without: Egil took straight to running from the house.

But within, in the fore-hall, men saw that they were both fallen, Bard and Oliver. Then came the King thither and let bear lights: then saw men what was betided, that Oliver lay there senseless, but Bard was slain, and all the floor swam with his blood. Then asked the King where might he be, that big man, that had drunken most there that evening. Men said that he went out.

"Search for him," said the King, "and let him come to me."

Now was search made for him about the house, but nought found of him. But when they came into the firehouse, there lay many men of Oliver's: the King's men asked if Egil perchance had come there. They say that he had leapt in there and taken his weapons, "And went out after that".

Then was that said unto the King. The King bade his men fare at their nimblest and take all the ships that were in the island; "But in the morning, when it is light, we shall ransack[8] all the island and then slay the man".

CHAPTER XLV. OF EGIL'S FLIGHT.

EGIL fared now through the night and looked about where the ships were. But wheresoever he came to the strand, everywhere there was men before him. He fared all that night and found never a ship: and when it began to be light, he was stood on a certain ness. He saw then an isle, and there was a sound there between, and marvellous broad. Then was this his rede, that he took his helm, sword, and spear, and broke that off its shaft and shot the shaft out to sea: but the weapons he wrapped in his overmantle and made him a bundle of it and bound it on his back. Then leapt he into the sound and stayed not till he came to the isle: it was named Sheppey, and is not a great isle, and grown over with bushes. There was in it cattle, neats and sheep, and that belonged to Atley. But when he came

to the isle he wrung out his clothes. Then was it daylight and
the sun risen.

Eric the King let ransack the isle as soon as it was light. That
went slowly, for the isle was great, and Egil was not to be found.
Then they went by ship to other isles to search for him.

That was about evening that twelve men rowed to Sheppey to
search for Egil. Even so there were many isles near by. He saw
the ship that fared to the isle. Now nine went up and split into
search-parties. Egil had laid him down in the bushes and hidden
him before the ship came to land. Now went three in each party,
but three minded the ship. And when the search-parties were
out of sight of the ship[1] then stood up Egil and went to the ship.
But they that minded the ship knew nought afore Egil was come
upon them.

He hewed one his bane-wound forthright, but another took
to running and there was there a certain bank to leap up: Egil
hewed after him and took off his foot. But one leapt aboard the
ship and pushed off with the quant-pole; but Egil drew in the
rope and leapt out aboard the ship, and there was no long
bandying of blows betwixt them before Egil slew him and
bundled him overboard. Then took he oars and rowed away in
the ship. Fared he all that night and the day after, and stayed
not till he came to Thorir the Hersir's.

Now Oliver and his fellows the King let fare in peace as for
these doings. But those men that were in Sheppey, they were
there many nights, and slew cattle for their meat, took fire and
made a cooking-place: they made it so great that it might be
seen from home, laid fire in and made a beacon. But when that
was seen, then folk rowed out to them. The King was by then
away: fared he then to another feast.

Oliver and his came home before Egil, and Thorir and Thorolf
and their folk were new come home from the bridal. Oliver said
the tidings: Bard's slaying and those chances that there had befallen, but he wist nought of Egil's farings, and Thorolf was all
unmerry, and so too Arinbiorn. It seemed to them as if he
would not come back again.

But the morning after, came Egil home. Now when Thorolf
was let know of this, then stood he up and went to find Egil and

asked him in what manner he had come off, and what to tell of
had befallen in his faring. Then quoth Egil a stave:[2]

> So have I farewell'd Listland's
> Landwarder's garth, and Gunnhild's,
> Rich in deeds (I'll draw no
> Darkling veil to hide them),
> As that some three thanes there
> Of Hlokk's thriving rowan,
> In Hell's huge dwelling,
> Hell-gone, end their goings.

Arinbiorn deemed well of this work: said that his father's duty
it was to make peace for him with the King.

Thorir saith, "That will be the talk of men, that Bard will
have gotten his deserts in this, that he was slain. And yet goeth
it over-much in Egil's family, to look too little before them lest
they stand in the King's wrath; and that turneth out for most
men a thing heavy to bear. Yet even so will I bring thee into
atonement with the King as for this time".

Thorir went to see the King; but Arinbiorn was at home, and
said one fate should go over them all. But when Thorir came to
see the King, then made he offer for behalf of Egil, bade himself
as surety, and the King's doom.[3] King Eric was of the wrathfullest, and nought easy was it to come to an agreement with
him.

The King spake and said that that would come true, even as
his father had said, that 'twould be long ere one put trust in
those kinsfolk: bade Thorir so devise as that, "albeit I do
somewhat of peace-making, Egil be not long a dweller in my
realm. But, for sake of thee, Thorir, will I take fee for those
men".

The King made the fine such as seemed him good, but
Thorir paid it all. Fared he then home.

CHAPTER XLVI. THOROLF AND EGIL HARRY IN KURLAND.

THOROLF and Egil were with Thorir in good honour and esteem; but they made ready in the spring a great long-ship and found men thereto and fared in the summer east-away and harried and gat them fee and had many battles. They held withal out to Kurland, and lay by the land there for a half month's peace and cheaping-mart.[1] But when that was ended, then took they to harrying and set on there at this stead and at that.

On a day, they set on by a certain great river-mouth; there there was withal a great forest. They took rede there for a going up aland, and split into bands of twelve men together. They went into the wood, and not long it was before the settled lands began. They robbed there and slew men, but the folk fled away and they found there no withstanding.

But when the day was far spent, Thorolf let blow to his folk for going down to the sea again. Turned men back then into the wood, there where each was standing, and so soon only could the folk be counted when they were come down to the strand. But when Thorolf was come down, Egil was not come. And then it took to darken unto night, and it seemed to them that they had no means to search for him.

Egil had gone over the wood, and twelve men with him, and they saw then great level spaces and settled land. One farmstead stood but a short way from them, and they set off to it, and when they came to it, leap they in into the house and were ware of no men there, but took those goods that were loose. There were there many houses and there was tarrying for them there a long while; but when they were come out and away from the buildings, then was the people come betwixt them and the wood, and set upon them. There was a high wood fence made betwixt them and the wood.

Then spake Egil, that they should follow him, so that they might not go at them on all sides. Went Egil then first, and then each after other, so near that there was no coming betwixt them. The Kurlanders set on fast against them, and mostly with thrust and shot, but went not to a battle of handy-strokes. Egil and his knew nought before they were gotten beside the fence, but the fence went on either hand of them and they might find no way to go forward. The Kurlanders set on after them into that pen, but some set on from without and thrust with spears and swords through the fence, while some threw clothes over their weapons.

They were wounded and next after that, laid hand on and all bound: led so home to the farmstead. That man who had that farmstead was a powerful and a wealthy. He had a son, well grown. And now it was talked on, what should they do with them. Said the bonder, that he thought that a good rede, if each were slain at the others' feet. The bonder's son said that it was now dark night, and they might not then have any sport with torturing[2] of them: he bade let them bide for morning. Then were they shot into a house and bound strongly; Egil was bound to a post, both hand and foot. And now was the house locked up strongly, but the Kurlanders went into the hall and took meat and were all merry and drank.

Egil set to work and made trial of the post till he gat it loosened up out of the floor. Therewith fell the post: Egil rid himself of the post then. And now loosed he his hands with his teeth. But when his hands were loosed, loosed he the bands off his feet. And now loosed he his fellows.

But when they were all loose, searched they about in the house, where it was likeliest to make a way out. The house was made with walls of great logs of timber, but at one end of the house was a flat shield-wainscot.[3] They leapt at that, and brake the wainscot. There was there another house that they came into. There were there too timber walls about it. Then heard they men's speech under their feet below. Then searched they about, and found a trap-door in the floor. They opened that up: there was under it a deep hole. They heard thence the speech of men.

And now Egil asked what men it might be there. That one named himself Aki, that spake with him. Egil asked if he would up out of the hole. Aki saith they would that willingly. Therewith Egil and his let down a rope into the hole (that one that they had been bounden with), and drew up there three men. Aki said that that was his two sons, and they were Danish men: had been taken in war there that last summer. "I was", said he, "well entreated i' the winter. I had much looking after of the bonders' goods, but the boys were made slaves of[4] and liked ill of their lot. In the spring we took rede and ran away, and then were found again. We were then set here, in this hole."

"It will likely be known to thee how the house here is built," saith Egil: "where it is hopefullest for us to make our way out."

Aki said that there was another shield-wainscot: "Break up that: you will then come forth into a corn-barn, and there may you go out as you will".

Egil and his folk did so: brake up the wainscot, went so into the barn and thence out. It was moonless dark. Then spake those companions, that they should speed to the wood.

Egil spake with Aki: "If the buildings here are known to thee, then mayst thou show us to some getting of goods".

Aki saith that there would be no lack there of loose goods: "Here is a great loft that the bonder sleepeth in: there lacketh not of weapons within there".

Egil bade then fare thither to the loft, and when they came up on the stair then saw they that the loft was open. There was light within there, and serving men, and they made men's beds. Egil then bade some be without and mind, so as none should come out. Egil leapt in into the loft: grabbed weapons there, because there lacked not of those within: slew there all those men that were within. They all took to themselves a full set of weapons.

Aki went to where a lid was in the floor-boards and opened it: spake, that they should go down there into the under chamber. They took them a light and went thither. There were there treasure-boxes of the bonder's, and good things of price and much silver. Men took them up burdens there and bare them out. Egil took under his arm a certain chest, big enow, and bare it under his arm.

Fared they then to the wood. But when they were come into the wood, then came Egil to a stand and spake: "This journey is altogether ill, and nought man-of-war-like. We have stole the bonder's fee, so as he knoweth nought on't. Never shall we take on us that shame.[5] Fare we back now to the house and let them know what is come about".

All spake against that: said that they would fare to the ship. Egil putteth down the chest; and now setteth he off a-running and ran to the farmstead. But when he came close to the farmstead then saw he that serving lads went from the firehall with trenchers and bare them in to the hall. Egil saw that in the firehouse was a great fire and kettles over it: went he thither. There had been big logs flitted home and so fires made, as there it is the wont to do, so as the fire shall take on the log's end, and burn so the log. Egil grabbed up the log and bare it up to the hall and shot that end, that blazed, up under the eaves and so up into the roof-barks. The fire caught swiftly on the rafters, and they that were sat a-drinking knew nought afore the whole roof stood in a blaze. Leapt men then to the doors, but there was nought of easy going out, both because of the wood and withal because Egil kept the door. Felled he men both in the doorway and out before the doors; and that was but a moment of time before the hall burnt, so that it fell in.

There perished there all the company that were within there; but Egil went back to the wood: found there his companions: fare then all together to the ship. Egil said that that chest that he came away with he will have for his private booty; but it proved to be full of silver.

Thorolf and his were right fain of Egil when he came back. Stood they out then straightway from the land when it began to be morning. Aki and his sons were in Egil's following. They sailed, as summer wore, to Denmark, and lay out there too for cheaping-ships, and robbed there when it served them.

CHAPTER XLVII. THOROLF AND EGIL HARRY IN DENMARK.

HARALD GORMSON[1] had then taken power in Denmark, but Gorm his father was then dead. The land was then open to harrying: vikings lay out much about Denmark.

Aki knew Denmark both by sea and land. Egil asked him much thereof, where those steads might be where big fee-

takings might lie to their hand. But when they came to Ere-
sound, then said Aki that there was up aland a great cheaping-
stead that was named Lund: said that there was fee to be looked
for, but likely that they would find some withstanding, where the
townsmen were. That matter was put before the men of their
host, whether they should take rede to go up thither or no. Men
took that all in divers ways: some were eager for it, but some
held back. The matter was left to the skippers. Thorolf was
somewhat eager for going up: then was counsel taken of Egil,
what seemed to him good rede. He quoth a stave:[2]

> Up with our swords a-glitter,
> O stainer of the wolf's teeth!
> Here have we deeds worth doing,
> This dalefish-bounty's season.
> Lightly up to Lund, then,
> Lads: and busk and hie ye!
> Make we there, 'fore sunset,
> Song unsweet of spear-clang.

And now men made them ready for the going up and fared
to the cheaping-stead. But when the townsmen were ware of
unpeace toward, then gathered they to meet it. There was a tree-
burg[3] about the stead: set they there men to defend it: then fell
they to battle. Egil goeth first into the burg: after that, the
townsmen fled. There was there great man-fall. They robbed
the cheaping-stead, and burnt it before they had done with it:
fared thereafter down to their ships.

CHAPTER XLVIII.   OF GUESTING WITH EARL ARNFID:
AND HOW THORIR THE HERSIR SPAKE WITH THE KING
CONCERNING THOSE SONS OF SKALLAGRIM.

THOROLF stood with his host north coasting by Halland,
and put in there to haven when the wind stopped them:
robbed there not at all. There was there a short way up
aland that Earl who is named Arnfid. But when he heard that
vikings were there come by the land, then sent he men of his to

find them, with this errand, to know whether they would there have peace-land, or harrying.[1]

But when the messengers were come with their errand and found Thorolf, then said he that there they would not harry: said that there was no need upon them to harry there and fare war-shield aloft: said that there was the land nowise wealthy.

The messengers fare back to the Earl and said to him their errand's speeding. But when the Earl was ware of this, that he need not summon a host for their sake, then rode he down with no host to meet with the vikings. But when they were met, then fared it all well there in their talk between them.

The Earl bade Thorolf to a feast with him, and his host too, so much of them as he would. Thorolf promised to come. But when it was the appointed time, the Earl let send riding-horses down to fetch them. They betook them to that journey, both Thorolf and Egil, and had with them thirty men: but when they came to the Earl he greeted them well. They were brought into the hall. There was straightway beer within there, and given them to drink. Sat they there till evening. But before it was time to take up the tables, then said the Earl that there should be lots cast for seats: there should drink together a man and a woman, so far as there were enough therefor, and those by themselves who were left over.

Men bare their lots then into the cloak, and the Earl took them up. The Earl had a daughter all fair and by then well grown: so said the lot, that Egil should sit by the Earl's daughter for the evening. She walked about the floor and made game: Egil stood up and went to that place where the Earl's daughter had sat during the day. But when men took their seats, then went the Earl's daughter to her own place: she quoth:

> What wilt thou, boy, in my seat?
> Seldom hast thou given
> Warm steaks to the wolf-folk:
> I'll be alone in my own place!
> Thou saw'st not raven yelling
> Last autumn o'er the corpse-swill:
> Thou wast not there where the shell-thin
> Sword-edges ran together.

Egil took her and set her down beside him. He quoth:[2]

> Fared I with bloody sword-blade
> (The wound-partridge follow'd me),
> And strong spear yelling:
> Set on there hard the vikings.
> Made we a wrathful rushing:
> Ran fire o'er men's dwellings:
> I let bloody bodies
> By the burg-gate gasp their lives out.

Then drank those two together through the evening, and were all merry. There was the feast of the best, and so too the day after. Fared then the vikings to their ships: they and the Earl parted with friendship, and gave and took gifts withal.

Thorolf and his folk held with their host towards the Brenneys. There in that time was a great lair for vikings, because there was much sailing of cheaping-ships through the isles. Aki fared home to his own place and his sons with him: he was a man wealthy in gold and had many dwellings in Jutland. They parted with loving-kindness and spake to great friendship betwixt them.

But when it turned to autumn, Thorolf and his men sailed north coasting along Norway and came at length into the Firths: fare to see Thorir the Hersir. He took to them well, but Arinbiorn his son much better: he bade that Egil shall be there through the winter: Egil took that with thanks. But when Thorir wist of Arinbiorn's bidding, then called he that somewhat quick-spoken: "I wot not", said he, "how King Eric will like that, seeing that he so spake, after Bard's taking off, that he would not that Egil should be here in the land".

"Thou mayst well, father," saith Arinbiorn, "take such rede with the King, as he should find no fault with Egil's being lodged here. Thou wilt bid Thorolf thy kinsman-in-law be here, but we two, Egil and I, will have but one and the same winter-quarters both of us."

But from this talk Thorir saw that Arinbiorn would have his way in this. That father and son then bade Thorolf have winter-quarters there, and he took that gladly. They were there with twelve men through the winter.

Two brethren are named: Thorvald the Overbearing and Thorfid the Strong: they were near kinsmen of Biorn the Franklin and had been brought up with him: they were big men and strong, very masterful men and self-willed. They followed Biorn then when he was a-viking; but afterward when he sat in quiet, then fared those brethren to Thorolf and were with him a-harrying. They were in the stem aboard his ship: but when Egil began to be skipper of a ship, then was Thorfid his fore-castle-man. Those brethren followed ever after Thorolf, and he set most store by them of all his shipmates. Those brethren were that winter in his company, and sat next to those brethren: Thorolf sat in a high-seat and had drink with Thorir, but Egil sat for his drink over against Arinbiorn. There was going on the floor there at every health.3

Thorir the Hersir fared in the autumn to see King Eric. The King took to him exceeding well. And when they took up their talk together, then bade Thorir of the King that he should not take that amiss that he had Egil with him for the winter. The King answereth well to that: said that Thorir might receive of him such thing soever as he would have: "But it would not fare so in this thing, if some other man had taken to Egil".

But when Gunnhild heard what they talked on, then spake she:4 "That think I, Eric, that now fareth it even as too oft it doth, that thou art much easily talked over and mindest thee not long of that where ill is done to thee. And thou wilt suffer those sons of Skallagrim to drag on5 till they shall yet smite down for thee some near kinsman of thine. Yet though thou make as if 'tis no matter to thee of Bard's slaying, for all that, it seemeth not so to me".

The King saith, "More houndest thou me on, Gunnhild, unto grim plays than all men else. Yet hath Thorolf had more kindness once at thine hands than now is; but I will not take back my word touching those brethren".

"Well was Thorolf here", said she, "before Egil spoilt him. But now I think there's nought to choose betwixt them."

Thorir fared home then when he was ready, and said to those brethren the words of the King and the Queen.

CHAPTER XLIX. OF THE DEALINGS BETWIXT EGIL AND EYVIND BRAGGART.

EYVIND BRAGGART and Alf[1] were named the brothers of Gunnhild, sons of Ozur Toti. They were big men and exceeding strong, and very masterful men. They had then the greatest esteem with King Eric and Gunnhild. They were not men well loved of the folk. They were then in their youthful age, and yet come to their full might and prime.

That was in the spring, that there should be great blood-offerings against summer at Gaular. That was the most famous high temple-stead: there sought thither great throng of men out of the Firths and from Fialir and out of Sogn, and almost all the great men of account. Eric the King fared thither. Then spake Gunnhild with her brethren: "That will I, that you two so devise it, amid this throng of men, that you get slain one or other of those sons of Skallagrim; and best, if 'twere both".

They said that so it should be.

Thorir the Hersir made him ready for that journey. He called Arinbiorn to speak with him. "Now will I", said he, "fare to the blood-offering. But I will not that Egil fare thither. I know this, of Gunnhild's tongue, and Egil's masterfulness, and the King's might,[2] that 'twill be nought easy to keep an eye on them all together. But Egil will not let himself be left, unless thou stay behind; but Thorolf shall fare with me," he said, "and the rest of their company. Thorolf shall do worship and seek the Gods' goodness for himself and his brother."

After that, Arinbiorn said to Egil that he will bide at home, "And both of us two together," said he. Egil said that so it should be.

But Thorir and his fared to the blood-offering, and there was there exceeding great throng of men and great drinkings. Thorolf fared with Thorir wheresoever he fared, and they parted never, day nor night. Eyvind said to Gunnhild that he found no way to come at Thorolf. She bade him then slay some man or other of his, "Rather than let everything go miss".

That was of an evening, then when the King was gone to

sleep, and so too Thorir and Thorolf, but those two still sat there, Thorfid and Thorvald, that thither came then those brethren, Eyvind and Alf, and sat them down beside them and were all merry. First drank they all in company. Then it came that they should drink half the hornful apiece: there drank together Eyvind and Thorvald, but Alf with Thorfid. But as the evening wore, then fell they to drinking unfairly, and next to that, with bandyings of words, and then with great boastings.

Then leapt Eyvind up and drew a sax-knife and stabbed Thorvald so that that was enough and more for his bane-wound. Therewith leapt they up of both sides, the King's men and housecarles of Thorir's; but men were all weaponless within there, because it was there the holy temple-stead, and men went betwixt them and parted those that were maddest wroth. Then was nought else befallen to tell of that evening.

Eyvind had slain in the sanctuary,3 and was become a wolf so, and needs must he forthwith fare away. The King bade boot for the man, but Thorolf and Thorfid said that they had never taken man-boot and they would nowise take this. They parted with things in such case. Thorir and his fared home.

King Eric and Gunnhild sent Eyvind south to Denmark to King Harald Gormson, because he might not bide there within the law of Norway. The King took well with him and his companions. Eyvind had along with him to Denmark a long-ship exceeding great. And now the King set Eyvind there for warding of the land against vikings. Eyvind was the greatest man of war.

But when spring was come after that winter, then made they ready, Thorolf and Egil, yet again to fare a-viking. But when they were ready, then stand they yet again eastaway. Now when they come into the Wick, then sail they south along Jutland and harry there, and then fare they to Frisland and tarry a long while there in the summer, but then stand they yet again back toward Denmark. But when they come to the lands-meet, there where Denmark meets with Frisland, and lay to then by the land, then was that of an evening, when men made them ready for sleep aboard their ships, that two men came to Egil's ship and said that they had with him an errand. They were brought to him. They say that Aki the Wealthy had sent them thither with this errand, that "Eyvind Braggart lieth out off Jutland-Side and meaneth to sit for you then when you fare from the south; and he hath a great host drawn together, so that there shall be for you no holding out against him, if you fall in with all that host of his. But himself fareth with two light ships, and is now but a short way from you".

But when those tidings were come to Egil, then let they straightway strike tilts. He bade them fare all silently. They did so. They came at dawn upon Eyvind and his, there where they lay at anchor. Forthwith they set upon them: let go both with stones and weapons: there fell there much folk of Eyvind's, but he himself leapt overboard and came aland by swimming, and so withal all that folk of his that escaped away. But Egil and his took the ships and their clothes and weapons.

Fared they back then by daylight to his folk: met then with Thorolf. He asketh, what way Egil had fared, or where had he gotten those ships that they fare with. Egil saith that Eyvind Braggart had had the ships, and they had taken them from him. Then quoth Egil:4

> Somewhat hard our work was
> Awhile by Jutland-Side there:
> Warréd well that viking,
> Warden of the Dane-realm;
> Till, swift-faring to strandward,
> Swimming with all his war host,
> East from back of wave-steed
> Off loup'd Eyvind Braggart.

Thorolf said, "In these things I think you have so wrought, that 'twill not be rede for us this autumn-long to fare to Norway".

Egil said that that was well, though they should seek now for another abiding-place.

CHAPTER L. THOROLF AND EGIL IN ENGLAND.

ALFRED THE GREAT ruled over England. He was the first of his kinsfolk to be sole King of all England. That was in the days of Harald Hairfair, Norway's King. After him was King in England Edward his son: he was father of Athelstane the Victorious, the fosterer of Hakon the Good.

In that time Athelstane took kingdom in England after his father. There were more brothers besides, sons of Edward. But when Athelstane had taken kingdom, then bestirred them to unpeace those lords that before had lost their dominions to the Kings of that house and line. It seemed to them as if now should be the happy time to claim their own, when a young King ruled the realm. That was both Welsh and Scots and Irish. But King Athelstane gathered unto him a host of war, and gave war-service to all those men that would have that for to get them fee, both outland men and inland.

Those brethren, Thorolf and Egil, stood south coasting by Saxland and Flanders. Then learned they that England's King thought he needed men, and that there there was great fee-gain to be looked for. Make they then that their rede, to betake them thither with their folk. Fared they then about autumn till they came and met with King Athelstane. He took to them well, and shewed that he thought there should be great strengthening of his forces with their following. Soon cometh it to this in the talk of England's King, that he biddeth them to him to take war-service there and become his land-warders. They settle that betwixt them, that they become Athelstane's men.

England was christened, and had long been so, when these things befell. King Athelstane was well christened. He was called Athelstane the Faithful. The King bade Thorolf and his brother that they should let themselves be prime-signed,[1] because that was then greatly the fashion both with chapmen and with those men that took war-service with christian men, because those men that were prime-signed had use of all matters in common alike with christian men and with heathen, but had that to trow in which was most to their liking. Thorolf and Egil did that according to the King's asking, and let prime-sign them both. They had there three hundred of their own men that took war-service with the King.

CHAPTER LI. OF OLAF THE SCOTS-KING, AND OTHERS.

OLAF THE RED[1] was named the King of Scotland. He was Scot by the father's side but Dane by the mother's side, and come of the line of Ragnar Hairybreeks.[2] He was a powerful man. Scotland was called a third part of the realm as against England.

Northumberland is called the fifth part of England, and that is northernmost next to Scotland on the eastern side. That had the Dane-Kings had in ancient days. York is there their chief stead. That realm Athelstane owned, and had set over it two earls: one was named Alfgeir and the other Godrek. They sate there for warding of the land, both against onset of the Scots and the Danes and the Northmen, who harried much in the land, and thought they had great claims to the land there, seeing that in Northumberland were those men only (of men of any account) that were of Danish blood by their fathers' or their mothers' side, and many by both the one and the other.

Over Wales ruled two brethren, Hring and Adils, and were scat-payers under Athelstane the King; and from that it followed that, when they were in the host with the King, they and their folk must be in the front of the battle-array before the King's banners. Those brethren were the greatest men of war, and not very young men.

Alfred the Great had taken from all the scat-kings both name and power. They were then named earls, that before were kings or kings' sons. That held all his days, and the days of Edward his son; but Athelstane came young into kingdom, and it seemed as if men should stand in less dread of him. Then began many to be untrustworthy, those that were before full of service.

CHAPTER LII. OF OLAF THE SCOTS-KING'S WARRING AGAINST ENGLAND.

OLAF the Scots-King drew together a great host of war, and therewith fared south to England. And when he came to Northumberland, he fared all ways war-shield aloft; but when the earls, that there held sway, heard tell of that, summon they forces together and fare against the King. But when they are met, there befalleth a great battle, and ended so, that King Olaf had the victory, and Earl Godrek fell; but Alfgeir fled away and the most part of that host that had followed them and that escaped away out of the fight.

Then found Alfgeir no means to make a stand. King Olaf laid then all Northumberland under him. Alfgeir fared to see King Athelstane and said unto him of their ill speeding. But straightway when King Athelstane learned that so great a host of war was come into his land, then sent he straightway men from him and summoned him forces: sent word to his earls and other great men. Then straightway turned the King on his way with that force that he had gotten, and fared against the Scots.

But when that was told abroad, that Olaf the Scots-King had gotten the victory and had laid under him a great part of England, then had he a much greater war-host than Athelstane's, and then sought unto him a mort of powerful men. And when Hring and Adils hear tell of this, they had drawn together a great host. Then turn they, and join force with King Olaf. Then had he and his a host beyond all telling.

Now when Athelstane learned of all this, then held he a meeting with his captains and counsellors: sought to find then what rede was likeliest to take to: said then clearly to the whole folk that which he had heard of the Scots-King's doings and of his great throng of men. All spake there on one wise: that Earl Alfgeir had herein held the worst part, and they thought that lay next to do, to take his titles from him. But this rede-taking was determined of: that King Athelstane should fare back again and fare into southern England, and then have a host-gathering before him northward through all the land; because they saw

that else it should be but slow work of gathering so great throng
of men as was need of, if the King himself drew not the folk
unto him.

But that host of war that then was come together there, thereover the King set then as captains Thorolf and Egil. They
should command that host which the vikings had had thither
unto the King, but Alfgeir himself had then still the command
over his own host. Then found the King withal captains of
companies, as seemed him good.

Now when Egil came back from the meeting to his fellows,
then asked they what he knew to tell them of tidings of the
Scots-King. He quoth:[1]

> Olaf hath hurl'd one war-lord
> In mad flight before him—
> ('S a hard man to hold Thing with,
> That Prince)—and fell'd another.
> Paths far a-gley must Godrek
> Tread in those deadly moorlands.
> Englanders' scourge hath 'neath him
> Of Alfgeir's land the half laid.

And now send they messengers to King Olaf, and find this
for their errand: that King Athelstane will hazel him a field,[2]
and will offer him for battle-place Winaheath[3] beside Wina-
wood; and he will that they harry not in his land, but let that
one of them rule the realm of England who shall get the victory
in that battle. He laid down a week's delay for their meeting,
and let that one bide a week for the other, whichsoever shall
come there first.

Now that was then the wont, as soon as a field was hazelled
for a king, that he could not harry (without shame unto himself)
until the battle was over. King Olaf did on such wise, that he
halted his war-host and harried not and bided till the day appointed. Then flitted he his war-host to Winaheath. A burg
stood to the north of the heath. King Olaf sat him down there
in the burg, and had there the most part of his folk, because
there were wide settled parts round about, and he thought it
better there for the getting in of that provision that the war-host
had need of. But he sent men of his up upon the heath, there

where the battle-place was appointed: they should take there places for tents and make things ready there before the host of war came.

But when those men came to the place where the field was hazelled, then were set up there hazel-poles all round to mark out where that place was where the battle should be. Needful it was to choose that place carefully, that it should be level, where a great host of war should be arrayed. And so it was there, where the battle-place should be, that there was a level heath, and one way from it fell a certain river, and another way from it was a great wood. But there where it was shortest betwixt the wood and the river, and that was yet a long way, there had King Athelstane's men pitched their tents. Their tents stood on all the ground betwixt the wood and the river. They had so pitched their tents that there were no men in every third tent, and few withal in any one; but when King Olaf's men came to them then had they thronged their men forth before all the tents, and King Olaf's men found no means of coming into them. Athelstane's men said that their tents were all full of men, so that there was nowhere near room for the host that was theirs. Withal, the tents stood so high that there was no seeing over them, whether they stood many deep or few only.

They thought, that there must be a war-host indeed.

King Olaf's men pitched their tents north of the hazels, and the ground was all somewhat falling away on that side. Athelstane's men said, too, from one day to another, that their King would then come (or would be come already) into that burg that was southaway under the heath. Folk drew to them both day and night. But when that appointed time was passed that had been fixed, then send Athelstane's men errand-runners to see King Olaf with these words, that Athelstane the King is ready for battle, and "Hath a host of war exceeding great. But he sendeth to King Olaf these words, that he will not that they make so great man-spill, as there it tended toward: bade him the rather fare home to Scotland; but Athelstane will find him, as gift of friendship, a shilling of silver for every plough in all his realm, and will that they league themselves together in friendship".

But when the messengers come to King Olaf, then was he in hand to make ready his war-host and was minded to ride out to battle; but when the messengers bare up their errand, then the King stayed his journey as for that day: sat then to take rede, and the captains of his host of war along with him. All unlike were men's counsels in this matter. Some urged much that they should take that choice: said that here was then befallen the greatest glory of their journey, if they should fare home and have taken gild so great of Athelstane. Some letted it, and said that Athelstane would bid much more the next time, if that were not taken; and this rede they determined on.

Then besought the messengers that King Olaf should give them time to see King Athelstane and try if he would pay yet more gild out of hand so that there might be peace. They bade a truce of one day for riding home, and another for taking counsel, and yet a third for coming back again. The King yea-said them this.

Fare the messengers home, and come back the third day, as was appointed: say to King Olaf that Athelstane will give all, even as he bade before, and besides, for a booty-sharing for King Olaf's host, a shilling for every man freeborn, and a mark for every captain of a company, to them that hold command over twelve men or more, and a mark of gold to every leader of a bodyguard, and five marks of gold to every earl. And now the King let bear this up before his folk. It was even as before, that some letted but some urged it. But in the end, the King gave his ruling: saith that this choice he will take, if that follow withal, that King Athelstane let him have all Northumberland with those scats and dues which there belong.

The messengers ask for yet three days' delay, and this withal, that King Olaf send now men of his own to hear the word of King Athelstane, whether he will or not have this choice: say that they think that King Athelstane would let few things stand in the way, so peace might be gotten.

King Olaf saith yea to that, and sendeth men of his own to King Athelstane. Ride then the messengers all together and find King Athelstane in that burg that was nighest to the heath on the south side. The messengers of King Olaf bear up their

errand before King Athelstane, and their peace-offer. King
Athelstane's men said too with what offers they had fared to
King Olaf, and this withal, that that was by the rede of wise
men, to delay so the battle while the King was not come.

But King Athelstane gave swift ruling in this matter, and said
unto the messengers as thus: "Bear these words of mine unto
King Olaf, that I will give him leave for this, to fare home to
Scotland with his folk: and let him pay back all that fee that he
took up with wrongfulness here in the land. Set we here thenceforth peace between our lands, and let neither harry other. That
shall follow too, that King Olaf shall become my man, and hold
Scotland from me, and be under-king of mine. Fare ye now",
saith he, "back again, and say to him that so it standeth".

The messengers turned back on their way forthwith that
evening, and came to King Olaf near middle night. Waked they
up the King then, and said to him straightway the words of King
Athelstane.

The King let straightway call to him the earls and other
captains: let then the messengers come to him and say out loud
their errand's ending and the words of King Athelstane. But
when these things were made known to the men of his host, then
was there but one thing in the speech of all of them, that that
would lie next to do, to make ready for battle. The messengers
said this withal, that Athelstane had a throng of folk, and that he
had on that same day come to the burg when the messengers
came there.

Then spake Earl Adils: "Now cometh it to light, King, even
as I said, that you would find what tricksters these English be.[4]
Here have we sat long whiles, and waited till they have drawn
to them all their force; and their King will have been nowhere
near then, when we came hither. They will now have gathered
great forces since we were sat down. Now this is my rede, King,
that we two brethren ride forth straightway in the night with our
host. That may be, that they have now no fear for themselves,
sith they have learnt that their King is nigh with a great host of
war. We two shall then give them an onfall; and when they are
put to a rout, then will they lose their folk, and be unbolder after
that for setting on against us".

This rede seemed to the King well thought on: "We will make ready our war-host soon as it is light, and fare to meet you".

They determined of this rede, and so brake up their meeting.

CHAPTER LIII. THE BATTLE ON WINAHEATH.

EARL HRING and Adils his brother made ready their war-host and fared straightway in the night south to the heath; and when it was light, then Thorolf's watchmen saw where that war-host fared. Then was blown the war-blast, and men clad them for war: took then to drawing up their folk for battle, and had two battles. Earl Alfgeir commanded one battle, and there was a banner borne before him. There was in that battle those people which had followed him, so too those people which had gathered there out of the countryside. That was a much greater host than that which followed Thorolf and his brother.

Thorolf was so arrayed that he had a shield wide and thick, a helm on his head exceeding strong; girt with that sword that he called Long,[1] a great weapon and a good. A halberd had he in his hand; the feather[2] was two ells long, and forged in the front-ward with a four-edged spike; but upwards was the feather broad, the socket both long and stout; the shaft was not so tall but that the hand might reach to the socket, and wondrous stout; an iron bolt was in the socket, and the shaft was all lapped with iron. Those spears were called byrny-twisters.[3] Egil had the same array as Thorolf. He was girt with that sword that he called Nadder. That sword had he gotten in Kurland: that was the best of weapons. Neither of them had a byrny.[4] They set up their banner and Thorfid the Strong bare it. All their folk had Norse shields and all Norse war-gear. In their battle were all the Norsemen, those that were there.

Thorolf and his drew up their battle near the wood, but the battle of Alfgeir fared beside the river.

Earl Adils and his brother saw this, that they would not come upon Thorolf and his folk at unawares. Then took they to drawing up of their host for battle. They, likewise, made two battles, and had two banners. Adils drew up his battle against Earl Alfgeir, but Hring against the vikings.

And now began the battle there. They went forth well of either side. Earl Adils set on hard before him, till Alfgeir began to fall back and give way, but Adils's men set on then twice as boldly. And no long time it was then, before Alfgeir fled. And there is that to be said of him, that he rode away south over the heath and a band of men with him. He rode so far till he was come near to that burg where the King sat. Then spake the Earl: "I mean not that we should fare to the burg. We found great clatter of words about us, when last we came to the King, then when we had fared without victory from before King Olaf; and nowise will he think we have bettered our estate by this journey. No need now to think on redress where he is". Therewith rode he south through the land, and it is to be said of his journey that he rode day and night till they came west to Earlsness. There the Earl found him passage south over the sea and came away to Valland. There had he his kinsfolk of one side. Never from that time forth came he to England.

Adils first drave the flight, but not long ere he turned back thither where the battle was and there made onset. But when Thorolf saw that, turned he to meet the Earl and bade thither bear the banner: bade his men follow up well and stand close: "Move we toward the wood," he said, "and let that cover our back, so that they may not go at us on all sides". They did so: drew up along the wood side. Then was the battle hard. Set on Egil against Adils, and hard dealings they had betwixt them. The odds of strength was exceeding great, and yet fell more folk on the side of Adils.

Thorolf began then to be so wood-wroth5 that he cast his shield over his back and took his spear in two hands: leapt he then forth and hewed or thrust on either hand. Sprang men back from him then either way, but he slew many. Cleared he so a path forward to the banner of Earl Hring, and then was no holding against him. He slew that man that bare Earl Hring's banner, and hewed down the banner-pole. And now laid he his spear through the Earl's chest, through byrny and body, so as out it went betwixt the shoulders, and heaved him up on the halberd over his head and shot down the tail of the spear into the earth. But the Earl perished on the spear; and that in the sight of all, both his own men and his unfriends likewise.

And now Thorolf drew his sword, and hewed he then on either hand. Then withal set on his men there. Fell then much folk, Welsh and Scots, but some turned to flight. But when Earl Adils saw his brother's fall, and great man-fall in his host, and some fled, and he thought a hard thing was come upon him, then turned he to flight and ran to the wood. He fled into the wood, and his company with him. Took then to fleeing all that host that had followed them. There befell then great man-fall among the men that fled, and the flight drifted then wide about the heath. Earl Adils had flung down his banner, and none knew then whether 'twas he that fared there or other men.

It began soon now to darken toward night, and Thorolf and Egil and their men turned back to their war-booths, and in that same hour came there King Athelstane with all his war-host and set up then their land-tents[6] and put them in order. A little later came King Olaf with his host of war. They pitched their tents and put them in order, there where their men had pitched. It was then said unto King Olaf that fallen were both those Earls of his, Hring and Adils,[7] and a great multitude besides of his men.

CHAPTER LIV. THE SECOND DAY'S BATTLE ON WINA-HEATH: WITH THE FALL OF THOROLF SKALLAGRIMSON.

KING ATHELSTANE had been the night before in that burg which was aforesaid, and there heard he that there had been fighting on the heath: made ready then straight-way, and all his war-host, and set forth north to the heath: learned then plainly of all that had betided, what way that battle had gone.

Came then to see the King those brethren, Thorolf and Egil. He thanked them well for their forwardness and for that victory which they had won: promised them his friendship full and perfect. Tarried they there all together for that night.

King Athelstane waked up his war-host straightway in the morning at point of day. He held talk with his captains and said what ordering there should be of his host. He ordered first his own battle, and then set he in the front of that battle those companies that were the keenest in fight. Then spake he, that over that host should be Egil; "But Thorolf", said he, "shall be with his own host and that other host that I set there. That shall be the second battle of our host, that he shall be captain over, because the Scots be ever loose in battle-array: leap they to and fro, and come forth in this place and in that. Oft can they give good scratches, if men be not wary of them, but they scatter on the field if face be made against them".

Egil answered the King: "I will not that we two, I and Thorolf, be parted in the fight. But well do I think it, if we be posted there where most need seemeth and hardest work toward".

Thorolf spake: "Let the King have his way,[1] where he will post us two. Let us do for him as he shall like. I will be, if thou hadst rather, there where thou art posted".

Egil saith: "You will have your way now. But of this ordering belike I'll oft repent me".

Went men then into their battle-array, even as the King had ordered, and the banners were set up. The King's battle stood on the open country reaching to the river, but Thorolf's battle fared the upper way along the wood.

King Olaf took then to drawing up of his host, when he saw that King Athelstane had drawn up his. He, too, made two battles, and he let fare his banner, and that battle that he himself had command of, against King Athelstane and his battle. They had then of either party a war-host so great that there was no odds betwixt them, which had the greater throng of men; but the other battle of King Olaf fared near the wood, against that host that Thorolf had command over. The captains there were Scottish earls. That was Scots for the most part, and that was a great host of men.

And now go their battle-arrays together, and there soon befell there a great battle. Thorolf set on hard and let bear his banner forward beside the wood, and was minded there to go so far forward as he might come at the King's battle at open shields.[2] They had their shields before them, but the wood was on their right: they let it cover them on that side. Thorolf went forth so far that few men of his were before him; and when he was least on his guard, then leap there out of the wood Earl Adils and that company that followed him. Turned there straightway many halberds at once against Thorolf, and he fell there by the wood-side; but Thorfid, who bare the banner, sprang back there where the host stood thicker, but Adils set on then against them, and there was then a great battle. The Scots whooped then the whoop of victory, since they had felled the captain.

But when Egil heard that whoop, and saw that Thorolf's banner turned heel, then he thought he knew that Thorolf himself would not be following it. And now leapt he thither, forth betwixt the battle-lines. He was quickly ware of those tidings that were there befallen, soon as he found his men. Then egged he on the host much to the onset. He was first in the battle-front. He had the sword Nadder in his hand. He set on there and hewed on either hand and felled many men. Thorfid bare the banner close after him, but the rest of the host followed the banner: the battle was there of the sharpest. Egil went forth till he was met with Earl Adils. They had few blows betwixt them before Earl Adils fell, and a mort of men about him; but after his fall, then fled that host that had followed him, but Egil and his host followed them and slew all they caught, for no need there was then to bid for quarter.

But those Scottish earls stood then no long time, soon as they saw that the others, their fellows, fled; took straight to running away. But Egil and his held on then to where was the King's battle, and came upon them at open shields, and wrought there swiftly great man-fall. Then was their battle-line riddled and all loosed asunder. Fled then many of Olaf's men, but the vikings whooped then the whoop of victory. Now when King Athelstane thought he found that the battle of King Olaf began to break, then egged he on his host and let bear forward the banners: made then a hard onset so that the host of Olaf rocked before it, and there befell there exceeding great man-fall. There fell King Olaf[3] and the most part of that host that Olaf had had, because they who turned to flight were all slain that were caught.

King Athelstane gat there an exceeding great victory.

CHAPTER LV. EGIL IN KING ATHELSTANE'S HALL.

KING ATHELSTANE turned from the battle, but his men drave the flight. He rode back to the burg and stayed not for night-quarters until he was in the burg; but Egil drave the flight, and followed them long, and slew every man that he could catch.

And now he turned back with the men of his company and fared thither where the battle had been, and there came upon Thorolf his brother, dead. He took up his corpse and washed it; and then did with it like as it was fit to do. Dug they there a grave, and set Thorolf therein with all his weapons and his clothes. After that, Egil clasped a gold ring[1] on either arm of him before he parted with him. And now piled they stones over him, and sprinkled earth. Then quoth Egil a stave:[2]

> He that ne'er quail'd for terrors,
> The earl-man's bane, went forth there:
> High-hearted, in the Thunder-God's
> Huge clash fell Thorolf.
> Earth greens beside the Wina,
> For me, but this remaineth:
> To hide—(Hell's sorrow is that!)—
> Grief for my noble brother.

And again he quoth:[3]

> West, with pil'd slain I loaded
> Field before the banners.
> 'Twas biting sleet I storm'd there
> 'Gainst Adils with my blue Nadder.
> With th' Englanders young Olaf
> Thunder-crash of steel rais'd.
> Hring (so ravens starv'd not)
> Out-stay'd the Thing of Weapons.

And now fared Egil with his company to find King Athelstane, and went straightway before the King where he sate a-drinking. There was great noise and cheer there. And when the King saw that Egil was come in, then spake he that room should be made for them on the lower bench, and spake, that Egil should sit there in the high-seat over against the King.

Egil[4] sat him down there, and shot down his shield before his feet. He had helm on head, and laid his sword across his knees, and whiles he drew it halfway, and whiles he slammed it back into the scabbard. He sat upright, but his head was much bent. Egil was great of face, broad of forehead, with great eye-brows: the nose not long, but marvellous thick: that place wide and long where the moustachios grow: the chin wonderfully broad, and so all about the jaw: thick-necked and great-shouldered beyond the measure of other men: hard-looking and grim-like whensoever he was wroth. He was of goodly growth and taller than any man else: his hair wolf-grey and close of growth, and become early bald.

Now while he sat as is afore-writ, he kept a-twitching now one now another of his eye-brows down toward the cheek, and the other up toward the hair-roots. Egil was black-eyed and his eye-brows joined in the middle.[5] Nought would he drink, though drink were borne to him, but twitched his eye-brows, now one now the other, down and up.

King Athelstane sat in the high seat. He laid his sword too across his knees: and when they had sat so for a while, then drew the King his sword from its scabbard and took a gold ring from his arm, great and good, and drew it over the sword's point: stood up and went upon the floor and reached it over the fire to Egil. Egil stood up and drew his sword and went upon the floor. He stuck the sword in the bend of the ring and drew it to him: went back to his place. The King sat him down in his high-seat. But when Egil sat him down, he drew the ring on to his arm, and then went his eye-brows into their right line. Laid he down then sword and helm, and took the beast's horn that was borne to him, and drank it off. Then quoth he:[6]

> The byrny's god hath granted
> Gleaming thong of paw-tongs
> To hang for me on hawk-trod
> Hanging-tree of Vingi.
> On spear-storm fish's gallows
> The snare of red gold mount I:
> The feeder of the battle-fowl
> To fresh lauds aredes me.

Thenceforth Egil drank his share, and spake with other men.

After that, the King let bear in two chests. Two men bare each. They were both full of silver. The King spake: "These chests, Egil, shalt thou have; and if thou come to Iceland, thou shalt bring this fee to thy father: as atonement for a son I send it him. But some of the fee shalt thou share with the kinsmen of thee and Thorolf, them that thou thinkest noblest. But thou shalt take here atonement for thy brother at mine hand, land or loose goods, whatsoever thou wilt rather. And if thou wilt tarry with me any long time then shall I here find thee worship and honours, even such as thou thyself canst think on to tell me of".

Egil took the fee, and thanked the King for his gifts and speech of friendship. Egil began from that time forth to be glad of himself,[7] and then quoth he:[8]

> The craggéd eaves, for grief sake,
> Of mine eye-brows droopéd.
> Now find I him who forehead's
> Unsmooth places righteth.
> My girdling rocks from face-ground
> The great Prince hath lifted—
> (Those scowls have left mine eyes now)—
> With pulling of an arm-string.

And now were those men healed who were wounded and there was yet hope of life for. Egil tarried with King Athelstane that next winter after the fall of Thorolf, and he had exceeding great honours from the King. There was then with him all that people that before had followed both those brethren and had come safe out of the battle. Then wrought Egil a drapa[9] on King Athelstane, and this is in it:[10]

> Now hath he that rouseth
> Our Ladies of the Battle-din,—
> ('Neath Ella's scion land fell)—
> Kings' head-stem, fell'd three war-lords.
> Otherwhat too wrought Athelstane:
> All's lower—(here we swear that,
> O flinger of the billow-fire!)—
> Than famous-father'd King-man.

And this is the burden in the drapa:[11]

> Now lieth loftiest reindeer-way
> Under lusty Athelstane.

Athelstane gave then to Egil, for skaldship's guerdon, two gold rings, and each stood at a mark; and there went with them a costly mantle, that the King himself had worn before.

But when it began to be spring, Egil made it known unto the King that he was minded to go away that summer, and to Norway, "And see what hath betided in the matter of Asgerd, that woman whom Thorolf hath had to wife, my brother. There standeth there much fee, and withal I know not whether there be children of theirs alive. I have them to look after, if they be alive, but I have all the inheritance if Thorolf hath died childless".

The King said, "That will be, Egil, for thine own ruling, to fare away from hence, if thou thinkest thou hast an errand of moment. But that way seemeth to me best, that thou take up here thy fixed abode with me, and such terms thereto as thou likest to ask for".

Egil thanked the King for his words: "I will now fare first, even as my duty beareth. But that is likely enough, that I shall come hither to call to mind these promises when I find I may".

The King bade him do so.

And now made Egil ready for going away with his folk, but much of them tarried behind with the King. Egil had a great long-ship, and aboard of her a hundred men, or well that. And when he was ready for his journey and had wind at will, then stood he out into the deep. He and King Athelstane parted with great friendship. He bade Egil come back at his speediest. Egil said, so it should be.

And now steered Egil for Norway, and when he came in sight of land he fared at his swiftest into the Firths. He heard this for tidings, that Thorir the Hersir was dead, but Arinbiorn had taken the inheritance and was made a landed man. Egil went to see Arinbiorn and found there good welcome. Arinbiorn bade him be there. Egil took that willingly. He let lay up the ship and find quarters for the folk. But Arinbiorn took to Egil and eleven of his men, and they were with him for the winter.

CHAPTER LVI. OF EGIL'S WEDDING AND OF HIS HOME-
COMING; AND OF HIS FARING ABROAD THE SECOND
TIME AND HIS SUIT AGAINST BERGONUND AT THE GULA-
THING.

BERGONUND,[1] son of Thorgeir Thornfoot, had then
gotten to wife Gunnhild, the daughter of Biorn the
Franklin. She was come to keep house with him at Ask.
But Asgerd, whom Thorolf Skallagrimson had had to wife, was
then with Arinbiorn her kinsman. Thorolf and she had one
young daughter that was named Thordis, and the maid was
there with her mother.

Egil said unto Asgerd of Thorolf's death, and bade her his
guardianship. Asgerd became very unmerry with that tale, but
answered well to what Egil said to her and showed little of what
was in her mind.

And as autumn wore, Egil took to great ungladness: sat oft
and drooped his head beneath the folds of his cloak. On a time
went Arinbiorn to him and asked what made his ungladness:
"Now, though thou'st gotten great scathe of thy brother, yet is
that like a man to bear that well. 'Man must outlive man', or
what quothee now? Let me now hear".

Egil said that but a short while since quoth he:[2]

> The young hawk-cliff's goddess
> Herself from me estrangeth.
> Well durst I lift aforetime
> The thwart crags of my forehead.
> Needs must skald, whenas 'girdle
> Of Bergonir' to mind comes,
> Haste to hide in cloak-folds
> High altar of his brow-fold.

Arinbiorn asked what woman that might be that he wrought
love-songs upon: "Thou hast hidden her name in the stave".

Then quoth Egil:[3]

> Seldom in Narfi's scion's,
> Suttung's, feast-fare hide I
> Name of sea-fire goddess,
> —(Sorrow swells the heart-burg),

'Cause dighters of the din-thing
Dear unto the Valkyries
Might feel with their poet-fingers
Fount of the Lord of Strife.

"Here will it be", saith Egil, "as oft is spoke, that 'All can
be said to a friend'. I will say to thee that which thou askest,
upon what woman I work my songs. 'Tis Asgerd, thy kinswoman; and there would I have thy backing, that I may get her
in marriage".

Arinbiorn saith that seemeth to him well thought on: "I shall
surely lay word thereto, that this rede be taken".

And now Egil bare that suit before Asgerd, but she left it to
the ruling of her father and of Arinbiorn her kinsman.

And now talketh Arinbiorn with Asgerd, and she for her part
had the same answer. Arinbiorn urged this marriage. And now
fare they, Arinbiorn and Egil, to find Biorn, and then beginneth
Egil his wooing and bade to wife Asgerd, Biorn's daughter.
Biorn took that suit well, and said that Arinbiorn would have
much of the ruling in this. Arinbiorn urged it much, and so
ended the matter that Egil plighted troth with Asgerd, and the
bridal should be at Arinbiorn's. So when the appointed day was
come, then was the feast there exceeding noble when Egil made
his wedding. He was then all merry the rest of that winter.

Egil made ready in the spring a cheaping-ship for Iceland-
faring. Arinbiorn counselled him that, to take not up his abode
in Norway while the might of Gunnhild was so great, "For she
is all heavy against thee," saith Arinbiorn; "and that hath spoilt
things greatly when thou and Eyvind met together off Jutland".

And when Egil was ready and had wind at will, then saileth
he into the main sea, and it speedeth him well of his journey.
He came about autumn to Iceland and stood in to Burgfirth.
He had then been abroad twelve winters.

Skallagrim was then become an old man. Joyful was he then,
when Egil came home. Egil fared to Burg for lodging, and with
him Thorfinn the Strong and very many along with them. They
were with Skallagrim for the winter. Egil had then fee beyond
all telling. But it is not told that Egil shared that silver which

King Athelstane had put into his hands, neither with Skallagrim nor with other men.

That winter gat Thorfinn to wife Saeunn, Skallagrim's daughter, and afterward in the spring Skallagrim found them homestead at Longwater-force and land in from Leirulech betwixt Longwater and Alptawater all up to the fell. The daughter of Thorfinn and Saeunn was Thordis, whom Arngeir of Holm had to wife, the son of Bersi the Godless. Their son was Biorn the Hitdale Champion.[4]

Egil tarried now with Skallagrim certain winters. He took to him the management of fee and the household business no less than Skallagrim. Egil was become bald-headed too.

Then was the neighbourhood begun to be settled far and wide. Hromund, brother of Grim the Halogalander, settled then in Thwartwater-lithe, and his shipmates. Hromund was father of Gunnlaug, the father of Thurid Dandle, the mother of Illugi the Black.[5]

Egil had then been, while many winters came and went,[6] at Burg. Then was it, of a certain summer, when ships came out of Norway to Iceland, that these tidings were heard from the east, that Biorn the Franklin was dead. There followed that tale, that all that fee which had belonged to Biorn, Bergonund had taken up, his son-in-law: he had flitted home to his own place all the loose goods, and the estates he had settled and set apart for himself all the land-rents. He had withal seized unto himself all those estates that had belonged to Biorn.

And when Egil heard these things, then asked he carefully whether perchance Bergonund had by his own redes gone forward in these things, or had he put his trust there in greater men. It was said to him, that Onund was come into great friendship with King Eric, and withal into dearer friendship yet with Gunnhild.[7]

Egil let that rest for the autumn. But when winter wore and it began to be spring, then let Egil set forth a ship that he had, that had been berthed in the shed by Longwater-force: he made ready that ship for the main sea, and gat him men. Asgerd his wife was minded for that journey, but Thordis, Thorolf's daughter, stayed behind. Egil sailed into the main sea when he was ready. Of his faring is nought to say until he came to Norway: he betook him straight to find Arinbiorn, the first he might. Arinbiorn took to him well, and bade Egil be with him. He took that thankfully: they fared, both he and Asgerd, thither, and certain men with them.

Egil came soon to talk with Arinbiorn about those fee-claims that Egil thought he had there in the land. Arinbiorn saith, "That suit seemeth to me unhopeful. Bergonund is hard, and ill to deal with, wrongful and greedy of fee, and he hath now great upholding of the King and the Queen. Now, Gunnhild is thy most unfriend, as thou knowest before; and she will not press Onund to make an agreement in the suit".

Egil saith, "The King will let us have the law and our rights in this suit. Besides, with thee to aid me, that groweth nought great in mine eye, to go to law with Bergonund".

They took that rede at last, that Egil mans a cutter: fared they aboard of her nigh twenty men. They fared south to Hordaland and come their ways to Ask. Go they there to the house, and meet with Onund. Then beareth Egil up his suit, and craveth of Onund a sharing of Biorn's inheritance, and saith that the daughters of Biorn were equal heirs of him at law, "Though it seemeth to me", quoth Egil, "as if Asgerd would seem to be born of much better lineage than Gunnhild, thy wife".

Then saith Onund very loud and saucily,[8] "Thou'rt a marvellous bold man, Egil, an outlaw of King Eric's, that thou farest hither into his land and thinkest here to attack his men. Thou mayst so bethink thee, Egil, that I have bowled over such as thou art, and for less cause than methinks is here, when thou claim'st heritage for behalf of thy wife; seeing 'tis known to all the folk that she's thrall-born o' the mother's side".

Onund was wild spoken for a time. And when Egil saw that Onund would make no agreement in this suit, then Egil summoneth him to the Thing, and leaveth the suit to the Gula-Thing's[9] Law. Onund saith, "Come will I to the Gula-Thing. And well I would that thence thou come not hale away".

Egil saith that he will take the hazard of this, to come yet to the Thing for all that: "Be it then as may, howso our suits shall end".

And now fare Egil and his men away, and when he came home he saith to Arinbiorn of his journey and of Onund's answers. Arinbiorn was exceeding wroth that Thora, his father's sister, was called bondwoman.[10]

Arinbiorn fared to see King Eric: bare up before him this suit. The King took his suit somewhat heavily, and saith that Arinbiorn had long much followed up Egil's suits: "He hath had thee to thank for this, that I have let him be here in the land. And now 'twill seem to me a steep thing,[11] if thou uphold him in this, to go against friends of mine".

Arinbiorn saith, "Thou wilt let us have the law in this suit".

The King was somewhat sulky at this suit. Arinbiorn deemed that the Queen would yet be much more ill-willed. Arinbiorn fareth back, and said that things turned somewhat unhopefully.

Weareth now the winter, and the time cometh when men fare to the Gula-Thing. Arinbiorn gathered great throng of men for the Thing. Egil was a-faring with him. King Eric was there, and had great throng of men. Bergonund was in the King's following and those brethren of his, and they had a great following. But when the Thing was to try the suits of men, then went they of either side thither where the court was set, to bring forward their proofs. Onund was then full of big words. But there, where the court was set, was a level field, and there were set hazel-poles in the field in a ring, and laid thereon on the outer side twisted ropes round about. That was called the hallowed bands. But in the inside of the ring sat the judges, twelve from the Firthfolk, and twelve from the Sognfolk, twelve from the Hordafolk: those three twelves of men must there judge the suits of men. Arinbiorn had the ruling in this, who the judges were from the Firthfolk, and Thord of Aurland, who they were from Sogn. They were all of one party.

Arinbiorn had had great throng of men to the Thing. He had a snake-ship all manned and had withal a mort of small ships, cutters and rowing-ferries, which the bonders steered. King Eric had there a great host: long-ships, six or seven. There was withal great throng of men of the bonders.

Egil so began his suit, that he craved that the judges should give him lawful judgement in his suit betwixt him and Onund. Then he set forth what proofs he had in his claim touching that fee that had been Biorn Bryniolfson's. He said that Asgerd, daughter of Biorn and wedded wife of Egil, was come into the inheritance, and that she was odal-born[12] and of landed men born in all branches of her kin, and noble-born[13] too further back in her lineage. He craved this of the judges, to adjudge unto the hand of Asgerd half of Biorn's heritage, lands and loose goods.

But when he ceased from his talking, then Bergonund took up the word.[14] "Gunnhild, my wife," said he, "is daughter of Biorn and of Alof, that woman whom Biorn had lawfully wed. Gunnhild is right heir of Biorn. For that cause took I up all that fee which Biorn had owned and left after him, because I knew that there was besides only that other daughter of Biorn who had no right to take heritage. Her mother was took by war, and thereafter taken like a harlot (and not by rede of her kinsfolk) and flitted from land to land. But thou, Egil, think'st to fare here, even as in other places wheresoever thou comest, with thine overmastery and unjustness. And now will that not avail thee here, because King Eric and Queen Gunnhild have promised me this, that I shall have my rights in every suit, there where their might standeth aloft. I will bring forward true witnesses before the King and the judges, that Thora Jewel-hand, the mother of Asgerd, was war-taken from the house of Thorir her brother, and another time from Aurland, from Bryniolf's. Fared she then abroad out of the land with vikings and outlaws of the King, and in that outlawry was gotten by Biorn of her a daughter, this Asgerd. Now is a marvel here, of Egil, when he thinketh to make unspoken[15] all the words of King Eric: that first, sith thou, Egil, hast been here in the land since King Eric made thee an outlaw—and that, though thou hast gotten to wife a bondwoman, to call her rightful heir. This will I crave of the judges, that they adjudge unto me all Biorn's inheritance, but adjudge Asgerd the King's bondwoman, because she was so begotten that then was her father (and her mother too) in outlawry of the King."

Then Arinbiorn took up the word: "Witness will we bring forward, King Eric, to this (and let oaths follow), that that was settled in the atonement betwixt Thorir, my father, and Biorn the Franklin, that Asgerd, the daughter of Biorn and Thora, was brought into the inheritance after Biorn, her father, and that withal, which to yourself is known, King, that thou madest Biorn be lawfully within the land, and then was an end put to all that matter that before had stood i' the way of men's being set at one".

The King maketh no speedy answer to his suit.

Then quoth Egil:[16]

> He saith, this Thorn of Thornés,
> My thorn-bearer thrall-born is.
> This Onund so, meseemeth,
> To serve his self-greed deemeth.
> My brooch-goddess, spear-brandisher,
> A bride to heirship born is:
> Oath-true is that: take now,
> Rich man, the oaths we'll make now.

Arinbiorn then let bear forward his witness twelve men, and all of good credit, and they had all been there and heard the atonement betwixt Thorir and Biorn, and offered then to the King and to the judges to swear thereto. The judges were willing to take their oaths, if the King banned it not. The King said he would not meddle there either way, to give leave for that or ban it.

Then took up the word Gunnhild the Queen: said as thus: "This is a wonder, King, how thou lettest this great Egil tangle all suits in thy despite. Or whether wouldst thou not open thy mouth against him, though he claimed thy kingdom at thine hand? But though thou wilt give no ruling when that might be of help to Onund, yet shall I not bear it that Egil tread so under foot friends of mine, that he take with his wrongfulness this fee from Onund. But where art thou, Ashman?[17] Fare thou to't with thy following, there where the judges be, and let them not judge this wrongful judgement".

Therewith leapt Ashman and they of his following to the court: cut asunder the hallowed bands and brake down the poles and scattered the judges. Then was made a great uproar at the Thing; but men were there all weaponless.

Then spake Egil: "Whether can Bergonund hear my words?"

"I hear," said he.

"Then will I bid thee to the holmgang:[18] and this, that we fight here at the Thing. Let that one have this fee, lands and loose goods, that shall get the victory. And be thou every man's dastard, if thou durst not."

Then answereth Eric the King: "If thou, Egil, art bent on fighting, then shall we now give thee that".

Egil answereth: "I will not fight with thee, nor with over-mastering odds. But before an even strength of men, then will I not flee, if that be granted me. And I should not pick and choose[19] then, neither".

Then spake Arinbiorn: "Fare we away. Nought shall we get done here, as for this time, that can help us". Therewith turned he away, and all his folk with him.

Then turned Egil back, and said: "Unto this call I to witness thee, Arinbiorn, and thee, Thord, and all those men that now may hear my words, landed men and lawmen, and all the common sort, that I ban all those estates that Biorn hath owned, whether to settle or to work: ban I thee, Bergonund, and all other men, inland and outland, with titles of honour or without, and upon whatso-ever man shall do that, lay I withal law-breaking against the rights of the land, and truce-sundering, and the anger of the Gods".[20]

Then Egil gat him gone with Arinbiorn. Fared they now to their ships, over a rising brow whereby the ships could not be seen from the Thing.

But when Arinbiorn came to his ship, he spake: "That is known of all men, in what sort here the Thing hath ended, that we have not gotten the law; but the King is wroth so exceedingly that methinks 'tis to be looked for that our men will suffer a hard choice from him, if he may. I will now that every man fare to his own ships and fare home". Then spake he with Egil, "Go thou now aboard thy ship, and thy companions, and get you away, and ward yourselves, because the King will seek to bring about a meeting betwixt you and him. Seek then to find us, whatever may befall betwixt you and the King".

Egil did as he spake. They went aboard a cutter, thirty men, and fared at their hardest. The ship was exceeding swift. Then rowed a throng of other ships out of the haven, that were Arinbiorn's, cutters and rowing-ferries. But a long-ship, that was Arinbiorn's, fared last because she was heaviest under oars. But Egil's cutter gat swiftly ahead. Then quoth Egil a stave:[21]

> The liar that lies to heirship
> Looks to sweep heirship from me:
> His hights I'll meet, and hates too,
> Howe'er, this heir of Thornfoot.
> Whenso, stock's sorrow's
> Syth'd of earth, I've gott'n him
> Apaid for all such robberies.
> (Earth-dweller's bed we strove for.)

King Eric heard those parting words of Egil's, which he spake latest at the Thing, and he became exceeding wroth; but all men had gone weaponless to the Thing; for that cause the King made no onslaught upon him. He bade his men all go to the ships, and they did as he spake. Then the King summoned a house-thing,[22] and spake his mind then: "We shall now let strike tilts on our ships. Now will I fare to find Arinbiorn and Egil. I will, withal, make this known to you, that I will take the life of Egil, if we may bring it about, and spare none of them that will stand i' the way of it".

After that, went they out to the ships and made them ready at their swiftest, and stood out with their ships and rowed thither where the ships of Arinbiorn had been. Then let the King row after them north into the sounds. But when they came into the Sogn-sea they saw the host of Arinbiorn; then turned the long-ships in toward Saudungsound, and then turned the King thitherward. He met there with Arinbiorn's ship, and the King straightway laid aboard of her and hailed her. The King asked whether Egil were there aboard the ship.

Arinbiorn answered: "He is not aboard of my ship. You will soon, King, be able to see that. There be those only here on board whom you will know; and Egil will not be a-skulking down under the decks, though ye chance to meet together".

The King asked what was the last Arinbiorn knew of him, but

he said that Egil was with thirty men in a cutter, "And they fared on their way out toward Steinsound".

The King and his had seen that many ships had rowed toward Steinsound. The King spake that they should row in along the inner sounds and so stand to meet with Egil and his folk.

A man is named, Ketil. He was a man of King Eric's body-guard. He gave the course for the King's ship, but he steered her himself.[23] Ketil was a big man in growth and fair to see and a near kinsman to the King, and that was the talk of men, that he and the King were alike in outward seeming.

Egil had let launch his ship and flitted her cargo aboard, before he fared to the Thing: and now fareth Egil thither where the cheaping-ship was, and they went up aboard the ship; but the cutter floated, with rudder shipped, between the ship and the land, and the oars lay in the loops.[24] But in the morning when it was scarce grown light, they become aware, who held watch, that big ships rowed at them. But when Egil knew that, then stood he up forthwith. Saw he at once that unpeace was come: there were there six long-ships and stood towards them. Then spake Egil that they should leap all into the cutter. Egil took up two chests that King Athelstane gave him: he had those ever with him: they leapt into the cutter. He took his weapons swiftly, and all they too, and rowed forth betwixt the land and that snake-ship that fared nearest to the land. Now that was the ship of Eric the King. But because it was all done of a sudden and there was yet but little daylight, the ships sped past one another, and, as the poops bare together, Egil shot a spear, and it came on that man's middle who sat a-steering. And that was Ketil the Franklin.

Then calleth out King Eric, and bade men row after Egil and his. But when the ships passed near the cheaping-ship, then leapt men of the King's up aboard of the ship, and those men that had been left behind of Egil's men and leapt not into the cutter were then all slain, those that were caught, but some leapt aland. There lost their lives there ten men of Egil's following.

Some of the ships rowed after Egil and his, but some robbed the cheaping-ship: there was there taken all the fee that was on board, but they burnt the ship. But they that rowed after Egil and his strove fiercely: took hold two on one oar. There was no lack of folk aboard there, but Egil's ship was thinly manned. They were then eighteen aboard the cutter. Then drew they together. But of the inner side of the island was a shoaling sound somewhat shallow betwixt it and another island. It was ebb-tide. Egil and his rushed the cutter into that shallow sound, but the snake-ships could not float there, and there was their parting with them. Then turned the King back south, but Egil fared north to find Arinbiorn.

Then quoth Egil a stave:[25]

> Now hath the thunder-lord of fight-flame,
> Fierce of heart (while I yet
> His wite escapéd) fell'd me
> Ten thanes of our following;
> 'Cause straight from mine hand sent,
> Wound-salmon goddess's
> Thick quivering thorn flew
> Thorough ribs of Ketil.

Egil came to find Arinbiorn and saith unto him these tidings. Arinbiorn saith that he could have hoped for nothing better from their dealings with King Eric. "But thou wilt not lack for fee, Egil. I shall pay boot to thee for the ship, and find thee another that thou mayest well be able to fare in to Iceland."

Asgerd, Egil's wife, had been with Arinbiorn since they fared to the Thing. Arinbiorn found Egil a ship that was fit for the main sea and let load her with wood. Egil maketh ready that ship for the main sea, and had then withal nigh thirty men. Then parted he and Arinbiorn with friendship.

Then quoth Egil:[26]

> So should the Powers pay him:
> This prince, O Gods, from land drive!
> High Ones, be wroth, and Odin:
> His robberies avenge Ye!
> Forth let the folk-despoiler
> Flee from the land, O Land's God!
> O Frey and Niord, abhor Ye
> The foe that wrongs the hallows!

CHAPTER LVII. EGIL MADE OUTLAW FROM END TO END
OF NORWAY: OF HIS VENGEANCE TAKEN UPON BER-
GONUND AND OTHERS, WITH HOW HE LAID A SCORN
UPON KING ERIC AND THE QUEEN AND CAME HOME
AGAIN TO ICELAND.

HARALD HAIRFAIR set his sons in power in Norway
then when he began to be old. He made King Eric over-
king over all his sons: and when Harald had been seventy
winters King, then gave he over his realm into the hand of his
son Eric. In that time bare Gunnhild a son,[1] and King Harald
sprinkled him with water and gave him his own name, and let
that follow, that he should be King after his father if his life
should last therefor. Harald the King sate then in his seat in
quiet, and sate oftenest in Rogaland or Hordaland. But three
winters later died Harald the King in Rogaland, and there was
made a howe after him beside Howesound. But after his death
was great strife betwixt his sons, because the dwellers in the
Wick took to them Olaf for King, and the Thrandheimers
Sigurd: but Eric felled then both these brethren of his in Tunsberg one winter after the death of King Harald. That was all of
one summer, that King Eric fared from Hordaland with his war-
host east to the Wick to do battle with his brethren, and before
this had they striven at the Gula-Thing, Egil and Bergonund,
and these tidings befallen that now were said of.

Bergonund was at home at his own place, then when the King
fared with his war-gathering, because it seemed to him unwary
to fare from his house so long as Egil was not fared away out of
the land. There was his brother Hadd then with him. There was
a man named Frodi, a kinsman of King Eric's and a fosterson
of his. He was the fairest of men, young of years, and yet grown
man. King Eric left him behind to take care of Bergonund:
Frodi sat at Alrekstead at the King's house and had there a company of men. Rognvald[2] is named, a son of King Eric and
Gunnhild: he was then of ten or eleven winters, and was the
fairest of hopeful young men. He was then with Frodi when
these tidings befell.

But before King Eric rowed on that war-gathering, he made Egil an outlaw from end to end of Norway, for every man to slay.

Arinbiorn was with the King in his war-gathering. But before he fared from home, then laid Egil his course to the main sea and held towards those outer fishing-grounds that are called the Beacons,3 out from Aldi: that lieth off the highway of the sea. There were fishermen there, and it was good there to learn tidings. Then learnt he that the King had made him an outlaw.

Then quoth Egil a stave:4

> For me the law-breaker makes laws—
> Long ways for me to journey:
> His bride it is hath blinded
> The brother-murthering shield-elf.
> Gunnhild I have to thank for't,
> To drive me from the land so.
> She's cruel. Ere now, when young, I've had
> Swift vengeance, whoso griev'd me.

The weather was with little wind, fell-wind a-nights but sea-breeze by day. On an evening sailed Egil and his out into the deep; but the fishermen rowed then in to land, those that had been set for espial of Egil's faring. They knew this to say, that Egil had put out and sailed to sea and he was away. They let bring this news to Bergonund; and when he knew these tidings, he sent then from him all those men that he had before had there for safety. Rowed he then in to Alrekstead and bade Frodi to him, because Bergonund had much ale at home at his house. Frodi fared with him and had with him certain men. They took there good feasting and had great gladness. Then was all there without fear.

Rognvald, the King's son, had a caravel:5 there rowed six men aboard her. She was painted all down to the water-line. He had with him ten men or twelve, those that followed him everywhere. And when Frodi was gone from home, then took Rognvald the caravel, and they rowed out to Herdla, twelve in company. There was a great house of the King's, and that man had charge of it who was named Skegg-Thorir. There had Rognvald been at fostering in his childhood. Thorir took joyfully to the King's son. There lacked not there, neither, great drinking.

Egil sailed out toward the main sea at night, as afore was written, and when it dawned the wind fell and there came a calm. They laid her then before the waves and let her ride so for certain nights, but when a sea-breeze came on, said Egil to his shipmates, "Now will we sail toward land, because I know not for sure, if the sea-wind come up stormy, where we shall then take land, but 'tis some likelihood of unpeace for us in most places".

The sailors bade Egil rule their journey. Then took they to sailing, and sailed in to Herdla-weir. There found they a good haven and tilted their ship and lay to then for the night.

They had aboard the ship a little boat, and Egil gat him into it with two men. Rowed he then in by night to Herdla: sent there a man up into the isle to ask tidings; and when that one came down to the ship he said that there at the farmstead was Rognvald, the King's son, and his men. "Sat they then a-drinking. I met one of the housecarles, and that one was drunk with ale and said that here should not less be drunken than at Bergonund's, for all that Frodi were there a-feasting and they five in company." No more men, he said, were there than the homemen, save Frodi only and his men.

So now rowed Egil back to the ship, and bade men stand up and take their weapons. They did so. They laid the ship out at anchor. Egil let twelve men mind the ship. But he fared in the cock-boat eighteen in company: rowed therewithal in up the sounds: they timed it so that they came at evening in to Fenhring and laid to there in a hidden creek. Then spake Egil: "Now will I go alone up into the isle and aspy what I may get to know, but you shall abide me here".

Egil had his weapons, them that he was wont to have: helm and shield, girt with sword, hewing-spear in hand. And now went he up into the isle and forth along a certain wood: he had a hood drawn low now over his helm. He came where some boys were, and along with them big shepherd's tykes, and when they came to words together he asked whence they were, or what for were they there and had hounds so big.

They spake: "Thou wilt be a full simple man. Hast not heard
that here goeth a bear[6] about the isle, the greatest mischief?
Slayeth here both men and cattle, and a price is set on the head
of him. Wake we here every night at Ask over our livestock, that
be shut in the folds. Or why farest thou with weapons i' the
night?"

He saith, "I am afeared of the bear. And few there be, methinks, that now fare weaponless. The bear hath long chased me
a-nights: ay, and see him now! there he is now! i' the neb o' the
wood. Whether be all men asleep at the farmstead?"

The boy said that Bergonund and Frodi would be still
a-drinking; "They sit all night long".

"Say to them, then," saith Egil, "where the bear is; but I
must hie me home."

He gat him gone then. But the boy ran home to the farmstead
and to the hall where they drank within. It was then so come
about as that all men were gone to bed save those three, Onund
and Frodi and Hadd. The boy saith where the bear was. They
took their weapons that were hung anigh them, and leapt out
forthwith and up to the wood. There jutted out nebs of wood[7]
from the mark, and thickets of brushwood in some places. The
boy saith to them where the bear had been in the thicket. Then
saw they how the branches moved: thought then for sure that
the bear would be there. Then spake Bergonund that they,
Hadd and Frodi, should run along 'twixt the thicket and the
main mark, and mind that the bear did not take to the wood.
Bergonund ran forward to the thicket. He had helm and shield,
girt with sword, halberd in hand.

Egil was there for him in the thicket, and no bear; and when
he saw where Bergonund was, then drew he sword, but there
was a looped band about the hilt of it, and he drew that over his
hand and let it hang there. He took in his hand his halberd and
ran forth then against Bergonund; and when Bergonund saw
that, then quickened he his pace and shot his shield afore him,
and before they were met each shot with his halberd at the other.
Egil caught the halberd on his shield and turned it aside, so that
it glented off the shield and flew into the ground; but Egil's
spear came on the middle of the shield and went through it a

long way up the feather, and the spear stuck fast in the shield. Onund's shield was thus become heavy to bear. Egil grabbed then swiftly the hilt of his sword. Onund too was about drawing of his sword, and when it was not half drawn Egil thrust him through with his sword. Onund reeled with the thrust, but Egil snatched back the sword hard, and hewed at Onund and nigh took off his head. After that, Egil took the halberd out of the shield.

Hadd and Frodi saw the fall of Bergonund, and ran thitherward. Egil turned to meet them. He shot the halberd at Frodi, and through his shield and into his breast, so that the point came out at his back. Fell he down straightway on his back dead. Egil took his sword then and turned to meet Hadd, and they bandied few blows betwixt them ere Hadd fell.

Then came up the boys, and Egil spake with them: "Look ye here to Onund your master and these his fellows, that beast nor fowl slit not their corpses".

Egil went then his ways, and not far before his fellows came to meet him, eleven, but six minded the ship. They asked what business[8] he had gotten done. Then quoth he:[9]

> Sat we too long in lowly
> Lot—(better erst I warded
> My fee)—beneath this bough of
> Bright home o' the ling-firth mackerel,
> Ere I let learn Bergonund
> Lie in's wounds, and deck'd out
> Bedfellow of Bor's Son
> With blood of Hadd and Frodi.

Then spake Egil: "We shall now turn back to the farmstead and fare like men of war: slay all the men that we catch, and take all that fee that we can come at".

They fare to the farmstead and leap there into the house and slay there fifteen or sixteen men. Some escaped their onset. They robbed there all the fee, but spoilt that which they might not fare away with. They drave the cattle to the strand and hewed them: bare aboard the boat so much as it could take: fared after that on their way, and rowed out by the island sound.

Egil was now all wrathful,[10] so that there was then no speaking to him. He sat at the tiller of the boat, and when they steered out into the firth towards Herdla, then rowed out to meet them Rognvald, the King's son, and they thirteen in company aboard that painted caravel of his. They had then heard that Egil's ship lay in Herdla-weir. They were minded to give Onund warning of Egil's faring. And when Egil saw the ship, then knew he her at once.

He steered his straightest at them, and when the ships drew together then came the beak of the cutter on the cheek of the caravel; she heeled over so that the sea fell in on the other side and filled the ship. Egil leapt then up aboard of her and grabbed his halberd: shouted to his men that they should not let one come off with his life that was aboard the caravel. That was then easy, seeing there then was no defence: they were all slain in the water, and not one came off. Died they there, thirteen, Rognvald and his companions.

Egil and his rowed then in to the isle of Herdla. Then quoth Egil a stave:[11]

> We battled: and with blood there
> Of Bloodaxe' son and Gunnhild's
> Glad redden'd I the war-flame—
> Nor reck I for their raging.
> And yet there fell of saplings
> Of ocean-moon thirteen, too,
> Aboard one single caravel.
> Stir-maker's task is done now.

And when Egil and his were come to Herdla, then ran they straightway up to the farmstead with all their weapons. But when Thorir saw that and his homemen, then ran they straightway from the farmstead, and saved themselves, all they that could lift foot, men and women. Egil and his robbed there all the fee that they might put their hands upon. So now fared they out to the ship. There was then withal not long to wait till a breeze sprang up from the land. They made ready to sail, and when they were about to set sail Egil went up into the isle.

He took in his hand a hazel-pole, and went to a certain point of rock that looked toward the land. Then took he a horse's head and set it up upon the pole. And now gave he forth his formular, and spake as thus:

"Here set I up a Scorn-Pole, and turn I this Scorn unto the hand of King Eric and of Queen Gunnhild" (he turned the horse's head in towards the land). "Turn I this Scorn unto those land-spirits which do these lands inhabit, so that they may all fare on wildered ways, and not one of them reach nor rest in her own home, until they shall have driven King Eric and Gunnhild forth from the land."

Therewithal he shot down the pole into a cleft of the rock, and there let it stand. And he turned the head in towards the land, but he scored runes on the pole, and those say all that formular.[12]

After that, went Egil ashipboard: they set sail and sailed out into the main sea. Then the breeze began to freshen, and it made stormy weather and a favouring wind. Then gat the ship mightily on her way.

Then quoth Egil:[13]

> Out 'fore the stem the storm-giant,
> Strainer of branches, planeth
> With chops of tempest-chisel
> Chill vast way of keel-deer;
> And swale-robéd sallow-fiend,
> Sweeping still without pity
> In gusts o'er swan of Gestil,
> Roars past gunnal and fore-stem.

And now sailed they into the main sea, and it sped them well of their journey, and they came out of the main sea into Burg-firth. Held he there his ship to harbour, and they bare their stuff aland. Then fared Egil home to Burg, and his sailors found them lodging.

Skallagrim was become then old and infirm with age. Egil took to him then the management of fee and the care and ward of the household.

CHAPTER LVIII. OF THE DEATH OF SKALLAGRIM.

THERE was a man named Thorgeir. He had to wife Thordis, Yngvar's daughter, the sister of Bera the mother of Egil. Thorgeir dwelt above Alptaness, at Lambistead. He had come out with Yngvar. He was rich and well esteemed of men. The son of her and Thorgeir was Thord, who dwelt at Lambistead after his father in that time when Egil came to Iceland.

That was then in the autumn, something before winter, that Thord rode in to Burg to see Egil his kinsman, and bade him home to a feast. He had let brew strong beer out there. Egil promised to come, and it was fixed for about a week hence. And when the week was gone, Egil made him ready for his journey, and with him Asgerd, his wife. They were in company ten or twelve.

And when Egil was ready, then went Skallagrim out with him, and turned to him before Egil went a-horseback, and spake:[1] "Slow methinks hast thou been, Egil, in paying over of that fee that King Athelstane sent me. Or what way art thou minded shall be done with that fee?"

Egil saith, "Art thou now much needy of fee, father? I knew not that. Straightway shall I let thee have silver when I know that thou needest: but I know thou must still have in thy keeping one chest, or twain, full of silver".

"So methinks", saith Skallagrim, "as that thou must think thou and I have shared out our loose goods between us. Thou'lt be content, may be, if I do as I like with that money that I have the keeping of."

Egil saith, "Thou wilt think there's no need to ask leave of me for that; because thou wilt have thine own will whatsoever I say".

And now rode Egil away, until he was come to Lambistead. They took to him there well and joyfully: he should sit there three nights.

That same evening that Egil had fared from home, Skallagrim let saddle him his horse. Rode he then from home, when other men went to bed. He carried at his knee a chest big enow, and he had in the crook of his arm a brazen kettle, when he set forth. Men have since had that for true, that he hath let fare one or both into Krumm's Well, and let fare down on the top of it a great flat stone.

Skallagrim came home about the midnight hour and went then to his place, and laid him down in his clothes. But in the morning, when it grew light and men clad themselves, then sat Skallagrim there against the post and was then dead, and so stiffened that men might nowise get him straightened out nor lift him, and 'twas tried all ways with him.

Then was a man set a-horseback. That one rode his hardest till he was come to Lambistead. Went he straightway unto Egil, and saith unto him these tidings. Then took Egil his weapons and clothes and rode home to Burg in the evening, and soon as he was gotten down from horseback went he in and into the passage which was round about the firehouse; but there were doors opening inwards from the passage to the seats. Egil ga him in to the seat and took Skallagrim by the shoulders and bent him backwards, laid him down in the seat and gave him then lyke-help. Then bade Egil take digging-tools and break open the wall of the south side, and when that was done, then took Egil under the upper part of Skallagrim but others took him by the feet. Bare they him across the house, and so out through the wall there where it had been broke open.[2] Bare they him then in that same hour down to Naustaness. There was a tilt rigged over him for the night. But in the morning, at flood-tide, was Skallagrim laid in a ship and rowed out to Digraness. There let Egil make a howe on the outward side of the ness. Therein was laid Skallagrim, and his horse and his weapons and smithy-tools. It is not told that any loose fee was laid in howe beside him.

Egil took the inheritance there, lands and loose goods. He ruled then over the household.

There was there with Egil Thordis, the daughter of Thorolf and of Asgerd.

CHAPTER LIX. OF EGIL'S FARING ABROAD THE THIRD TIME; WITH HOW HE WAS CAST ASHORE IN ENGLAND AND WAS FALLEN INTO THE HAND OF KING ERIC BLOOD-AXE AND QUEEN GUNNHILD.

ERIC the King ruled one winter over Norway after the death of his father, King Harald, before Hakon, Athelstane's-Fosterling,[1] another son of King Harald, came to Norway from the west out of England; and that same summer fared Egil Skallagrimson to Iceland.

Hakon fared north to Thrandheim. He was there taken for King. They were, he and Eric, that winter, both Kings in Norway. But after, in the spring, drew they of either part a war-host together. Hakon had much the greater throng of men. Eric saw then no other choice for him but to flee the land. He fared abroad then with Gunnhild his wife and their children.

Arinbiorn the Hersir was fosterbrother of Eric the King, and fosterer of his child. He was dearest to the King of all the landed men. The King had set him to be lord over all the Firthfolk. Arinbiorn fared out of the land with the King.

They fared first west over seas to the Orkneys. Then gave he Ragnhild his daughter to Earl Arnfinn. After that, fared he with his host coasting south by Scotland, and harried there. Thence fared he south to England, and harried there. And when King Athelstane heard that, he summoned forces and fared against Eric. And when they were met, there were borne speeches of peace betwixt them; and that was in the peace-making that King Athelstane gave Eric rule over Northumberland,[2] but he should be warden of the land for King Athelstane against the Scots and Irish. King Athelstane had made Scotland pay scat to him after the fall of King Olaf, and yet was that folk ever untrue to him. King Eric had ever his seat and state in York.

So it is said, that Gunnhild let work a spell, and let that be in the spellworking, that Egil Skallagrimson should never bide in peace in Iceland until she should look upon him.

Now that summer, when Hakon and Eric had met and striven

together for Norway, then was banned all faring to other lands out of Norway, and there came that summer no ships to Iceland and no tidings out of Norway. Egil Skallagrimson sat at his own house. But that second winter that he dwelt at Burg after the death of Skallagrim, then was Egil become unmerry, and so much the more was his ungladness as more the winter drew by. And when summer came, then Egil gave out that he is minded to make ready his ship for faring abroad that summer. He took then sailors. He is minded then to sail to England. They were aboardship thirty men. Asgerd was then left behind and took care of their house, but Egil was minded then to go and see King Athelstane and look to those promises that he had promised Egil at their parting.

Egil was not early ready, and when he put out into the main sea then were they somewhat late in getting a fair breeze. It began to draw towards autumn, and the wind grew strong. They sailed about Orkney from the north. Egil would nowise put in there, because he deemed that the might of King Eric belike would stand over all in the isles. They sailed then coasting south by Scotland, and had a great storm and cross winds. They beat about off Scotland, and so off England from the north. But of an afternoon when it began to grow mirk, there was a fierce gale. They find nought afore there were shoal breakers on their outer beam, and the like ahead. There was then no other choice, but to stand in towards land; and so did they: sailed then till she was wrecked ashore, and came aland by Humber mouth. There were all the men saved and the most part of the goods, except the ship; that was broken into shivers.

And when they found men to talk to, they learned these tidings, which Egil thought perilous: that King Eric Bloodaxe was there hard by, and Gunnhild, and they had there the realm to rule over, and he was but a short way thence, up in the burg of York. That learned he too, that Arinbiorn the Hersir was there with the King, and in great loving-kindness with the King.

And when Egil was sure of these tidings, then took he counsel with himself. It seemed to him there was little hope of coming off, even though he should try this, to fare with hidden head so long a way as it would likely be before he might come out of the realm of King Eric. He was then easily known to any who might see him. It seemed to him that that was but the fashion of a little man,3 to be took in flight. Hardened he then his heart, and made this his rede, that straight that very night that they were thither come, then getteth he him a horse and rideth straightway to the burg.

He came there at evening time, and he rode straightway into the burg. And now he had a hood over his helm, and all his weapons had he. Egil asked where might be that garth4 in the burg, that belonged to Arinbiorn. That was told him. He rode thither into the garth. But when he came to the hall, gat he down from his horse and found a man to speak to. It was then said to him that Arinbiorn sat at meat. Egil spake: "I would, good lad, that thou go in, into the hall, and ask Arinbiorn: whether will he rather without-door or within, to talk with Egil Skallagrimson".

That man saith, "That is little pains for me, to run this errand".

He went in into the hall and spake loud and clear: "A man is come here, out before the doors," saith he, "great as a troll; and that one bade me go in and ask whether thou wouldst without-door or within, to talk with Egil Skallagrimson".

Arinbiorn saith, "Go and bid him bide without, and he will not need to bide long".

He did as Arinbiorn spake: went out and said as was spoken unto him. Arinbiorn bade take up the tables. Thereafter went he out and all his housecarles with him. And when Arinbiorn saw Egil he hailed him and asked why was he come thither.

Egil saith in few words, the plainest he might, of his journey; "And now shalt thou see to it, what rede I shall take, if thou wilt give aught of help to me".

"Hast thou met any men in the burg", saith Arinbiorn, "who will have known thee, before thou camest here into the garth?"

"Not one," saith Egil.

"Take men their weapons, then," saith Arinbiorn.

They did so, and when they were weaponed, and all the housecarles of Arinbiorn, then went he into the King's garth.

But when they came to the hall, then clapped Arinbiorn on the door and bade open, and saith who was there. The door-keepers straightway opened the gates.

The King sate at table. Arinbiorn bade go in then twelve men; named for this Egil and ten men besides: "Now shalt thou, Egil, bring unto King Eric thine head, and take him by the foot, but I will plead thy suit".

So now go they in. Arinbiorn went before the King and greeted him. The King welcomed him, and asked what he would. Arinbiorn spake: "I have followed hither that man that is come a long way to seek to you at home and be set at one with you. That is great honour unto you, Lord, when your unfriends fare of their own free will from other lands, and think they cannot bear your wrath, though you be nowhere anigh. Let thyself now be lordly in thy dealings with this man. Let him get of thee good peace-making, for that he hath made thine honour so great as now may be seen: fared over many mains and difficult ways from home from his own dwelling. There was no need bare him on this journey, save only good will to you".

Then looked the King about him, and he saw over the heads of men, where Egil stood. And he glared with his eyes upon him, and spake: "Why wast thou so bold, Egil, that thou durst fare to find out me? On such wise last time wentest thou hence, that there was no hope of thy life from me".

Then went Egil to the table and took the King by the foot. Quoth he then:5

> Iva's firth-trampling stallion
> Long surging ways hath borne me
> To seek to him that sitteth
> In sway o'er land of England.
> Now hath the wound-sheen's shaker
> (Too stout of heart) sought hither,
> Unto the very rope-core
> Of Harald's hard-spun line.

King Eric said, "No need have I to tell up the guilts at thine hands, and yet are they so many and so big, that any single one may well be sufficient that thou come never from hence with life. Thou hast no other thing to hope for, but that here thou shalt surely die. Thou mightest have known that before, that thou wouldst get no peace-making from me".

Then quoth Egil:*

Gunnhild spake: "Why shall's not straightway slay Egil? Or mindest thou not now, King, what Egil hath done? slain friends of thine and kinsmen, and more than that, thy son; and scorned thine own self? Or where did ever men wot of such doings to a King-man?"

Arinbiorn saith: "If Egil hath spoke ill against the King, then may he boot that by words of praise, such as may stand up for all ages".

Gunnhild spake: "We will not harken to his praise. Let thou, King, lead Egil out and hew him. I will not harken to his words, and not look upon him".

Then spake Arinbiorn: "The King will not let himself be egged on to all thy dastard's work. He will not let slay Egil at night, because night-slayings are murthers".6

The King saith, "So shall it be, Arinbiorn, as thou biddest, that Egil shall live this night. Have thou him home with thee, and bring me him in the morning".

Arinbiorn thanked the King for his words: "We hope, Lord, that from this belike will Egil's matter be settled a better way. And albeit Egil hath in great matters made himself guilty in your sight, yet look you at that, that he hath had mighty losses through your kindred. King Harald thy father took the life of a famous man, Thorolf, his father's brother, because of the slander of wicked men, but for no cause. And you, King, did break the law for Egil for the sake of Bergonund; yea, and more than that, you would have had Egil a dead man, and did slay men of his, and robbed him of all his fee, and more than that, you did make him outlaw and drive him from the land; and Egil is not a man to be mocked and teased.7 But in every matter that a man must judge, needs must he look to what beareth on it. I will now", saith Arinbiorn, "have Egil with me for the night at home in my garth".

So it was now. And when they came into the garth, then go those two into a certain little loft and talk over this matter. Saith

* This stave is lost. E.R.E.

Arinbiorn as thus: "All wrathful was the King now; and yet methought rather his frame of mind was softened somewhat, before the end. And now will luck settle it, what must come of it. I know that Gunnhild will set all her mind to it, to spill thy matter for thee. Now will I give thee this rede, that thou wake this night and work a praise-song upon King Eric: methinks that were well, if that were to be a drapa of twenty staves, and thou mightst say it forth in the morning, when we two come before the King. So did Bragi,[8] of my kindred, when he stood before the wrath of Biorn the Swede-King, that he wrought a drapa of twenty staves upon him in one night and received therefor his head. Now might it be that we might bear luck here with the King, so that that should bring thee into peace with the King".

Egil saith, "I shall try this rede, since 'tis thy will. But this have I never prepared me for, to work a praise upon King Eric".

Arinbiorn bade him try. And now he went away to his own men. Sat they a-drinking until middle night. Then went Arinbiorn to the sleeping-house and his following, and before he did off his clothes, went he up into the loft to Egil and asked him how it sped of the song.

Egil saith that he had gotten nothing wrought: "Hath here sat a swallow by the window and twittered all the night, so that I have never bided in peace for it".

With that, went Arinbiorn away and out by those doors where a man might go up onto the house, and sat him down by that window in the loft that the fowl had before sat by. He saw where some shape-changer[9] fared the other way from the house. Arinbiorn sat there by the window all night until it dawned. And after Arinbiorn had come there, then wrought Egil all the drapa, and had so gotten it by heart that he might say it forth in the morning when he met Arinbiorn.

They held themselves in readiness against the time should come for them to meet the King.

CHAPTER LX. HOW EGIL QUOTH HIS DRAPA THAT IS
NAMED *HEAD-RANSOM* IN KING ERIC'S HALL IN YORK.

KING ERIC went to table according to his wont, and
there was then great throng of men with him. And when
Arinbiorn was ware of that, then went he with all his
following all weaponed into the King's garth then when the King
sate at table. Arinbiorn craved leave to go into the hall: that, too,
was allowed him as of right. They go in, he and Egil, and the half
of their following: the other half stood without before the doors.

Arinbiorn greeted the King, and the King gave him good
welcome. Arinbiorn spake: "Now is here come Egil. He hath
not sought to run away in the night. Now will we know, Lord,
what his lot shall be. I hope for good from you. That have I
done (as worthy was) that I have spared nothing for this, so to
do and to speak as that your honour might so be greater than
afore. I have left, too, all my possessions and kinsfolk and friends
that I had in Norway, and followed you, but all your landed men
fell off from you. And that is right and seemly, seeing that thou
hast in many a thing done unto me exceeding well".

Then spake Gunnhild: "Give over, Arinbiorn, and talk not
so long of this. Much hast thou done well unto King Eric, and
he hath to the full rewarded that. There lieth on thee a much
greater duty to King Eric than to Egil. This is not to be asked by
thee, that Egil should fare unpunished hence from before the
face of King Eric, such things as he hath been guilty of".

Then saith Arinbiorn, "If thou, King, and Gunnhild have
fast resolved on this, that Egil shall here get no peace-making,
then is that the manly part to give him truce and safe-conduct
for a week's space, to get him gone; he hath, when all's said, of
his own free will fared hither to see you, and had hope for himself of peace therefor. And then let your dealings together fare
even as they must, from thenceforth".

Gunnhild spake: "I can see in this, Arinbiorn, that thou art
more careful of Egil than of King Eric. If Egil shall ride hence
for a week away in peace, then will he be come to King Athelstane by that time. But King Eric needs not now to hide this
from himself, that all kings are now become men of greater

might and mastery than he. But a short while since would that not have been thought likely, that King Eric should not have the will nor the marrow for this, to avenge his griefs on every man, such-like as Egil is".

Arinbiorn saith, "No man would call Eric the greater man, though he should slay one bonder's son, an outlander, that hath walked into his power. But if he will fain grow great by that, then shall I do this for him, that these tidings shall be thought somewhat worth the telling; because we two, Egil and I, will now hold together, so that at one and the same time must we both be met with. Thou mayst then, King, buy dear the life of Egil, when we be all laid on the field, I and my following. I might have looked for some other thing from you, than that thou wouldst have the will to lay me to earth rather than let me receive the life of one man at mine asking".

Then saith the King, "Exceeding great masterfulness layest thou on this, Arinbiorn, to give Egil aid. Loth must I be to do thee scathe, if it must come to this, if thou wilt rather lay down thy life than he were slain. Yet enough and to spare be my causes against Egil, whatsoever I may let do unto him".

And when the King had spoken these words, then went Egil before him and began his song, and quoth it high, and had a hearing forthwith:[1]

> West over sea
> Bear I with me
> God's wish-strand's spray;
> Such is my way.
> Launch'd I mine oak
> When the ice broke;
> Loaded I her
> With praise-plunder.
>
> Guest came I to Prince.
> Of praise-song methinks:
> I bear Odin's drink
> To England's brink.
> The great Lord's ways
> Surely I praise:
> Skald silence prays
> Praise-song to upraise.

Lord, harken to't
(Well beseems that),
What song I've wrought,
If there's silence got.
Most men heard say
How the King made fray;
But Odin saw
Where the slain men lay.

Wax'd rattle of swords
With clank of wards;
Stour wax'd round Lord:
Lord rangéd for'rd.
Heard was the croon
Of the iron-storm's tune:
Sword-river's moan,
Where the spate swirl'd down.

No jot waver'd
The web dart-broider'd,
Where the King's merry
Spear-fields serry.
In bloody shallows
'Neath banners wallows
Seal's plain, and thunder
Gives tongue from under.

On the shore the folk sink
'Neath javelins' clink.
Loud fame gat
Eric from that.

More can I tell ye
If harken will ye:
There's more worth hearing
Of that war-faring.
Waxéd wounds
With war-lords' stounds:
Breaking of blades
'Gainst blue shield-braids.

Brands were slashing
And helms a-flashing:
Wound-graver goes through—
(That's sword-point shows through).

Fall'n 'fore the slice
Of the sword-belt's ice
Odin's oaks lay
In the iron-play.

   'Twas points' crash
   And edges' gnash.
   Loud fame gat
   Eric from that.

King's sword wax'd red:
Ravens gath'réd.
Spears sought men's hearts:
Flew bloody darts.
Fed night-hags' horses
Scots' scourge on corses:
Hell's feet slubber
The eagles' supper.

Flew battle-cranes
Down carrion lanes:
Of blood's no drouth
In the wound-mew's mouth.
Wolf slits wounds:
Sword-billow sounds,
Plashing red
'Gainst raven's head.

   Came battle's lees
   On Gialf's horses.
   Eric by sea
   Bade wolves feast free.

The Sword-God wakes
Our Lady of Sakes,
And on skerry of Hake's
The bulwark breaks.
Spear-points batter
And sword-points shatter;
Bow-strings singing
Bear arrows winging.

Bit flying blade there:
Peace was bewray'd there:
Elm-bow did strain there:
Wolf was fain there:

Folk-shepherd out-fac'd
Death that lays waste:
While the yew-bow sang
To edges' clang.

War-lord bent yew:
The wound-bees flew.
Eric by sea
Bade wolves feast free.

Yet would I fain
To men make plain
The hero's ways
(I must speed my praise).
War-lord flings gold,
And lands doth hold
The Bird of the North:
Most praise he's worth.

Wrist-glow he breaketh
Who gem-gifts maketh:
No niggard's ways
Will the ring-breaker praise.
A hath goodly store
Of the hawk-strand's ore:
Glads folk galore
With Frodi's flour.

Spear-guard he flings
With seat of rings,
The sword-game's haster,
The strong blood-waster.
East beyond seas
The rumour flees,
Blown big and far,
Of Eric at war.

War-lord, hark to't—
The song I wrought:
Good meseems that,
That I silence gat.
With speech of my tongue
From mind's deeps I've wrung
Odin's sea,
War-dighter, for thee.

King's leave I bore
Till silence was o'er.
Words' measure I ken
In the seats of men.
From the hold of cheer
Lord's praise I bear:
So forth did't fare
As that most should hear.

CHAPTER LXI. OF EGIL'S LIFE GIVEN HIM BY THE KING.

KING ERIC sat upright while Egil quoth the song, and glared with his eyes upon him. And when the drapa was ended, then spake the King: "On best wise is the song given forth; and now have I bethought me, Arinbiorn, of this matter 'twixt me and Egil, where it shall be come. Thou hast pressed Egil's suit with great hardihood, when thou didst offer to make thy troubles bite against me. Now shall that be done for thy sake, even that thou hast bidden, that Egil shall fare from before my face hale and without harm. But thou, Egil, give heed to't in thy journeys, that, from that time when thou comest from before my face out of this hall, thou come never into the sight of mine eyes or my sons' sight, and be never in the way of me nor of my folk. But I give thee now thy head, for this time; for that sake, that thou didst walk into my power, therefore will I do no dastard's work upon thee. But thou shalt know that for truth, that this is no peace-making with me nor with sons of mine nor any kinsman of ours, them that have will to wreak their rights".

Then quoth Egil:[1]

I am not loth,
Though laidly 'tis,
This helm-crag,
Prince, t'accept of.
Where's he that gat
From lofty-minded
All-wielder's son
A goodlier gift?

Arinbiorn thanked the King with fair words for that honour and friendship that the King had done him. Then go they, Arinbiorn and Egil, home to Arinbiorn's garth.

And now Arinbiorn let his folk make ready riding-horses. He rode away with Egil, and a hundred men all weaponed along with him. Arinbiorn rode with that host till they came to King Athelstane's and found there a good welcome. The King bade Egil be with him, and asked what way it had fared betwixt them, him and King Eric.

Then quoth Egil:[2]

> Haster of Hugin's rest-day
> —(High heart of kinsman sav'd there)—
> Gave eyes with their black eyebrows
> For Egil to be fain of.
> So have I right to rule yet
> Right throne of hat of Ali,
> Now like as't far'd aforetime,
> 'Fore lord of battle-adders.

But at the parting of Arinbiorn and Egil, then gave Egil to Arinbiorn those two gold rings that King Athelstane gave him, and they stood each at a mark: but Arinbiorn gave Egil that sword that was named Dragvandil. That had been given to Arinbiorn by Thorolf Skallagrimson, but before had Skallagrim received it of Thorolf his brother, but Thorolf was given the sword by Grim Hairycheek, son of Ketil Haeng. That sword had Ketil Haeng owned, and had it in holmgangs, and that was of all swords the best biter.

They parted with the greatest loving-kindness. Arinbiorn fared home to York, to Eric the King. But Egil's companions and his shipmates had there good peace, and sold their wares under Arinbiorn's safe keeping. But when winter wore they flitted themselves south to England, and fared to find Egil.

CHAPTER LXII. OF EGIL'S FARING TO NORWAY WITH
THORSTEIN ERICSON, THE SISTER'S SON OF ARINBIORN
THE HERSIR.

ERIC ALL-WISE was the name of a landed man in
Norway; he had to wife Thora, daughter of Thorir the
Hersir and sister of Arinbiorn. He owned estates east in
the Wick. He was a man exceeding wealthy and the greatest man
of account, wise of understanding. Thorstein was named their
son; he was at fostering with Arinbiorn and was then much
grown, and yet in his youthful age. He had fared west to England with Arinbiorn.

Now that same autumn that Egil had come to England, there
was heard from Norway these tidings: that Eric All-wise was
dead, but his heritage had the King's bailiffs taken, and cast
thereon the King's ban. And when Arinbiorn and Thorstein
heard these tidings, then took they that rede, that Thorstein
should fare east and look to the heritage. And when spring drew
on and men made ready their ships, they that were minded to
fare betwixt land and land, then fared Thorstein south to London
and fell in there with King Athelstane. He bare forward tokens
and word-sending of Arinbiorn to the King (and so, too, to Egil
that he might be his upholder with the King), that King Athelstane might send word unto King Hakon his fosterson that
Thorstein should get the heritage and estates in Norway. King
Athelstane was easy-besought in this, because Arinbiorn was
known to him for good. Then came Egil too to talk with King
Athelstane and said to him that which he had in mind: "I will
this summer", saith he, "fare east to Norway, to look to that fee
which King Eric robbed me of, he and Bergonund. There
sitteth now over that fee Atli the Short, Bergonund's brother.
I wot, if word-sending of yours come too, that I shall have the
law in this matter".

The King saith that Egil shall rule his own journey, "But best
'twould seem to me, that thou wert with me and wert made my
land-warder and hadst rule over mine host of war: I will find
thee big revenues".

Egil saith, "This choice seemeth to me much to be wished for: I will say yea to that, and never nay. Yet must I first fare to Iceland and look to my wife and that fee that I have there".

King Athelstane gave Egil a good cheaping-ship and lading therewith: there was aboard of her wheat and honey and much fee beside in other wares. And when Egil made ready his ship for the main sea, then took rede to fare with him Thorstein Ericson that before was spoke of, who afterwards was called Thorason;[1] and when they were ready, then sailed they. They parted, King Athelstane and Egil, with the greatest friendship. It sped them well of their journey, Egil and his; they came to Norway in the Wick east and held in with their ship all into Oslofirth (there had Thorstein his dwelling up aland), and so inland all as far as Raumrealm. And when Thorstein came there aland, then brought he up his claim to his father's heritage with the bailiffs, that had sat them down in his dwelling. Many brought Thorstein aid in this. Meetings were summoned there: Thorstein had there many noble kinsmen: the end of it was that it was left to the King's ruling, but Thorstein took over the keeping of that fee that his father had owned. Egil fared to winter-lodging with Thorstein, and they twelve in company. There was flitted home thither to Thorstein's both wheat and honey: there was there that winter great gladness, and Thorstein dwelt like a man of largesse, because there was provision enow for it.

CHAPTER LXIII. OF EGIL AND KING HAKON ATHELSTANE'S-FOSTERLING.

KING HAKON Athelstane's-Fosterling ruled then over Norway, as before was said. The King sate that winter north in Thrandheim. But when winter wore, Thorstein began his journey and Egil with him: they had near thirty men; and when they were ready, fared they first to the Uplands, thence north over Dovrafell to Thrandheim, and came there to meet with Hakon the King. They bare up their errand with the

King: Thorstein said clearly forth his suit and brought forward witnesses to back him, that he was owner of all that inheritance that he laid claim to. The King took that suit well: he let Thorstein have his possessions; and therewith was he made landed man of the King's, even as his father had been.

Egil went to see King Hakon, and bare before him his errand and therewith the word-sending of King Athelstane and his tokens: Egil claimed that fee which had belonged to Biorn the Franklin, lands and loose goods. He claimed for himself the half of that fee, and for Asgerd his wife: bade forth there witnesses and oaths to back his suit: said, too, that he had borne forward all this before King Eric: let that follow, that he had then not gotten the law because of the might of King Eric and Gunnhild's egging on. Egil told up all the process of that suit that had before taken place at the Gula-Thing: bade he the King then grant him the law in that suit.

King Hakon answereth: "So have I heard tell, that Eric my brother will reckon, he and Gunnhild both, that thou, Egil, wilt have cast a stone beyond thy strength[1] in your dealings together. I should a thought thou mightest be well content, Egil, if I should take no hand i' this suit, for all that we two, Eric and I, have not had the luck to see eye to eye together".

Egil spake: "Nowise mayest thou, King, be silent over so big matters, seeing that all men here in the land, inland men and outland, must obey your bidding. I have heard that you set laws here in the land and right for every man: now know I that you will let me have them, as other men: methinks I have birth for that and strength of kin here in the land to hold mine own 'gainst Atli the Short. But as for my matter with King Eric there is that to say unto you, that I went to see him and we two parted in such wise that he bade me fare in peace whereso I would. I will bid you, Lord, my following and service. I know that there must be here with you men who will not be thought more warlike to see i' the field than I am. My mind bodes me that it shall be no long while before your path and King Eric's shall bear you face to face, if your lives last thereto: wondrous methinks were that if it shall not come to this, that it shall seem to thee that Gunnhild hath reared up many sons".

The King saith, "Nowise shalt thou, Egil, go under mine hand. Much greater gaps have you kinsmen hewn in our line than that it should do for thee to make thine abiding-place here in the land. Fare thou out to Iceland, and be there in heritage after thy father. Then will there no harm befall thee from us kinsfolk. But here in the land is this to be looked for all thy days, that our kinsfolk will be the mightiest. But for sake of King Athelstane my fosterfather, then shalt thou have here peace in the land, and have the law and the land's rights; because I know that King Athelstane hath dear love of thee".

Egil thanked the King for his words, and asked this, that the King should find him sure tokens of his to Thord in Aurland and other landed men in Sogn and Hordaland. The King saith that so should it be.

CHAPTER LXIV. OF EGIL'S COMING TO FRIDGEIR'S, AND OF HIS DEALINGS WITH LJOT THE PALE.

THORSTEIN and Egil made ready their journey as soon as they had ended their errands: fare they then back on their way, and when they come south over Dovrafell, then saith Egil that he will fare down to Raumsdale and so south by the sound-way: "I will", saith he, "make an end of mine errands in Sogn and Hordaland, because I will make ready my ship this summer out to Iceland".

Thorstein bade him rule his own journey. They part, Thorstein and Egil. Thorstein fared south by the Dales and all the way till he came to his own place: bare he then forward the King's tokens and word-sending before the bailiffs, that they should let go all that fee which they have taken up and which Thorstein laid claim to.

Egil fared his own way, and they twelve in company: they came forth into Raumsdale, found them convoy there, and fared now south to Mere. There is nought said of their journey before they came into that isle that is named Hod and fared a-guesting to that farmstead that is named Blindheim:[1] that was a worshipful farmstead. There dwelt a landed man that was named Fridgeir: he was young of years: had newly taken his father's heritage. His mother was named Gyda; she was a sister of Arinbiorn the Hersir, a great lady and a worshipful. She kept house with her son Fridgeir: they had there a household of great largesse. There gat they exceeding good welcome.

Egil sat that evening next Fridgeir, and his fellows there outward from him: there was there great drinking and costly feast. Mistress Gyda went that evening to talk with Egil: she asked after Arinbiorn her brother and after more kinsmen of hers besides and friends, them that had fared to England with Arinbiorn. Egil said to her that which she asked. She asked what things had been done to tell of in Egil's journeys: he saith unto her thereof at the clearest.

Then quoth he:[2]

> Laidly to me was loathly
> Land-hankerer's anger:
> Gowk sings not if he knoweth
> Snarl-vulture after him goeth.
> There best (as oft) bested me
> Bear of eagle's stall-stone.
> Fails he not all nor founders
> Who finds such friends to speed him.

Egil was all merry that evening, but Fridgeir and his homemen were somewhat silent.[3] Egil saw there a maid fair and well arrayed; it was said to him that she was a sister of Fridgeir's. The maid was unmerry and wept ceaselessly all the evening: that seemed to them wonderful.

There were they that evening; but in the morning was wild weather, and no going to sea. There needed they conveyance out of the isle. Then went Fridgeir, both he and Gyda, to find Egil: they bade him sit there with his fellows till it should be good faring-weather, and have thence furtherance on their journey, whatsoever they needed. Egil took that thankfully: they sat there weather-bound three nights, and there was there the greatest good cheer.

After that, became the weather calm. Stood they up then, Egil and his, early in the morning, and made them ready: went then to meat, and there was given them ale to drink, and they sat awhile. And now took they their clothes. Egil stood up and thanked the bonder and the mistress for their entertainment, and therewithal went out. The bonder and his mother went on the road with them: then fell Gyda to speech with Fridgeir her son and talked with him low. Egil stood meanwhile and waited for them.

Egil spake with the maid: "What for weepest thou, maid? I see thee never merry".

She had no might to answer, and wept the more.

Fridgeir answereth his mother out loud: "Nowise will I now ask for this: they be now ready for their journey".

Then went Gyda to Egil and spake: "I will say to thee, Egil, the tidings that be here amongst us. There is a man named Ljot the Pale:4 he is a berserk and a holmgangs-man: he is unloved of the folk: he came here and bade to wife my daughter, but we answered speedily and denied him the match. Therewith, challenged he to the holmgang5 Fridgeir my son; and shall come to-morrow to the holm, in that isle that is named Vorl. Now would I, Egil, that thou mightest fare to the holm with Fridgeir: that would be seen for true, if Arinbiorn were here i' the land, that we would not bear the overweening might of such a man as Ljot is".

"Binding on me is that, mistress, for sake of Arinbiorn thy kinsman, that I should fare with thy son, if he think that aught of help to him."

"Then doest thou well", saith Gyda. "We shall then go in into the hall, and be all together this day long."

Egil and his go then in into the hall and drank: sat they there that day, but in the evening came friends of Fridgeir's, those that were minded to fare with him, and there was throng of men that night. There was then a great feast there. But the day after, Fridgeir made him ready for his journey and a mort of men with him. There was Egil a-faring: then was it good faring-weather: and now fare they and come into the isle of Vorl. There was a fair field a short way from the sea, where the meeting on the holm should be. There was marked the holm-stead: stones laid round on the outside.

Now came Ljot there with his company. He maketh him ready then for the holmgang: he had shield and sword. Ljot was an exceeding big man and strong-looking. And when he walked forth on the field to the holm-stead, then came upon him berserks-gang;[6] took he then to bellowing evilly, and bit into his shield. Fridgeir was a man not big, slim-built and fair to look on, and not strong; he had withal never stood in battles.

And when Egil saw Ljot, then quoth he a stave:[7]

> Nowise fit is Fridgeir—
> (Fare we to holm, my messmates:
> We'll ban the man the maiden)—
> To move the fray with quickener
> Of Gondul's storm, who biteth
> Shield, and unto Powers
> Blood-offering doth. The ring-god
> Rolleth his eyes all-fey.

Ljot saw where Egil stood, and heard his words, and spake: "Walk thou hither, that big man, to the holm, and fight with me, if thou art all eager for it, and let us two try it out together. That is much fairer, than I should fight with Fridgeir, sith I should be thought nought the greater man albeit I lay him to earth".

Then quoth Egil:[8]

> To Ljot a little service
> 'Twere nowise right to nay-say:
> Play I with the Pale one
> With quivering sprout of byrny.
> Busk we to fight: but mercy
> Leave I him no hope for.
> Needs must we two, swash-buckler,
> Shape with our shields in Mere.

Therewith Egil made ready for the holmgang with Ljot. Egil had that shield which he was wont to have, and he was girt with that sword that he called Nadder, but he had Dragvandil in his hand: he walked in over that mark where the meeting on the holm should be: but Ljot was then not ready. Egil shook his sword and quoth a stave:9

> Hew we with shining hilt-wand:
> Hack the shield with brand:
> Try we out the shield's moon:
> Redden we sword with blood:
> Chop we Ljot from life:
> Play we sore with Pale one:
> Champion with iron lull we:
> Come, eagles, to the carrion!

Then came Ljot forth on the battle-field, and therewithal they ran together, and Egil heweth at Ljot, but Ljot turned it with the shield; but Egil hewed one blow after another so that Ljot gat no blows in against him. He hopped away round the holm-ring, but Egil fared with like speed after and hewed his fiercest: Ljot fared out beyond the mark-stones and wide about the field. So went it the first bout. Then Ljot bade for a rest: Egil let that be: take they their stand then, and rest them.

Then quoth Egil:10

> Somewhat ahead, O flood-fires'
> Flinger, as I bethink me—
> (The treasure-hankerer fears now)—
> The hapless champion fareth.
> Stands he not fast, the dart-storm's
> Staff, who cries halt to hewings.
> Wide fareth the woe-hankerer
> On field before the bald-head.

That was the holmgang law in that time, that that one who challengeth another man for anything and he getteth the victory, he who challenged, then should that one have as meed of victory the thing for which he had challenged him; but if he get not the victory, then should he ransom himself with such fee as might have been agreed upon. But if he fell on the holm, then had he forfeited all his possessions, and that one should take heritage after him, he that had felled him on the holm. That was law, too: if an outland man died, one that there in the land had no heir, then went that heritage into the King's garth.

Egil bade that Ljot should make ready: "I will that we try out now this holmgang".

And now leaped Egil upon him and hewed at him: went he then so near him that he staggered back, and then was the shield borne aside from him. Then hewed Egil at Ljot, and it came on him below the knee and took off the foot: then fell Ljot, and straightway was the breath out of him. Then Egil gat him to where Fridgeir was and his folk. There was very good thanks given him for this work.

Then quoth Egil:[11]

> Feaster of wolvés fell there—
> (Foot the skald from Ljot hew'd)—
> Who worst of ill hath workéd.
> Brought I peace to Fridgeir.
> O breaker of lowe of sea-loch,
> I look to no reward for't:
> To me but game and sport 'twas,
> The spear-din with the Pale one.

Ljot was little sorrowed after by most men, because he had been the unkindest of men. He was a Swede by race, and had no kinsfolk there in the land. He had come thither and gathered him fee by holmgangs. He had felled many good bonders, and challenged them before to the holmgang for their estates and odal rights: was then become greatly wealthy both in lands and loose goods.

Egil fared home with Fridgeir from the meeting on the holm; he tarried there then a little while, before he fared south to Mere. They parted, Egil and Fridgeir, with great loving-kindness; Egil gave charge to Fridgeir to claim those estates which Ljot had owned. Fared Egil on his way: came forth into the Firths: thence he fared into Sogn to see Thord at Aurland. He took to him well. He bare forward his errand and the word-sending of Hakon the King. Thord took well with Egil's talk, and promised him his help in that suit. Egil tarried there long through the spring with Thord.

CHAPTER LXV. OF THE DEALINGS BETWIXT EGIL AND ATLI THE SHORT.

EGIL made his journey south to Hordaland. He had for that journey a rowing-ferry and aboard of her thirty men: they come on a day to Ask in Fenhring: Egil went thither with twenty men, but ten minded the ship. Atli the Short was there with certain men: Egil let call him out, and say that Egil Skallagrimson had an errand with him. Atli took his weapons, and all those men that were there meet for fight, and thereafter went they out.

Egil spake: "So is it said to me, Atli, that thou wilt have the keeping of that fee which is mine by rights and Asgerd's, my wife's. Thou wilt have heard talk of that before, that I called mine the heritage of Biorn the Franklin which Bergonund thy brother held in my despite. Now am I come to look to that fee, lands and loose goods, and to crave of thee that thou let it go and pay it into my hands".

Atli saith: "Long have we heard that, Egil, that thou beest an unjust man; but now may I come to proof of it, if thou art minded to claim this fee at mine hands which King Eric adjudged to Onund my brother: King Eric had then the rule, both to bid and ban here in the land. I bethought me now, Egil, that thou wouldst be come here for this, to bid me atonement for my brethren, that thou tookst the life of; and that thou wouldst have the will to boot that robbery, when thou robbedst here at Ask. Then would I make answer in this suit, if thou wouldst flit forward those things as thine errand. But here can I nought to answer".

"That will I", saith Egil, "bid thee, as I bade unto Onund, that the Gula-Thing's law settle our case. I count thy brethren to have fallen without atonement by their own works, because they had before robbed me of the laws and the land's rights and taken my fee as spoil of war. I have for this the King's leave, to go to law with thee about these matters. I will summon thee to the Gula-Thing, and have there the laws' ruling in these matters."

"Come will I", saith Atli, "to the Gula-Thing, and there may we two talk about this matter."

Therewithal fared Egil away with his company: fared he then north into Sogn and inland to Aurland to Thord his kinsman-in-law, and tarried there until the Gula-Thing.

And when men came to the Thing, then came Egil thither. Atli the Short was also thither come. They took then to pleading of their suits, and set them forth before those men that should judge thereon. Egil set forth his fee-claim, but Atli pleaded a lawful defence against it, an oath of twelve, that he had not that fee in his keeping which belonged to Egil. But when Atli went to the courts with his band of oathmen, then went Egil to meet him and saith that he will not take his oaths for his fee: "I will bid thee another law, to wit, that we two go to holm here at the Thing, and let that one have this fee who getteth the victory".

That was the law, too, as Egil spake, and the ancient custom, that it was every man's right to challenge another to the holm-gang, whether he were defendant in the suit or plaintiff.

Atli said that he would not deny to go to holm with Egil, "Sith thou speakest that which was mine to speak, sith harm enough and more have I to revenge upon thee. Thou hast laid to earth two brothers of mine, and far indeed must I be from holding of a rightful suit, if I shall rather let go my possessions unlawfully because of thee than fight with thee when thou bidst me that".

And now take they hands together, Atli and Egil, and make that fast betwixt them, that they shall go to holm, and he that getteth the victory shall have those estates that they strove about aforetime.

After that make they ready for the holmgang. Egil went forth and had helm on head, and shield before him, and halberd in hand, but the sword Dragvandil he fastened by his right hand. That was the fashion of holmgang-men, so as not to need to draw sword on the holm, rather to let the sword follow his hand, so that straightway might the sword be taken hold on, when he would. Atli had the same array as Egil: he was wonted to holm-gangs: he was a strong man and the greatest man of valour. There was led forth a bull, big and old. That was called the neat of sacrifice. That should he hew, who had the victory. That was sometimes one neat; sometimes each let lead forward his own, of them that went to holm.

And when they were made ready for the holmgang, then leapt they to it and shot first with spears, and neither spear took fast in the shield: stood they both in the earth. Therewith take they both to their swords: then went fast to it and hewed away. Nowise did Atli turn on heel. They hewed swift and hard, and speedily were the shields spoilt. And when Atli's shield was much spoilt, then cast he it from him: took then his sword with two hands, and hewed at the swiftest. Egil hewed at him on the shoulder-bone and the sword bit not.[1] He hewed a second time, and a third. It was then easy for him to find hewing-steads on Atli, seeing he had no guard. Egil smote with the sword with all his might; but it bit not, wheresoever he hewed. Then seeth Egil that it will not do as things are, because his shield then becometh spoilt. Then Egil let go sword and shield and leapt at Atli and grabbed him with his hands. Then was known the odds of strength, and Atli fell over backwards: but Egil was crawled upon him down there, and bit asunder his weasand.[2] There Atli lost his life.

Egil leapt up swiftly, and thither where the neat of sacrifice stood: grabbed with one hand in the lips of it, with the other the horn, and twisted it so that the feet looked upward, and asunder the neck-bone. Therewithal walked Egil thither where stood his company. Then quoth Egil:[3]

> Brandish'd I blue Dragvandil:
> It bit not on the shield-rim;
> And aye because the edge on't
> Atli the Short had deavéd.
> The odds of strength then us'd I
> 'Gainst wordy-blust'ring swordster:
> Garr'd I gag-tooth's brother
> Gnaw [quite through his windpipe].

And now Egil took possession of all those estates which he had striven about, and which he claimed that Asgerd his wife had had to take after her father. It is not said that there befell aught else to tell of at that Thing. Egil fared then first in into Sogn and set in order those estates that he had gotten into possession: tarried he there very long that spring. And now fared he with his company east into the Wick: fared he then to see Thorstein, and was there awhile.

CHAPTER LXVI. OF EGIL'S HOME-COMING AND DWELLING IN ICELAND: THE CHILDREN OF HIM AND OF ASGERD.

EGIL made ready his ship that summer and fared as soon as he was ready: he held his course for Iceland. It went well with him of his journey. He held into Burgfirth, and came with his ship a short way from his own farmstead. He let flit home his wares, and laid up the ship.

Egil was that winter at his own place. Egil had now had out to Iceland exceeding great fee: he was a man exceeding wealthy: he had a great house and a high. Nowise was Egil a meddler in the affairs of men, and not quarrelsome with most men when he was here in the land: nor did men in any wise go about to pry into his affairs. Egil was then at his own place while no few winters[1] shifted by.

Egil and Asgerd had these children that are named: Bodvar was named a son of theirs, Gunnar another, a daughter Thorgerd, and Bera; Thorstein[2] was the youngest. All Egil's children were hopeful and well witted from birth. Thorgerd was the eldest of Egil's children, Bera the next.

CHAPTER LXVII. OF EGIL'S GOING ABROAD ONCE MORE TO NORWAY, AND HIS GUESTING WITH ARINBIORN IN THE FIRTHS.

EGIL heard these tidings from east over sea, that Eric Bloodaxe had fallen in west-viking, but Gunnhild and their sons were fared south to Denmark, and there was gone away from England all that folk that had thither followed Eric and them. Arinbiorn was then come to Norway. He had gotten his revenues and possessions, them that he had had, and was come into great loving-kindness with the King.

It seemed to Egil again then a thing becoming much to be desired, to fare to Norway. That followed too with the tidings-telling, that King Athelstane was dead. There ruled then over England Edmund his brother.

Egil made ready then his ship and found him sailors thereto. Onund Sjoni[1] was minded for that journey, the son of Ani of Anisbrent. Onund was big and of those men the strongest, that then were there in the countryside. There was not all one tale about it, that he were not shape-strong. Onund had oft been a-faring betwixt land and land. He was something older than Egil. Between them had long been good friendship.

And when Egil was ready, he put out to sea, and it sped them well of their journey: came amidmost of Norway. And when they saw land, they stood in to the Firths. And when they gat tidings from the land, it was said to them that Arinbiorn was at home at his own place. Held Egil thither with his ship into haven, as near as might be to the farmstead of Arinbiorn.

And now fared Egil to find Arinbiorn, and a great joyful meeting was that betwixt them. Arinbiorn bade Egil thither to lodging and his company, them that he would should thither fare. Egil took that thankfully, and let put his ship on the rollers, and the sailors gat them lodging. Egil fared to Arinbiorn's, and they twelve in company. Egil had let make a long-ship's sail, much wrought: that sail gave he to Arinbiorn, and more gifts besides, that were fit to send. Egil was there for the winter in good entertainment. Egil fared that winter south into Sogn about his land-rents: tarried there much long time: thereafter fared he north into the Firths.

Arinbiorn had a great Yule-bidding:[2] bade to him friends of his and bonders of the neighbourhood. There was there great throng of men and good feast. He gave Egil for a Yule-gift a gown made of silk and much broidered with gold, set all down the front with gold knobs: Arinbiorn had let make that raiment according to the stature of Egil. Arinbiorn gave Egil a full suit of clothes, new-cut, at Yule: they were cut in English cloth of many colours. Arinbiorn gave many kinds of gifts of friendship

at Yule to those men who had come to his house, because Arinbiorn was of all men the most open-handed and the most lordly.
    Then wrought Egil a stave:3

> By his own rede the hero
> Robe of silk gold-knobbéd
> Let fetch forth for the poet:
> (Friend better I'll ne'er get).
> Arinbiorn hath the warding
> Withal—(late shall be born us
> His like, much less a greater)—
> Of a lord's unpitying might.

CHAPTER LXVIII. OF EGIL'S CLAIMING OF THE HERITAGE
OF LJOT WHOM HE HAD SLAIN, AND HOW ARINBIORN
BROUGHT THAT CLAIM BEFORE KING HAKON, AND WITH
WHAT ISSUE.

EGIL gat great ungladness after Yule, so that he quoth
never a word.1 And when Arinbiorn found that, then took
he to speech with Egil and asked what that betokened, that
ungladness which he had. "I will", saith he, "that thou let me
know whether thou beest sick, or beareth somewhat else hither?
We may then work some remedy."

    Egil saith, "Nought have I of ailments, but great concern
have I of this, how I shall get that fee which I won, then when
I felled Ljot the Pale, north in Mere. 'Tis said to me that the
King's bailiffs have taken up all that fee and cast the King's ban
on it. Now will I fain have thy help over this fee-claiming".

    Arinbiorn saith, "Nought far deem I that from the law of the
land, that thou shouldst have gotten for thine own that fee. And
yet methinks now, the fee is come in a fast place: 'tis roomy
going in to the King's garth, but a strait way out. There hath
befallen us many hard-sought fee-claims with men of might and
mastery, and sat we then in greater trust with the King than now
is; 'cause shallow standeth our friendship with King Hakon,
though needs must I so do as the word is spoken of old, that
'Needs must they cherish the oak who will dwell beneath it'".

"And yet thither swingeth my mind," saith Egil: "if we have law of our side, that we should try it. May so be, that the King grant us right here, for 'tis said to me that the King is a righteous man and holdeth well those laws that he setteth here in the land. That is what my mind most telleth me, that I should fare to meet the King and make trial of this suit with him."

Arinbiorn saith that he was nought eager for this. "Meseems as if that should be an unhandy coming together, Egil, of thy masterfulness and braving ways, and the King's frame of mind and his might; because I hold him to be no friend of thine, and thinks he hath cause for it too. Rather will I that we two let this suit fall to the ground, and not bring it up. But if thou wilt have it so, Egil, then rather shall I fare to meet the King with seeking of this suit."

Egil saith he oweth him great thanks and beholding for this, and will willingly take this choice. Hakon was then in Rogaland, but whiles in Hordaland. It was no hard matter to seek him out, and that was come about not much after their talk had been. Arinbiorn made ready his journey: it was then given out to men that he was minded for a meeting with the King. Manned he with housecarles of his a twenty-bencher that he had. Egil should be at home: Arinbiorn would not that he should go.

Fared Arinbiorn soon as he was ready, and it sped him well of his journey. Found he Hakon the King, and gat there a good welcome. And when he had a little while tarried there, bare he up his errand with the King and saith that Egil Skallagrimson is thither come into the land, and thought himself owner of all that fee that had belonged to Ljot the Pale: "So is it said to us, King, that Egil belike hath the law of his side in this; but the fee have your bailiffs taken up, and cast thereon your ban. I will bid this of you, Lord, that Egil may get the law thereof".

The King answereth his suit and was slow in taking up the word. "I know not why thou goest with such-like suit in behalf of Egil. Came he upon a time to see me, and I said to him that I would not have his abidings here in the land, for those sakes that be already known to you. Now needs not Egil to heave up such-like claims with me as with Eric my brother. But to thee, Arinbiorn, there is that to say: that thou mayest so long only be here in the land as thou settest not more account by outland men than by me or my words. For I know that thy thoughts stand thitherward where Harald is, Eric's son,[2] fosterson of thine; and that choice is best for thee, to go and find those brethren and be with them; because I greatly misdoubt me that such men as thou will be ill for me to lean on, if that be needful, to try things out betwixt me and the sons of Eric."

And when the King took this suit so thwartly, then saw Arinbiorn that it would not do to follow up those suits with him: he made ready then for his journey home. The King was somewhat sulky and unblithe toward Arinbiorn, after he knew his errand. Arinbiorn had then, withal, no frame of mind for it, to make himself meek with the King in these matters. Parted they with things in such case. Fared Arinbiorn home and said unto Egil his errand's ending: "I will not follow up such suits again with the King".

Egil became all frowning with this tale: seemed to himself to have lost great fee there, and nowise rightfully.

A few days later, that was early one morning, when Arinbiorn was in his chamber (there was there then not many men), then let he call thither Egil, and when he came there, then let Arinbiorn open up a chest and weighed out therefrom four times ten marks of silver, and spake thus: "This fee pay I unto thee, Egil, for those estates that Ljot the Pale had owned. That seemeth to me fair, that thou have this payment from us kinsmen, me and Fridgeir, since thou didst ransom his life from Ljot; and I know that thou didst this for love of me. I am bounden, then, not to let thee be robbed of thy lawful rights in this suit".

Egil took the fee, and thanked Arinbiorn. Then was Egil become joyful again.

CHAPTER LXIX. OF THE HARRYING OF EGIL AND ARIN-
BIORN IN FRISLAND, AND OF THEIR PARTING.

ARINBIORN was that winter at home at his own place,
but afterward in the spring he gave it out that he is
minded to fare a-viking. Arinbiorn had good choice of
ships: he made ready in the spring three long-ships, and all big.
He had three hundred men: housecarles had he on his own
ship, and that was exceeding well manned; he had, withal, many
bonders' sons with him. Egil took rede to fare with him: he
steered a ship, and there fared with him much of that company
that he had had with him from Iceland. But that cheaping-ship
that Egil had had from Iceland he let flit east into the Wick. He
found there men for her, to fare with his goods.

But they, Arinbiorn and Egil, held with their long-ships
south along the land: and now stood they with their host south
to Saxland and harried there that summer and gat them fee.
But when it began to be autumn, held they north again and lay
off Frisland. Upon a night, when the weather was quiet, they
laid their course up into a certain tidal river, where it was ill for
harbouring and a great outflow of the tide. There were up aland
great flats and a short way to the wood: there were the fields wet,
because there had been great rain. There took they rede for going
up, and left behind a third of the folk to mind the ships. They
went up along the river, betwixt it and the wood: then was there
soon in their way a certain thorp, and many bonders dwelt there.
The people ran out of the thorp landwards, whereso they might,
soon as they were ware of the war-host, but the vikings set on
after them. There was then later on another thorp, and a third:
the people fled, all that might come off: there was it level land
and great flats. Dykes were cut wide about the land, and water
stood therein: they had so fenced about their cornlands and
meadows, but in some places were big poles set over the dykes.
There where a crossing should be, were bridges, and timbers laid
over. The landsfolk fled into the forest; but when the vikings
were come a long way into the settled parts, then gathered the
Frislanders together in the wood, and when they had over three

hundred men then set they forth against the vikings and take rede for a battle with them. There befell then a hard fight, but so it ended that the Frislanders fled, but the vikings drave the flight. The company of the townsfolk drifted wide afield, that which ran away: so did they likewise, who fared after them: then came it so about that of either part few fared in company.

Egil set on hard then after them, and few men with him, but very many ran away. The Frislanders came there where was a dyke before them, and fared over it: after that, they took away the bridge. Then come Egil and his, at the other side: Egil straightway took and leapt over the dyke: but that was no leap for other men, and withal none had a mind for it. And when the Frislanders saw that, then they set upon him, but he warded himself: then set upon him eleven men, but so ended their dealings betwixt them that he felled them all. After that, Egil shot the bridge over and fared then back again over the dyke. Saw he then that all their folk had turned to the ships: he was then stood near the wood: so now fared Egil along the wood and so to the ships, so as he had choice of the wood if he needed.

The vikings had had down great war-takings and strand-hewings, and when they came to the ships some hewed the farm-stock, some flitted out their fee to the ships. Some stood higher up in a shield-burg,[1] because the Frislanders were come down and had a great host and shot at them: the Frislanders had then a second battle-array. And when Egil came down and he saw what was betided, then ran he at his speediest there where the rabble stood. He had his halberd before him, and took it in two hands, and cast his shield on his back. He laid forth with the halberd, and back sprang all that stood before him, and so was room given him clean through their battle: he set on so, down to his own men: it seemed to them that they had gotten him home from Hell.

Go they now aboard their ships, and held their course away from land. Sailed they then to Denmark. And when they come to the Limfirth and lay at the Neck,[2] then held Arinbiorn a house-thing with his folk and said to men his mind and purpose: "Now will I", saith he, "seek and find the sons of Eric, with that company that hath a will to follow me. I have now learnt that those brethren be here in Denmark, and keep great followings, and be in summer-time a-harrying, but sit a-winters here in Denmark. Now will I give leave to all men to fare to Norway, them that have a will to that, rather than follow me. That rede seemeth good to me, Egil, that thou turn back to Norway, and seek again at thy soonest out to Iceland, forthwith when we two part."

And now men changed ships: betook them to Egil those who would fare back to Norway; but it was by much the greater part of the folk that followed after Arinbiorn.[3] They parted, Arinbiorn and Egil, with blitheness and friendship.[4] Fared Arinbiorn to find out Eric's sons, and into the following of Harald Greycloak, his fosterson, and was thereafter with him while they both lived.

Egil fared north to the Wick, and held his course in up Oslo-firth: there was his cheaping-ship waiting, that he had let flit south that spring. Also there was there his wares and his followers, they that had fared with the ship. Thorstein Thorason came to meet Egil and bade him be with him for the winter, and those men whom he would have with him. Egil took that thankfully: let lay up his ships and bring his wares into safe-keeping. But of that folk which followed him some had lodging there, but some fared north into the land, there where they had their homes. Egil fareth to Thorstein's, and they were there in company ten or twelve. Egil was there for the winter in good welcome.

CHAPTER LXX. OF THE VERMLAND SCAT, AND HOW KING HAKON WOULD SEND THORSTEIN THORASON TO GET IT IN, OTHER ELSE TO GET HIM GONE OUT OF THE LAND.

KING HARALD HAIRFAIR had laid under him Vermland in the east. Olaf Tree-shaver had first won Vermland, the father of Halfdan Whiteleg that first was king in Norway of his kinsfolk; and King Harald was come from thence by his forefathers' line, and all those forefathers had ruled over Vermland and taken scat thereof and set men over it for the land's guarding. And when King Harald was become old, then ruled over Vermland that Earl who was named Arnvid. It was then (as in many another place far and wide), that the scat was worse paid than then when King Harald was in the lightest run of his age; and so too when the sons of Harald strove for the realm of Norway. There was then little overseeing of the scat-lands, those that lay afar. But then when Hakon sat in peace, then sought he to get again all that realm which Harald his father had had.

King Hakon had sent men east to Vermland, twelve in company: they had gotten the scat from the Earl; and when they fared back again by Eidwood, then came at them highwaymen[1] and slew them all. The same way fared it with other messengers that King Hakon sent east to Vermland, that the men were slain and the fee came not back again. That was then the talk of some men, that Earl Arnvid would set men of his, belike, to slay the King's men, and to have the fee to bring to the Earl.

Then sendeth King Hakon yet the third time men: he was then in Thrandheim; and they should fare into the Wick east to find out Thorstein Thorason with these words, that he should fare east to Vermland to fetch home the scat for the hand of the King, but, for his other choice, should Thorstein fare out of the land; because the King had then heard that Arinbiorn, his mother's brother, was come south to Denmark and was with Eric's sons: that too, withal, that they had there great followings and were a-harrying in summer-time. It seemed to King Hakon that all they together were no ways to be trusted in, because there was unpeace to be looked for from Eric's sons if they should have aught of strength for this, to make an uprising against King Hakon. Then did he unto all kinsfolk of Arinbiorn, and unto them of his affinity or friends of his: drave he then many out of the land, or made for them other hard choices. That came about there too, where Thorstein was, that the King made offer unto him, for that sake, of this choice.

That man who bare this errand, he was a man of all lands: had been long in Denmark and in the Swede-realm: it was known to him there every deal both about the ways and the men: he had fared withal wide about Norway. And when he bare these matters before Thorstein Thorason, then saith Thorstein to Egil, with what errand these men fared, and asked what way he should answer.

Egil saith: "Clear as day it looketh to me, of this word-sending, that the King will have thee out of the land, even as other kinsmen of Arinbiorn's; because that call I this for-sending,[2] of so worshipful a man as thou art. That is my rede, that thou call to speak with thee the messengers of the King, and I will be by at your talk: see we then what is here a-doing".

Thorstein did as he spake: brought them to speech with him. Then said the messengers all the truth of their errand, and the word-sending of the King, that Thorstein should fare on this journey, or be an outlaw for his other choice.

Then saith Egil: "I see plainly of your errand: if Thorstein will not fare, then must you fare to fetch home the scat".

The messengers said that he guessed right.

"Nowise will Thorstein fare on this journey, because he is nought bounden for this, so worshipful a man, to fare on such unseemly journeys. But this will Thorstein do, which he is bounden to, to follow the King,[3] inland or outland, if the King's will it is to ask this. So too, if ye will have some men from hence for this journey, then will that be your due, and all such further-ance for your journey that ye may demand of Thorstein."

And now talked the messengers among themselves, and that came to an agreement betwixt them, that they should take this choice, if Egil would fare on that journey. "The King", said they, "is all ill-willed against him, and it will seem to him our journey is all good if we so bring it about as that he be slain. He may then drive Thorstein out of the land if it likes him." And now say they to Thorstein that they will be content if Egil fare, and Thorstein sit at home.

"That shall be, then," saith Egil, "that I will ransom Thor-stein from this journey. Or how many men think ye it needful to have from hence?"

"We be eight in company," said they. "We will, that hence fare four men. Then we are twelve."

Egil saith that so should it be. Onund Sjoni and certain of Egil's following had fared out to the sea to look to their ships and wares besides that they had put into safe keeping that autumn, and they were not come home. That seemed to Egil a great miss, for the King's men were wild for the journey and would not wait.

CHAPTER LXXI. OF EGIL'S JOURNEY INTO VERMLAND, AND HIS GUESTING WITH ARMOD BEARD.

EGIL made him ready for the journey, and three other men his companions. They had horses and sledges, like as the King's men. Then were there great snows, and all the ways changed. They betake them now to their journey, when they were ready, and drove up aland; and when they made east toward Eid, then was it of a night that there was great fall of snow, so that nought clear was the way to see. Their faring was slow then the day after, because a man was over head and ears in snow, soon as he left the path; and as the day wore, they tarried and baited their horses. That was near a wooded hause.

Then spake they with Egil: "Now parteth here the ways; but here under the hause dwelleth that bonder who is named Arnald, a friend of ours:[1] we companions will fare thither to guesting. But ye shall fare here up to the hause, and then, when ye be come there, will shortly be before you a great farmstead, and there are ye sure of guesting. There dwelleth a very wealthy man that is named Armod Beard. But in the morning betimes we shall meet together and fare the next evening to Eidwood: there dwelleth a good bonder, Thorfinn by name".

So now part they. Egil and his fare up to the hause. But of the King's men is that to say, that, soon as they were hidden from sight of Egil and his folk, then took they their snowshoes[2] that they had had and put them on. Then made they their way back again with all their might. Fared they night and day, and turned to the Uplands and thence north by Dovrafell, and stayed not till they came to meet King Hakon and said to him of their journey, even as it had fared.

Egil and his companions fared in the evening over the hause. That was swiftest to say of them, that they forthwith lost the road. There was great snow. The horses fell into drifts every other while, so that they must be dragged up. There were cliffs sometimes, and woods full of undergrowth, and about the undergrowth and cliffs was exceeding hard going. There was then great delay for them with the horses, and the going for the men was of the heaviest. Then were they much outwearied, and yet made their way down from the hause, and saw there before them a great farmstead and held on thitherward. And when they came into the home-mead then saw they that there stood men without, Armod and his boys. They came to speech and asked tidings of one another, and when Armod knew that they were King's messengers, then bade he them guesting there. They took that thankfully. Armod's housecarles took their horses and gear, and the bonder bade Egil go into the hall, and they did so.

Armod set Egil in the high-seat on the lower bench, and his fellows there out from him on either side. They talked much of it, how toilsomely they had fared that evening, and to the home-men it seemed great wonder that they had come through, and said that there was no fit going for any man, even were it without snow.

Then spake Armod: "Think ye not that entertainment best, that tables be set for you and your supper given you, and then ye may go to sleep? Ye will then rest you best".

"That likes us very well," saith Egil.

Armod then let set tables for them, and thereafter were set forth great bowls full of curds.[3] Then Armod let it seem that he thought that ill, that he had no strong beer to give them. Egil and his were much thirsty for weariness: took they up the bowls and drank deep of the curds, and yet Egil by much the most. There came not any other victuals forth for them.

There was there a mort of household folk. The mistress sat at the cross-bench, and women there beside her. The bonder's daughter was on the floor, of ten winters or eleven: the mistress called her to her and spake her in the ear: therewith

fared the maid out before the table, there where Egil sat. She
quoth:[4]

> My mother sent me,
> Me with thee to talk,
> And word bear to Egil
> That you should be ware:
> So spake the Hild of Hornés—
> Manage so thy maw now:
> Our guests anon may
> Eat of nobler victual.

Armod struck the maid and bade her be silent: "Speakst thou
that always which worst befitteth".

The maid gat her gone; but Egil shot down the curd-bowl,
and it was then near empty, and then were the bowls taken from
them. Then went the homemen now into their seats, and tables
were set up throughout all the hall, and victuals set forth: next
to that, came in chargers of meat, and were then set before Egil
as before other men. Next to that was ale borne in, and that was
the strongest of beer. There was then soon drinking each man
by himself: each man alone should drink off the beast's horn.
There was the most heed given to it, where Egil was and his
followers, that they should drink their hardest.

Egil drank fairly at first, a long while. But when his companions became speechless, then drank he for them that which
they had no might for. So went it until the tables were taken
away; and then were they all become very drunk, they that were
within. But every cup that Armod drank, then spake he,
"Drink I to thee, Egil"; but the housecarles drank to the companions of Egil, and had the same form of speech. A man was
appointed for this, to bear to Egil and his men every cup, and
that one egged them on much that they should swiftly drink.[5]
Egil spake with his companions that they should then not drink
at all; but he drank for them that which they might no other way
be rid of.

Egil found then that, with things going that gate, it must ill
bestead him. Stood he then up, and walked across the floor
thither where Armod sat. He took him with his hands by the
shoulders and bent him back up against the pillars. Therewith

yawked Egil up out of him great spew, and it gushed into the face of Armod, into his eyes and nostrils and into his mouth: ran so down over his chest; but Armod was near smothered, and when he had gotten his breath again, then gushed up spew. But all spake that were by, housecarles of Armod's, that Egil must be of all men the vilest, and he would be yet the worst of men for this work, when he should not go out when he had a will to spew, and not be a gazing-stock within-door in the drinking hall.

Egil saith, "No need to speak cross at me for this, albeit I do as the bonder doth. Speweth he with all his might, no less than I".

Therewith Egil gat him to his place and sitteth him down: bade then give him to drink. Then quoth Egil with a rouse:[6]

> That I this journey hazarded
> Readily witness bear I—
> To thy meat weighty witness—
> The witness of my cheek-surge.
> Many a guest for's guesting
> Yieldeth—(seldom meet we)—
> Costlier pay: the ale-dregs
> Is left in Armod's beard.

Armod leapt up and out, but Egil bade give him to drink. Then spake the mistress with that man who had poured out for them that evening that he should give drink, so that it should not run short, while they had will to drink. So now took he a great beast's horn and filled and bare it to Egil. Egil quaffed off the horn at one drink. Then quoth he:[7]

> Drink we off—(though Ekkil's
> Ocean-steed's bestrider
> Still to song-god's hand bear
> Horn-mere)—every brimmer!
> Leave we nought, though sword-play's
> Stirrer unto me fetch
> Froth-mash tarn in horn-a
> From now till day at morn-a!

Egil drank for a while, and quaffed off every horn that came to him: but little was then of gladness in the hall, albeit some men drank. And now standeth up Egil and his companions, and take their weapons from the walls, that they had fastened up, and now go to that corn-barn that their horses were in. There they laid them down in the straw, and slept through the night.[8]

CHAPTER LXXII. OF EGIL'S LEAVE-TAKING OF ARMOD, AND HIS COMING TO THORFINN'S.

EGIL stood up in the morning, soon as it began to be day. Those companions array them and fared, soon as they were ready, back to the farmstead to look for Armod. And when they came to that bower which Armod slept in and his wife and daughter, then Egil kicked open the door and went to Armod's bed. He drew then his sword, but with the other hand grabbed he Armod by the beard and jerked him forward to the bedpost. But the wife of Armod and his daughter leapt up and besought Egil that he should not slay Armod. Egil saith that he should do that for their sake, "For that is seemly. Yet had he his deserts for it, were I to slay him".

Then quoth Egil:[1]

> The ill-spoke giver of arm-snakes
> Hath his own wife to thank for't—
> (To us of terror-eker
> No awe is)—and his daughter.
> Yet so belike will seem to thee,
> The scot this poet for drink pays,
> (Yet on our way we'll waddle),
> Nought worthy, as't befalleth.

Therewithal sliced Egil the beard off him close to the chin. Therewithal crooked he his finger in his eye, so that it lay out on the cheek. After that Egil gat him gone and to his companions.

Fare they then on their way: come at day-meal time to the farmstead of Thorfinn. He dwelt beside Eidwood. Egil and his craved day-meal, and to bait their horses: goodman Thorfinn took it as if that were their due. Go they then, Egil and his, in into the hall.

Egil asked if Thorfinn had seen aught of his companions: "We had here bespoken tryst between us".

Thorfinn saith as thus: "Fared here six men together something before day, and were much weaponed".

Then spake a housecarle of Thorfinn's: "I drove last night to fetch wood, and I found six men in the way, and that was house-carles of Armod's; and that was much before day. Now know I not, whether those will be all one and the same with the six men that thou saidst of".

Thorfinn saith that those men that he had met had fared later than when the housecarle came home with the load of wood.

And when Egil and his sat and took their meat, then saw Egil that a sick woman² lay on the cross-bench. Egil asked Thorfinn what woman that might be, who there was holden so heavily. Thorfinn saith that she was named Helga and was a daughter of his: "She hath long had lack of strength"; and that was a great fever. She gat never a night's sleep, and was as if beside herself.

"Hath aught been looked to in it", saith Egil, "about her hurt?"

Thorfinn saith, "Runes have been scored, and that is a certain bonder's son a short way from here who did that: and is since then much worse than before. Or canst thou, Egil, do aught for such hurts?"

Egil saith, "May be it will not spoil things utterly, even if I come into it".

And when Egil had eat his fill he went there where the woman lay and talked with her. He bade then lift her out of the bed and lay under her clean clothes, and now was it so done. And now he ransacked the bed that she had rested in, and there found he a whalebone, and thereon were the runes. Egil read them, and therewithal he scraped off the runes and shaved them off into the fire. He burnt all the whalebone, and let bear into the wind those clothes which she had had before.

Then quoth Egil:³

> Runes shall a man not score,
> Save he can well to read them.
> That many a man betideth,
> On a mirk stave to stumble.

> Saw I on scrapéd whalebone
> Ten dark staves scoréd:
> That hath to the leek-linden
> Over-long sickness broughten.

Egil scored runes and laid them under the bolster in the resting-place where she rested. It seemed to her as if she wakened out of sleep, and she said that she was then healed; yet was she of little might. But her father and mother became exceeding joyful. Thorfinn offered that Egil should have there all furtherance, whatso he thought he needed.

CHAPTER LXXIII. OF EGIL'S COMING TO ALF THE WEALTHY.

EGIL saith to his companions, that he will fare on his journey and bide no longer. Thorfinn had a son who was named Helgi: he was a stalwart man. That father and son bade Egil their companionship through the wood. They said that they knew for truth that Armod Beard had put six men in the wood to sit for them; and yet 'twas likelier that there would be more sittings in the wood, if the first should go miss. Thorfinn and his were four in company, that offered themselves for the journey.

Then quoth Egil a stave:[1]

> Wot you, if I with four fare,
> Fare there not six that 'gainst me
> Should hold exchange with red shield-
> Snicking knives of Din-God.
> But if I with eight be,
> Are never twelve that shake should,
> With swords together hurtling,
> The heart of black-brow'd me.

Thorfinn and his had their way in this, that they fared to the wood with Egil, and they were then eight in company. And when they came there, where was the sitting for them, then saw they men there. But those housecarles of Armod's, that sat there, saw that there fared eight men, and it seemed to them that they were nought fit to have to do with them. Stole they away then into the wood. But when Egil and his came there where the look-out men had been, then saw they that it was not all peaceful. Then spake Egil, that Thorfinn and his should fare back again; but they offered to fare further. Egil would not that, and bade them fare home, and they did so, and turned back; but Egil and his held on on their journey and were then four in company. And as the day wore, Egil and his were ware that there were six men in the wood, and thought they knew that there would be Armod's housecarles. The look-out men leapt up and made at them, and they against them; and that befell of their meeting, that Egil felled two men, but those that were left leapt then into the wood.

And now fared Egil and his on their ways, and there was done then nought to tell of before they came out of the wood and took guesting beside the wood with that bonder whose name was Alf, and was called Alf the Wealthy. He was an old man and wealthy of fee, a man self-willed, so that he might not have household folk about him, save few only. Good welcome had Egil there, and Alf was free of speech with him. Egil asked much of tidings, but Alf said such as he asked. They talked most about the Earl and about the messengers of Norway's King, them that before had fared eastward thither to fetch home the scat. Alf was no friend of the Earl's in his talk.

CHAPTER LXXIV. HOW EGIL CAME TO EARL ARNVID AND HAD THE SCAT OF HIM, AND OF THE EARL'S CHARGE UNTO HIS MEN CONCERNING EGIL.

EGIL made him ready betimes in the morning for his journey, he and his companions, but at their parting Egil gave Alf a hairy cloak. Alf took the gift thankfully: "And may here make me of it a hairy cape": and bade Egil come thither to him, when he fared back again.

They parted friends, and Egil fared on his journey and came

in the afternoon to the court of Arnvid the Earl, and gat there all good welcome. Room was made for those companions next to the high-seat man. And when Egil and his had been there a night, then bear they up their errand with the Earl and the King's word-sending out of Norway, and say that he will have all that scat from Vermland which had before stood over, since Arnvid was set in power there.

The Earl saith that he had paid out of hand all the scat and put it into the hands of the King's messengers. "But I know not what they have done with it after that, whether they have brought it to the King or have run away out of the land with it. But sith ye bear sure tokens hereof, that the King hath sent you, then will I pay all that scat which he hath a right to, and put it into your hands. But I will not be answerable afterwards, what way ye fare with it."

Egil and his tarry there a while, but before Egil fares away, the Earl payeth them the scat. That was some in silver, some in grey-wares. And when Egil and his were ready, then fared they back on their way. Saith Egil to the Earl at their parting: "Now will we bring the King that scat that we have taken; but that shalt thou know, Earl, that this fee is much less than the King thinketh he hath here; and yet is that not counted, that it will seem to him that you have to pay him back for his messengers with man-gilds,[1] them that men reckon that you will have let slay".

The Earl saith that that was not true.

Part they on that. And when Egil was away, then called the Earl to him two brethren, that were each named Wolf.[2] He spake as thus: "That great Egil, that was here this while, I am minded 'twill be clean unuseful to us that he should come to the King. We may mark from this, what way he will bear our matters before the King, when he splashed this up in our eyes,[3] the taking off of the King's men. Now shall ye two fare after them and slay them all, and let them not bear these slanders before the King. It seems to me that is your likeliest rede, that ye sit for them in Eidwood. Have with you men so many that it be certain no one of them come off, but ye get nought of man-spill from them".

Now make they ready, those brethren, for their journey, and had thirty men. Fared they to the wood; and they knew there every path before them. Held they then espial of the faring of Egil. In the wood were two ways: by the one was a hill to fare over, and there was there a steep cliff and a one-man's path to fare by: that road was the shorter. But by the other the faring was round the end of the hill, and there were there big fens and felled trees laid over them, and there was there too a one-man's path to fare by. And fifteen sat in either place.

CHAPTER LXXV. OF EGIL'S BRINGING OF THE SCAT OUT OF VERMLAND, AND OF HIS GREAT FIGHTS AGAINST THE EARL'S MEN THAT SAT FOR HIM IN EIDWOOD.

EGIL fared till he came to Alf's, and was there for the night in good entertainment. The morning after, stood he up before day: made ready then for their journey, and when they sat over their day-meal then came there goodman Alf. He spake: "Betimes do ye make ready, Egil; but that would be my rede, nowise to rush on the journey, rather look before you, for I am minded that men will be set for you in the wood. I have no men I may find to follow thee, such as might be aught of strength for thee. But that will I offer, that thou tarry here with me until I can say to thee this, that 'tis clear for faring through the wood".

Egil saith, "That will be nought but fairy-babes.[1] I will fare mine own way, as I have before determined of".

Egil and his make them ready for the journey, but Alf letted it, and bade him fare back again if he became ware that the way was trodden: said that there had no man fared over the wood from the east since Egil fared eastaway, "Unless those have fared who methinks are like to have a will to meet you".

"What deemest thou, how many will they be belike, if so it is as thou sayest? We are not to be picked up like forfeit goods,[2] though there be some odds of strength."

He saith, "I was fared forth to the wood and my housecarles

with me, and we came on men's footmarks, and that slot lay forward towards the wood, and they would likely have been many in company. But if thou believe not that which I say to thee, then fare thither and see the slot, but turn back if it shows to thee as I say to thee".

Egil fared on his way. And when they came to the road, that which led into the wood, then saw they there both men's tracks and horses'. Then spake Egil's companions, that they should turn back.

"Fare will we," said Egil. "That seemeth to me nought wonderful, though men have fared through Eidwood, seeing that is the common highroad."

And now fared they, and the trodden way held, and there was then a multitude of tracks; and when they come there where the ways parted, then parted the slot too, and was then of equal bigness in either place. Then spake Egil: "Now meseemeth it may be, that Alf hath said true. We shall now make us ready so, as if it were to be looked for that a meeting should be betwixt us".

And now cast they off their cloaks, Egil and his men, and all their loose clothes. They lay that in the sledges. Egil had had in his sledge a line of bast, very long, because that is the fashion of men who drive a long way, to have with them loose cords, if there be need to make tackling. Egil took a great flat stone[3] and laid it before his breast and his belly; and now he bent the cord about it and lapped it round and round and did it so all up about his shoulders.

Then quoth Egil:*

Eidwood is on this wise, that the forests are big all as far as the settled parts of either side, but in the midst of the wood is small timber and undergrowth far and wide, and in some places un-wooded altogether. Egil and his men turned on the shorter way, that lay over the hause. All had shields and helms and hewing-weapons and thrusting-weapons. Egil fared before them, and when they fared up the hause then was there wood down below, but unwooded up on the cliff, and when they were come up to the cliff, then leapt seven men out of the wood and

* The stave is lost. E. R. E.

up into the steep part after them, and shot at them. Egil and his turned against them, and they stood in even array across the path. Then came other men down at them on to the crag, and stoned at them thence, and that was for them much more perilous.

Then spake Egil: "Now shall ye fare back under the cliff and shelter you as ye may, but I will seek up on to the berg".

They did so. And when Egil came up from the cliff, then were there before him eight men, and went all at once against him and set upon him. Now there is nought to say of their bandying of blows: so ended it that he felled them all. And now went he forth on the berg, and bowled down stones, and there was no withstanding it. There were left lying there three of the Vermlanders, but four came off into the wood, and they were wounded and battered.

And now took Egil and his their horses and fared forth on their way till they came over the hause. But those Vermlanders that had come off brought the news to their fellows, them that were beside the fens. Set they forth then by the lower road, and so forth and in the way of Egil and his men.

Then said Wolf to his fellows, "Now shall we fare with counsel against them: watch our time so as they get not the chance to run. Here fareth it on such wise", saith he, "that the way lieth along by the hause, but the fen reacheth up to it, and there is there a crag above, but the broken road lieth there between and is not broader than a footpath's breadth. Some shall fare forth round the crag, and take them if they will go forward, but some shall lie hid here in the wood and then leap upon the back of them when they come past. See we to it so, that not one come off".

They did so, as Wolf spake. Fared Wolf forth round the berg, and ten men with him. Egil and his fare on their way, and knew nought of this rede-taking before they were come into the one-man's path. Then leapt there men upon the back of them and bare straightway weapons against them. Egil and his turned about to meet them and defended themselves. Now drive yet more men at them, they that had been of this side of the crag. And when Egil saw that, turneth he about to meet them. There was short hewing betwixt them, and Egil felled there some in the path but some turned back, there where there was more of even ground. Egil set on then after them. There fell Wolf, and in the end Egil alone slew there eleven men.

And now set he on thitherward where his companions warded the path against eight men. They were then wounded of either party. And when Egil came to it, then fled straightway the Vermlanders, but the wood was hard by. There came off there five, and all much wounded, but three fell there. Egil had many wounds and none big. Fared they now on their way. He bound the wounds of his companions, and they were none like to be bane-wounds. They sat them then in the sledges, and drove for what was left of the day.

But those Vermlanders, that came off, took their horses and dragged themselves east out of the wood to the settled parts. Then were bound their wounds. They gat them conveyance till they came to meet the Earl, and say unto him their ill faring. They say that either Wolf is fallen, and dead were five-and-twenty men, "But five alone came off with life, and they yet all wounded and battered".

The Earl asked what then might be the tidings of Egil and his companions.

They answered: "Nought clearly knew we, how much they were wounded; but boldly enough they set on against us. Then when we were eight, but they four, then fled we. Came we five to the wood, but three perished, and we saw nought else but what Egil and his should be then span-new".[4]

The Earl said that their journey was fallen out the worst it might: "Content might I have been with that, that we had great loss of men, if ye had slain those Northmen. But now when they come west out of the wood and say these tidings unto Norway's King, then have we to look for of him the hardest of choices".

CHAPTER LXXVI. OF THE BRINGING OF THE VERMLAND
SCAT TO KING HAKON, AND OF THE KING'S FARING INTO
VERMLAND AND THOSE EASTERN PARTS, AND OF EGIL'S
COMING HOME TO ICELAND.

EGIL fared till he came west out of the wood. Sought they
then to Thorfinn's at eventime, and gat there all good
welcome. Then were bounden the wounds of Egil and his
men. Certain nights were they there. Helga, the daughter of the
bonder, was then on her feet and well of her hurt. She and all
they gave thanks to Egil for that. They rested them there and their
draught-horses. But that man who had scored runes for Helga
was a short way from there. That came up then, that he had
bidden her to wife, but Thorfinn would not give her. Then
would the bonder's son have beguiled her, but she would not.
Then thought he to have scored love-runes for her, but he knew
not how, but he had scored that for her that she gat her hurt
from.

And when Egil was ready to fare away, then Thorfinn
brought him on his journey, he and his son. They were then in
company ten or twelve. Fared they then all that day with them
for safety because of Armod and his housecarles. And when
these tidings were spread, that Egil and his had fought against
overmastering odds in the wood and had the victory, then
Armod thought there was no hope that he should be able to
lift shield with Egil. Sat Armod therefore at home with all his
men.

Egil and Thorfinn gave and took gifts at their parting, and
spake to friendship betwixt them. And now fared Egil and his
on their way, and it is not said that aught befell to tell of on their
journey before they came to Thorstein's. There were their
wounds healed. Tarried they there, Egil and his, till spring.

But Thorstein found him messengers to Hakon the King, to
bring him that scat that Egil had fetched from Vermland. And
when they came and found the King, then said they unto him
those tidings that had come about in Egil's journey, and brought
him the scat. The King thought he knew then that that would

be true, which before he had been jealous of, that Earl Arnvid must have let slay his two sets of messengers that he had sent east. Said the King, that Thorstein should then have his abiding in the land and be in peace with him. Fare the messengers therewithal on their homeward way. And when they come back to Thorstein, then say they to him that the King made much of that journey, and Thorstein should then be in peace and friendship with the King.

King Hakon fared into the Wick east that summer, but thence made he his journey east to Vermland with a great host. Earl Arnvid fled away, but the King took large gild off those bonders that he thought were guilty at his hands, by the saying of them that fetched home the scat. Set he there another Earl over them, and took hostages of him and of the bonders.

King Hakon fared in that journey wide about western Gautland and laid that under him, even as is said in his saga, and is found in those songs that have been wrought upon him.[1] Then is it said too that he fared to Denmark and harried wide there: then cleared he, with two ships, twelve ships of the Danes; and then gave he the king's name to Tryggvi Olafson, his brother's son, and dominion over the Wick eastaway.

Egil made ready his cheaping-ship that summer, and gathered a ship's company; but that long-ship which he had had in the autumn out of Denmark he gave to Thorstein at parting.[2] Thorstein gave Egil good gifts, and they spake to great friendship betwixt them. Egil sent messengers to Thord at Aurland, his kinsman-in-law, and gave him charge to take order for those estates that Egil owned in Sogn and in Hordaland, and bade him sell if there were buyers for them.

And when Egil was ready for his journey and had wind at will, then sailed they out down by the Wick, and so on their way coasting north by Norway, and so out into the main sea. It blew for them fair enough: came from the main sea into Burgfirth, and Egil held his ship's course in up the firth and to harbour a short way from his own homestead, and let flit home his cargo and put his ship on the rollers.

Egil fared home to his own house. Men were joyful to see him. Tarried Egil there that winter.

CHAPTER LXXVII. OF THE BURNING OF THORD LAMBISON;
AND OF THE GIVING IN MARRIAGE OF THORDIS, EGIL'S
STEPDAUGHTER, TO GRIM OF MOSSFELL.

WHEN these tidings were befallen, that Egil was come
out again from this journey, then was the neighbourhood all settled. Then were dead all the land-taking
men, but their sons lived, or sons' sons, and they dwelt then
in the neighbourhood.

Ketil Gufa came to Iceland then when the land was much
settled. He was the first winter at Gufascales at Rosmhvalness.
Ketil had come from west over seas from Ireland. He had
with him many Irish thralls.[1] The lands were all settled at
Rosmhvalness in that time; Ketil took rede therefore to get him
gone thence, and inland to the Nesses, and sat a second winter
at Gufaness and gat there no settled abode. So now fared he up
into Burgfirth and sat there the third winter, where it is since
called Gufascales, but the river [is called] Gufa, that there had
its outfall, wherein he had his ship that winter.

Thord Lambison dwelt then at Lambistead. He was married,
and had a son who was named Lambi: he was then grown man,
big and strong for his age. The summer after, then when men
rode to the Thing, rode Lambi to the Thing. But Ketil Gufa
was then fared west into Broadfirth to look there for a place to
dwell in. Then ran his thralls away. They came a-night-time to
Thord's at Lambistead, and bare there fire to the houses, and
burnt there within-door Thord and all his household folk, but
brake open his store-house and bare out treasures and wares.
Therewith, drave they home horses and loaded them, and fared
therewith out to Alptaness.

That morning, about sunrise time, came Lambi home, and
he had seen the fire through the night. They were some few
men in company. He rode straightway to look for the thralls:
ride there men from the farmstead to meet him. And when the
thralls saw that hue and cry, they made haste away and let go
their robbery-takings. Leapt some out to the Myres, but some
out along by the sea, till the firth was before them. Then set on

after them Lambi and his men, and slew there that one that was named Kori (therefore is it called there since Korisness), but Skorri and Thormod and Swart dived in and swam from land. And now looked Lambi and his men for ships, and rowed to look for them, and they found Skorri in Skorrey and slew him there. Then rowed they out to Thormodskerry, and slew there Thormod: after him is the skerry called. They laid hand on yet more thralls, there where since are place-names called after them.

Lambi dwelt thenceforth at Lambistead, and was a worthy bonder. He was stout and able: nowise was he a quarrelsome man.[2]

Ketil Gufa fared thereafter west to Broadfirth and set up house in Codfirth. After him is called Gufadale and Gufafirth. He had to wife Yrr, daughter of Geirmund Hellskin. Vali was a son of theirs.

There was a man named Grim, and was Sverting's son.[3] He dwelt at Mossfell below the Heath: he was wealthy and of great kin. Rannveig was his sister by the same mother, whom Thorodd the Priest in Olfus had to wife. A son of theirs was Skapti,[4] the Speaker of the Law. Grim too was Speaker of the Law later He bade to wife Thordis, Thorolf's daughter, Egil's brother's daughter and his stepdaughter. Egil loved Thordis no whit less than his own children. She was the fairest of women. But because Egil knew that Grim was a worshipful man and that that match was good, then was that determined of. Thordis was given to Grim. Egil then let go out of hand her father's heritage. She went to keep house with Grim, and they dwelt long at Mossfell.

CHAPTER LXXVIII. OF THE WEDDING OF THORGERD, EGIL'S DAUGHTER, TO OLAF THE PEACOCK: OF EGIL'S LOSS OF HIS SONS BODVAR AND GUNNAR: HIS *SONS'* *WRECK* AND HIS *ARINBIORN'S LAY*; AND OF HIS OLD AGE IN ICELAND AND THE FRIENDSHIP BETWIXT HIM AND EINAR JINGLE-SCALE.

THERE was a man named Olaf,[1] son of Hauskuld, Dale-Koll's son, and of Melkorka, daughter of Muir-Kiartan the Erse-King. Olaf dwelt at Herdholt in Laxriverdale, west in the Broadfirth dales. Olaf was exceeding wealthy of fee. Fairest to look upon was he of those men that then were in Iceland. He was a lordly man.

Olaf bade to wife Thorgerd, daughter of Egil. Thorgerd was a comely woman and the tallest of women, wise and somewhat proud-minded, but of gentle ways from day to day. Egil understood every deal about Olaf, and knew that that match was worshipful, and therefore was Thorgerd given to Olaf. She went to keep house with him in Herdholt. Their children were these: Kiartan, Thorberg, Halldor, Steindor, Thurid, Thorbiorg, Bergthora: her, Thorhall the Priest, Odd's son, had to wife. Thorbiorg was had to wife first by Asgeir Knattarson, and later by Vermund Thorgrimson.[2] Thurid, Gudmund Solmundson had to wife: their sons were Hall and Slaying Bardi.[3] Ozur Eyvindson, brother of Thorodd of Olfus, gat to wife Bera, daughter of Egil.

Bodvar, son of Egil, was then well grown. He was the best make of man, fair to look upon, big and strong, like as had been Egil or Thorolf at his age. Egil loved him greatly, and Bodvar withal was dearly fond of him.

That was one summer, that a ship was in Whitewater, and there was there a great cheaping-fair. Egil had there bought much wood and let flit it home ashipboard: his housecarles went, and had an eight-oared ship that belonged to Egil. That was then on a time, that Bodvar begged to fare with them, and they granted him that. Fared he then up to the Meads[4] with the housecarles. They were six in company in the eight-oared ship, and when they should fare down again then was the flood-tide late in the day, and since they needs must bide for it, then fared they late in the evening. Then leapt up a raging south-wester, and there went against it the outfall of the tide. Then it made heavy seas in the firth, as there can oft-times befall there. Ended it so, that the ship foundered under them, and they were all lost.

But the day after were the bodies thrown up ashore. Bodvar's body came in by Einarsness, but some came on the south side of the firth, and thither drave the ship: that was found up by Reekhammer. That day learned Egil these tidings, and straightway rode he to look for the bodies. He found, washed ashore, the body of Bodvar. Took he that up, and set it on his knees, and rode with it out to Digraness, to Skallagrim's howe. He let then open the howe, and laid Bodvar down there beside Skallagrim. Thereafter was the howe shut again; and the work was not ended until about day-set time. After that, rode Egil home to Burg.

And when he came home, then went he straightway to that shut-bed⁵ that he was wont to sleep in. He laid him down and shot to the lock. None durst crave speech of him. Now so, it is said, was Egil arrayed, then when they set Bodvar down, that his hose were tied fast at the leg: he had a kirtle of red fustian, tight in the upper part, and laced at the sides. But that is the tale of men, that he was swollen so that the kirtle burst on him, and the hose likewise.

But the day after, Egil opened not the shut-bed. He had then, too, neither meat nor drink. Lay he there that day and the night after. Not a man durst to speak with him.

But the third morning, soon as it was light, Asgerd let set a man a-horseback: rode that one his hardest west to Herdholt, and let say to Thorgerd all these tidings at once. And that was about the time of nones⁶ when he came there. He said that withal, that Asgerd had sent word to her to come, first she might, south to Burg. Thorgerd let straightway saddle her a horse, and there followed her two men. Rode they that evening and through the night, until they came to Burg. Thorgerd walked straightway into the fire-house.

Asgerd hailed her, and asked whether they had eaten supper.

Thorgerd saith loudly: "Nought have I had of supper, nor nought will I, till it be at Freyja's.7 Know I no better rede for me than my father's. No will have I to live after my father and brother".

She went to the shut chamber and called, "Father, open up the door. I will that we two fare one way, both of us".

Egil sprang the lock. Thorgerd went up into the bed-chamber and locked the door behind her. She laid her down in another bed that was there. Then spake Egil: "Well doest thou, daughter, sith thou wilt follow thy father. Dear love hast thou shown unto me. What hope is there that I should have the will to live with this sorrow?"

And now held they their peace for a while.

Then spake Egil: "What is it now, daughter? Chewest thou now somewhat?"

"I chew dulse,"8 saith she; "because I am minded that then will it be worse with me than before. I am minded that else will I be over-long alive."

"Is that bad for a man?" saith Egil.

"Exceeding bad," saith she. "Wilt thou eat?"

"What can it matter?" saith he.

But a while later called she and bade give her to drink. So now was given her water to drink.

Then spake Egil: "So worketh it with one that eateth dulse, thirsteth he aye the more for that".

"Wilt thou drink, father?" saith she.

He took it, and swallowed a big draught, and that was in a beast's horn.

Then spake Thorgerd: "Now are we cheated! This is milk".

Then bit Egil a shard out of the horn, all that his teeth took hold on, and therewith cast down the horn.

Then spake Thorgerd: "What rede shall we two now take to? 'Tis ended now with this plan. Now would I, father, that we two lengthen our life, so that thou mightest work a funeral song after Bodvar; and I will score it on a roller;9 and then let us two die if it seems us good. Slow methinks will thy son Thorstein

be to work the song after Bodvar, and that would not do if there
were no right funeral held for him. For I am not minded that
we two shall be sitting at the drinking of his funeral feast".

Egil saith that that was then not to be looked for, that he
would have might to work then though he sought to: "Yet try
this I may", saith he. Egil had then had a son that was named
Gunnar, and that one too had died a little before. And this is the
beginning of the song:[10]

> Heavy meseems
> Is stirring of tongue now,
> 'Neath air-weight
> Of the ode's balance.
> 'Tis not now hopeful
> For Odin's plunder:
> From heart's well
> No handy drawing.
>
> 'Tis not rais'd easy
> ('Cause ruleth here
> Heavy sobbings)
> From soul's abode—
> The fair thing found
> Of Frigg's kinsfolk,
> Borne of yore
> From Jotunheim.
>
> Faultless: the one thing
> Left for me:
> My last, best
> Boat unsunken.
> The giant's wound-stream
> Waileth under,
> Past boat-house door
> Of my blood and kin.
>
> For my line
> At's latter end
> Standeth, storm-bent
> Like forest maples.
> 'Tis no blithe man,
> He that must bear
> A dear one's corpse
> From his dwelling down.

Yet for me
A mother's corpse,
A father dead,
Is first to tell of.
That bear I out
From temple of words,
Timber for song-craft
Speech-beleaféd.

Grim was the breach
The breaker wrought
In the kin-built fence
Of my father's garth.
I know, unfill'd
And open standeth
My son's place
That the sea swept bare.

Greatly hath Ran
For-ruin'd me.
I am over-stript
Of loving friends.
The sea hath cut
The cords of mine house,
The hard-spun line
That held from me.

Wot thou, if my wrongs
Could be wreak'd with the sword,
With the Ale-Smith
'Twere soon over.
Had I might to fell
The fierce storm's brother,
'Gainst Aegir's darling
I'd fare to battle.

Yet had I nothing,
(As I bethought me),
Of might to strive
'Gainst my son's slayer.
To the common folk's
Eyes lies bare
The helplessness
Of an old man.

Me hath the sea
Sorely robbéd:
Grim 'tis the death
Of kinsfolk to tell of:
Since for me
My house's shield
To the way of bliss
From life hath turn'd.

This know I for sure:
In this son of mine
No stuff of an ill man
Was ever waxen.
If the tree had gotten
Grown to's prime,
To the War-God's hand
'Should a reach'd at last.

Aye valu'd he most
What his father said,
Though all beside
Should speak against it.
Me he upheld
In mine householding,
And mine estate
Most he strengthen'd.

Oft cometh me
In the light wind
Of the Moon's bride
My brother lost.
I bethink me of him
When Hild rageth;
Look round for him,
And think on this:

Who else, high-hearted,
His place can fill me,
To stand by me
When mad talk riseth?
Need I that oft
'Gainst thrawart folk:
Wary I wing,
Sith friends are ebbing.

Much hard to find
Is he we may trust in,
'Mid all folk
In Iceland dwelling;
For the good-for-nought
Who a great house wrecketh
Barters for rings
His brother's corpse.

Find I that oft,
Where fee is bidden....

Nay, and that's said:
That none may get
Right boot for his son
'Less he breed another:
Nor get that man
Who might to other
Stand in the stead
Of a brother born.

It likes me not
Of the common people,
Not though each keep him
Quiet with other.—
—My boy's come
Where the bee's path beareth:
My wife's son,
To seek to his kin.

But 'gainst me still,
With's mind unmov'd
The Judge of the Froth-mash
Standeth yet.
'Neath unrest's hood
Hold I may not
Up and aright
My riding thoughts,

Since my son
By the fire of sickness
In hateful wise
From his home was took:
Him that, I wis,
Warded him well
Withouten blemish
From blameful speech.

That mind I too,
That He which holdeth
Converse with men
In the Gods' home rais'd
Mine house's ash-tree
From me that grew,
The kindred wood
Of my wife's kin.

Well stood I
With the Lord of Spears:
I made me trusting
To trow on Him;
Till the Ruler of Wains,
The Awarder of Vict'ry
Cut bonds of our friendship
And flung me off.

Worship I not, then,
Vilir's Brother,
The Most High God,
Of mine own liking.
Yet Mimir's Friend hath
To me vouchsaféd
Boot for my bale
That is better, I ween.

Mine Art He gave me,
The God of Battles,
Great Foe of Fenrir,—
A gift all faultless,
And that temper
That still hath brought me
Notable foes
'Mid the knavish-minded.

All's hard to wield now.
The Wolf's right Sister
—All-Father's Foe's—
On the sea-ness stands.
Yet will I glad,
With a good will,
And without grief,
Abide Hell's coming.

Egil began to be brisk as it went forward with working of the song. And when the song was ended, then said he it over to Asgerd and Thorgerd and them of his household. Rose he then up out of his bed, and sat him in his high seat. This song called he *Sons' Wreck*.

Thereafter let Egil hold funeral for his sons after the ancient manner. But when Thorgerd fared home, then Egil led her on her way with gifts.

Egil dwelt at Burg a long tide, and became an old man; but it is not said that he had dealings at law with men here in the land. Nought is said, neither, of holmgangs of his or warlike dealings after he settled down here in Iceland. So say men, that Egil fared not abroad out of Iceland since these tidings came to pass that were now aforesaid; and that had most to do with this, that Egil might not be in Norway because of those guilts, as before was said, that the Kings thought they had against him. A household had he of the greatest largesse, because there lacked not of fee. He had, too, a good frame of mind for this.

King Hakon Athelstane's-Fosterling ruled over Norway a long while; but the latter part of his life, then came the sons of Eric to Norway and strove for the realm of Norway with Hakon the King, and they had battles together, and Hakon had ever the victory. Their latest battle had they in Hordaland, in Stord at Fitiar.[11] There gat King Hakon the victory, and therewithal his bane-wound. After that, took those sons of Eric kingdom in Norway.

Arinbiorn the Hersir was with Harald Ericson and became his counsellor, and had of him exceeding great revenues. He was overseer of his host and of the warding of the land. Arinbiorn was a great man of war and a victorious. He had to revenue the Firthfolk.

Egil Skallagrimson heard these tidings, that a shifting of Kings was come about in Norway, and that withal, that Arinbiorn was then come into Norway to his own home, and was then in great esteem. Then wrought Egil a song upon Arinbiorn, and this is the beginning thereof:[12]

> I am pat of speech
> For praising of princes,

But slow-spoke
Of the stingy-minded;
Open-mouth'd
Of war-lord's deeds,
But tongue-tied
'Mid tittle-tattle.

With scoffs dower'd
'Gainst scandal-bearers,
I am free of speech
For friends of mine.
Sought have I many
Seats of the great,
With the pure mind
Of poesy.

Had I of old
The Yngling's child's,
The rich King's,
Wrath upon me.
Over my dark hair
Daring's hood
Drew I, and home
To the Hersir sought I,

There where all-wielder
'Neath helm of awing,
As folk-lord, over
The land did sit.
Steer'd the King
With stern intent
From York-town
The dank demesne.

That was a moonlight
Nought to trust to,
Nor without terror,
On Eric's brow;
When the moon of his forehead,
Worm-glance darting,
Shone from all-wielder's
Flaming eyen.

Yet bolster-hire
Of Him that is make
Of the fish of the wildwood
Durst I to lord bear,
So as Ygg's cup
O'er-brimming came
Unto the mouths
Of each man's ears.

Nor fair of shape
To folk beseeméd
Skald-fee I won
From house's ruler,
Then when my wolf-grey
Knob of hats
As price of my song
From prince I gat.

That took I;
But with noddle follow'd
The darkling pits
Of my drooping brows,
And that mouth
Which for me did bear
Mine HEAD-RANSOM
'Fore prince's knee.

There stood for me,
Than many better,
The treasure-bestower
On t'other side:
True friend of mine
That I'd learnt to trust to,
In glory enhancéd
At every rede:

Arinbiorn,
Who alone us kept,
Of kempés foremost,
From King's hatreds;
The ruler's friend,
Who never yet
Brake faith in the war-wont
Prince's garth.

And.........
.........let
The much-advancer
Of deeds of mine,
As.........
....
That it should be in
Kindred's....

Friendship's thief
I were justly naméd,
And hope-belier
Of Odin's cup,
Of praise-song unworthy,
A promise-breaker—
Made I not payment
For that upholding.

Now is that seen
Where set I shall,
Steep for the scaling
Of skalds' footsteps,
Before men's eyes
In their multitude,
Praise-song of mighty
Offspring of Hersirs.

Easy of shaping
With my voice-plane
Is the praise-timber
Of son of Thorir
—Of mine own friend—
'Cause chosen lieth
Two things or three
Upon my tongue.

That tell I first,
Which most men wot,
And the common sort
Do seek with their ears:
How bounteous-minded
Beseem'd to men
The Bear of the Table
Of Birches' Dread.

To all the host
'Tis holden for wonder
How the world of men
With wealth he dowereth;
They have enrich'd
The Bear of the Stone,
Both Frey and Niord,
With fee's abundance.

Yea, at the house of
Hroald's head-stem
Streams wealth o'ermounting
To hands of men;
There's riding of friends
From all the ways
Over the wind-bowl's
Wide bottom.

Like as a prince
He hath gotten
A draw-rope unto
Hearing-baskets;
Lov'd of the Gods
'Mid the throng of men;
Friend of Vethorm;
Weaklings' defender.

That winneth he
Which the most of men
Fail of, albeit
Fee they've gotten;
I mean, short's not the going
'Twixt great men's houses,
Nor easy shafting
Of all men's spears.

Ne'er went one out
From Arinbiorn,
Forth of his long-built
Bedstead-ship,
With scorn led forth
Nor with scathing words
Nor dwelling-stead
Of spear empty.

He is grim toward fee
Who dwells in the Firths;
That one's right dour
Toward Draupnir's scions;
An adversary
To sons of stealers:
To rings a terror:
A treasure-slayer.

Still hath he had
His whole life long
Full........
Of peace-breakings.

That were not good,
If the gold-waner
Should on the mews'-path,
Much-beridden
Of Rokkvi's steed,
Have strewn to waste
Those many gains
That to me he wrought.

I was waking betimes:
I bare words together,
With the morning's work
Of the servant of speech
Pil'd I a praise-howe
That long shall stand
Not easy-broken
In Bragi's mead.

There was a man named Einar.[13] He was the son of Helgi, the son of Otter, the son of Biorn the Easterner who took land in Broadfirth. Einar was brother of Osvif the Wise.[14] Einar was straightway in his youthful age big and strong and the greatest man at feats of strength. He took to working of songs straightway when he was young, and was a man ready to learn. That was one summer at the Althing, that Einar went to the booth of Egil Skallagrimson, and they took to words, and speedily it came to this in their talk that they discoursed of skaldship. To either of them such-like discoursing seemed delightful. After that, Einar was wont oft-times to go to talk with Egil; there began to be there great friendship. Einar had a little while before come home from

faring abroad. Egil asked Einar much of tidings from the east,
and of his friends: so too of those who he thought he knew were
unfriends of his. He asked much too about the great men.
Einar asked Egil too, in return, of those tidings that aforetime
were come about in Egil's journeys and his mighty works; and
that talk seemed good to Egil, and it made good telling. Einar
asked Egil where he had been so bested that he had most tried
himself, and bade him say to him that.

Quoth Egil:[15]

> Battled I one 'gainst eight,
> Ay, with eleven twice.
> So brought we food for beast:
> Their bane was I alone.
> Swapp'd we hard with hate
> With horrible shield-knives:
> Let I o'er Embla's ash
> The sword-fire cast.

Egil and Einar spake to friendship betwixt them at parting.
Einar was long in the outlands with men of high estate. Einar
was an open-handed man, and oftenest had little money, but
he was a lordly man and a good fellow: he was of the bodyguard
of Earl Hakon Sigurdson.[16]

In that time there was in Norway great unpeace and battles
betwixt them, Earl Hakon and the sons of Eric, and now one
now the other were packed out of the land. King Harald
Ericson fell south in Denmark at the Neck in the Limfirth, and
he was betrayed.[17] There battled he against Harald Knutson,
that was called Gold-Harald; against him and Earl Hakon. There
fell then too, with Harald the King, Arinbiorn the Hersir that
before was spoke of.

And when Egil heard tell of Arinbiorn's fall, then quoth he:[18]

> Minish'd are those who minish'd
> The mew-field's day,—O where now
> Shall I find men as bounteous?—
> Thing-brighteners of Ingvi:
> They that on hawk's high-fell
> Hail'd for me with limbeck's
> Snow for earth's girdle
> Island-nail'd with words.

Einar Helgison the skald was called Jingle-scale. He wrought a drapa upon Earl Hakon that is called Gold-lack,[19] and that was for a very long time that the Earl would not listen to the song, because he was wroth with Einar.

Then quoth Einar:[20]

> Made I the ale of Odin,
> While others slept; for captain
> That sits o'er earth, all eager
> Wrought I—I'm sorry for it!
> Little methought (with longing
> The lord sought I) 'twas likely
> To strong prince, treasure-scatterer,
> This skald should seem the worst.

And yet again quoth he:[21]

> Seek we that earl that heart takes
> To eke with swords the wolf's feast:
> To twi-row'd bark repair we
> Of ring-shielded Sigvaldi.
> Drop hand with me he will not,
> That wound-serpent swayer,
> When lord we find. Targe bear we
> Aboard of Endil's snow-shoe.

The Earl would not that Einar should fare away, and listened then to the song, and thereafter gave he Einar a shield, and it was the greatest treasure: it was drawn upon with tales of old,[22] but all between the drawings were spangles of gold laid over it, and set with stones.

Einar fared to Iceland and to lodging with Osvif his brother; but in the autumn rode Einar from the west and came to Burg and guested there. Egil was then not at home, for he was fared north into the countryside, but he was looked for home again. Einar waited for him three nights, but that was not the custom to sit longer than three nights at a friend's. Einar made him ready then to be gone, and when he was ready then went he to Egil's bed and hung up there the shield, that precious one, and said to the homemen that he gave Egil the shield. So now rode Einar away, but that same day came Egil home. But when he came in to his bed, then saw he the shield, and asked who owned that treasure. It was said to him that Einar Jingle-scale had come there, and he had given him the shield.

Then spake Egil: "Of all men, curse him for his gift! Is he minded that I shall wake there over it and work songs upon his shield? Now fetch my horse. I shall ride after him and slay him!"[23]

It was then said to him that Einar had ridden early in the morning, "He will now be come west to the Dales".

After that Egil wrought a drapa, and this is the beginning thereof:[24]

> Time 'tis the lauds to 'lumine
> Of glitt'ring fence I've gotten
> Of ships: (home to mine hand came
> Greeting of treasure-sender).
> Mishandled (my words hear ye)
> Of me shall ne'er the reins be
> Of stallion of Gylfi's land
> That 'longeth to the earth-born.

Egil and Einar held to their friendship so long as they both lived. But so, it is said, fared it with the shield at last, that Egil had it with him in that bridal-journey, when he fared north to Withymire with Thorkel Gunnvaldson, he and those sons of Red-Biorn, Trefil and Helgi. Then was the shield spoilt, and cast into the whey-vat;[25] but thereafter Egil let take off the mountings, and there were twelve ounces of gold in the spangles.

CHAPTER LXXIX. OF THORSTEIN EGILSON, AND OF THE DEATH OF ASGERD, EGIL'S WIFE, AND HOW EGIL SHIFTED HOUSE FROM BURG TO MOSSFELL.

THORSTEIN the son of Egil, then when he was waxen up, was of all men the fairest to look upon, white of hair and bright of aspect. He was big and strong, and yet not to compare with his father. Thorstein was a wise man and of gentle ways, even-minded and the best-tempered of men. Egil loved him little.[1] Thorstein too was nothing warm-hearted towards him; but Asgerd and Thorstein loved each other greatly.

Egil was then becoming very old. That was of a certain summer, that Thorstein rode to the Althing, but Egil sat then at home. But before Thorstein should fare from home, he and Asgerd watched their time and took out of a chest of Egil's that silken gown, Arinbiorn's loom, and Thorstein had it to the Thing. And when he had it at the Thing, then was it too long and trailed behind him and became filthy underneath, then when they were a-going to the Hill of Laws.[2] And when he came home, then Asgerd put away the gown, there where it was before; but a long while later, when Egil opened his chest, then found he that the gown was spoilt, and looked into the matter with Asgerd, how that might have come about. She said then the truth of it.

Then quoth Egil:[3]

> No heir have I to inherit
> Mine heritage, as need were:
> Living, a son hath cheated me;
> Cheating, forsooth, I call that.
> Well might the water-horse's
> Bestrider yet have bided
> Till they that own the sea-sleighs
> The stones have pil'd above me.

Thorstein gat to wife Jofrid, daughter of Gunnar Hlifarson:[4] her mother was Helga, daughter of Olaf Feilan,[5] and sister of Thord the Yeller.[6] Jofrid had Thorodd had to wife aforetime, the son of Odd-a-Tongue.[7]

A little after this died Asgerd. After that, Egil broke up his household and put it in the hand of Thorstein; but Egil fared then south to Mossfell to Grim, his son-in-law, because he loved most Thordis his stepdaughter of those folk that then were alive.[8]

That was one summer, that a ship came out into Leiruwick, and that man steered her who was named Thormod: he was a Northman and a housecarle of Thorstein Thorason's. He had along with him a shield that Thorstein had sent to Egil Skallagrimson, and that was a noble treasure. Thormod brought Egil the shield, and he took it thankfully. Afterwards in the winter wrought Egil a drapa on the gift of the shield, that is called Targe-Drapa,[9] and this is the beginning thereof:[10]

> King's thane, lithe and listen
> To my lofty force of the altar's
> Falling-tresséd Friend (let
> Thy folk give heed to silence).
> Oft shall be heard through Hordland
> Mine harvest good of eagle's
> Chaps,......a-stirring,
> O steerer of the Raven.

Thorstein Egilson dwelt at Burg. He had two sons gotten out of wedlock, Hrifla and Hrafn, but since he was married he and Jofrid had ten children; Helga the Fair[11] was their daughter, whom they strove for, Skald-Hrafn and Gunnlaug the Worm-tongue. Grim was the eldest of their sons; another Skuli; the third Thorgeir, the fourth Kollsvein, the fifth Hiorleif, the sixth Halli, the seventh Egil, the eighth Thord. Thora was named a daughter of theirs that Thormod Kleppiarnson had to wife. From the children of Thorstein is come a great line of kindred and a mort of great men: that is called the Myresmen's kindred, all that which is come from Skallagrim.

CHAPTER LXXX. OF STEINAR, THE SON OF ONUND SJONI, AND HIS HIGH HANDED DEALINGS WITH THORSTEIN EGILSON.

ONUND SJONI dwelt at Anisbrent then when Egil dwelt at Burg. Onund Sjoni had to wife Thorgerd, daughter of Biorn the Thick from Snaefellstrand.[1] The children of her and Onund were Steinar and Dalla, whom Og-mund Galtison had to wife (their sons, Thorgils and Kormak[2]). And when Onund became old and his eyesight little good, then handed he over his household: Steinar took it then, his son. That father and son had a wealth of fee.

Steinar was of all men the biggest, and mighty of strength; an ugly man, crooked of growth, long-legged and short of body;

Steinar was a very quarrelsome man and a headstrong, ill to deal with and hard to take hold of, and the most masterful of men. And when Thorstein Egilson dwelt at Burg, then came about straightway a coldness betwixt him and Steinar.

South of Hafslech lieth a marsh that is named Stacksmire: there standeth water over it in winter-time, but in the spring when the ice is loosed then is there grazing there so good for beasts that it was called equal with a stack of home-mead hay. Hafslech made the landmarks there in old days; but in spring went Steinar's beasts much upon Stacksmire when they were driven out towards Hafslech, and Thorstein's housecarles grumbled at it. Steinar gave no heed to it; and so fared it through the first summer that nought befell to tell of.

But the second spring Steinar held on with the grazing; but Thorstein betook him then to a talk with him, and talked yet quietly; he bade Steinar hold the grazing of his farm cattle even as in old times it had been. Steinar saith that the cattle would go where it liked;3 he talked of it all somewhat stiffly, and he and Thorstein had some bandying of words.

And now Thorstein let chase the beasts out into the marshes over Hafslech. And when Steinar was ware of that, then set he Grani, a thrall of his, to sit over the beasts on Stacksmire, and he sat there every day. This was in the latter part of summer; there were grazed bare then all the ings4 of the south side of Hafslech.

Now that was one day that Thorstein had walked up to Burg to look about: he saw where Steinar's beasts fared. He walked out to the marsh (that was late in the day): he saw that the beasts were then come a long way out into the bays of fen between the hillocks. Thorstein ran out along the marsh, and when Grani saw that, then drave he the beasts without stint or stay till they came to the milking-shed. Thorstein came then after him, and they met, he and Grani, in the wall-gate. Thorstein slew him there. That is named since Grani's-gate: that is in the wall of the home-mead.5 Thorstein kicked the wall down on the top of Grani, and covered so his corpse.

And now fared Thorstein home to Burg. But those women that fared to the milking-shed found Grani there where he lay.

After that, fared they home to the house and said unto Steinar these tidings. Steinar buried him up in the holts, but thereafter set Steinar another thrall to follow the beasts, and that one is not named. Thorstein made then as if he knew nought about the grazing, for that which was left of the summer.

That befell to tell of, that Steinar fared in the first spell of winter out to Snaefellsstrand, and tarried there awhile. Steinar saw then a thrall that was named Thrand: he was of all men the biggest and strongest. Steinar bargained for that thrall, and bade for him a great price; but he that owned the thrall valued him at three marks of silver, and valued him twice as dear as a common thrall, and that was their bargain. He had Thrand home with him. And when they came home, then talked Steinar with Thrand: "Now is it come to this, that I will have work of thee. Here hath division been made already of all pieces of work. Now will I lay down a piece of work for thee that thou wilt find little toil in. Thou shalt sit over my beasts. On that set I much account, that there be good holding of them to pasture: I will that thou follow no man's judgement save thine own, where the pasture is best in the marshes. Nought know I of the looks of a man, if thou have not the heart and the might for this, to hold thine own with any one of Thorstein's housecarles".

Steinar put into Thrand's hands a great axe, near an ell across the mouth, and it was edged like a hair. "So it looketh to me of thee, Thrand," saith Steinar, "as if 'twill not be clear how much thou valuest Thorstein's priesthood, if you two look one another in the eye."

Thrand answereth: "I am nought beholden methinks to Thorstein, but it seems to me I understand what kind of work thou hast laid down for me. Thou wilt think thou hast little at stake where I am;[6] and methinks 'tis a good choice for me, come up what may, if we two, I and Thorstein, must try it out betwixt us".

And now took Thrand to minding of the beasts. He had understood, albeit he had not been there long, what way Steinar had let hold his beasts to pasture, and Thrand sat over the beasts on Stacksmire. And when Thorstein was ware of this, then sent he a housecarle of his to find out Thrand and bade tell him of the landmarks betwixt his land and Steinar's. And when the housecarle met Thrand, then said he to him his errand and bade him hold the beasts another way: said that that was the land of Thorstein Egilson, that the beasts were then come into.

Thrand saith: "That reck I not a jot, which of them owneth the land. I will have the beasts there where it seemeth to me is the pasture best".

So now part they. Fared the housecarle home, and saith to Thorstein the answer of the thrall. Thorstein let that rest. But Thrand took to sitting over the beasts night and day.

CHAPTER LXXXI. OF THE SLAYING OF THRAND, AND OF THE SUIT AT LAW BETWIXT STEINAR AND THORSTEIN.

THORSTEIN stood up one morning with the sun, and walked up to the Burg. He saw where Steinar's beasts were. And now walked Thorstein out upon the marshes until he came to the beasts. There standeth a wooded rock beside Hafslech, and up on the rock slept Thrand, and had loosed and done off his shoes. Thorstein walked up to the rock, and had an axe in his hand, not big, and no weapons more. Thorstein prodded Thrand with the axe-shaft, and bade him wake. He sprang up swift and hard and grabbed his axe with two hands and swung it up. He asked what Thorstein would.

He saith, "I will say to thee that I own this land, but you own the grazing-pastures of the outer side of the brook. That is not to be wondered at though thou know not the landmarks here".

Thrand saith: "Nought seemeth it to me to matter, who owneth the land. I will let the beasts be there where it seemeth to them best".

"That is likelier", saith Thorstein, "that I will now have a mind to rule mine own land, rather than shall Steinar's thralls."

Thrand saith: "Much art thou, Thorstein, an unwiser man than I deemed, if thou wilt have night-quarters under my axe[1] and make hazard against this of thy nobility. 'Tis clear, as I reckon, that I will have strength belike for two of thee; and I lack not heart. I am, besides, weaponed better than thou".

Thorstein spake: "On that hazard will I lie, if thou do nought about the grazing. I have hope there may be great unlikeness in good luck[2] betwixt us two, even as the matter of our causes is unequal".

Thrand saith: "Now shalt thou see, Thorstein, whether I am any whit afraid of thy threats".

And now Thrand sitteth him down and tied his shoe; but Thorstein swung up the axe hard and hewed at the neck of Thrand, so that his head fell on his chest. Therewithal bare Thorstein stones to him and covered his corpse: walked thereafter home to Burg.

But that day came late home Steinar's beasts; and when all hope was given up of their coming, then took Steinar his horse and laid saddle on it. He had all his weapons. He rode south to Burg, and when he came there he met men to speak to. He asked where Thorstein was: it was said to him that he sat within-door. Then bade Steinar that Thorstein should come out: said he had an errand with him. And when Thorstein heard that, he took his weapons and went out into the doorway. And now asked he of Steinar what errand his might be.

"Hast thou slain Thrand, my thrall?" saith Steinar.[3]

"So it is truly," saith Thorstein. "Thou'st no need to turn thy thoughts towards other men for that."

"Then see I, that thou wilt seem to thyself a hard-handed warder of thy land, sith thou'st slain two thralls of mine: but to me that seemeth nought so mighty a piece of work. Now will I give thee a much better choice in this, if thou wilt with valiancy ward thy land, and there shall be no more relying on other men to drive the beasts; but this shalt thou know, that the beasts shall both day and night be upon thy land."

"So it is", saith Thorstein, "that I slew last summer a thrall of thine, him which thou didst set to graze the beasts on my land, and thereafter I let you have grazing as you would, all through till winter. Now have I slain another of thy thralls for thee: laid I on this one the same guilt as on the first. Now shalt thou have grazing from henceforth this summer, as thou wilt;

but next summer if thou graze my land and set men to drive hither thy cattle, then will I yet slay for thee one man or another, him that followeth the cattle, yea, though thou thyself shouldst follow them. I will so do every summer, so long as thou holdest to this habit thou'st taken to in the grazing."

Therewith rode Steinar away and home to Brent; and a little later rode Steinar up into Staffholt: there dwelt then Einar,[4] he was a priesthood's-man. Steinar asked his aid and bade him fee therefor. Einar saith: "It will little avail thee of my help, unless more men of worth back this suit".

After that rode Steinar up into Reekdale[5] to find out Odd-a-Tongue, and asked his aid and bade him fee therefor. Odd took the fee and promised his help, that he should strengthen Steinar to bring the law into force against Thorstein. Steinar therewithal rode home.

But in the spring fared they, Odd and Einar, with Steinar a-summoning, and had great throng of men. Steinar summoned Thorstein for the thrall-slayings, and let the penalty be the lesser outlawry for either slaying; because that was the law where a man's thralls were slain for him if so be that the thrall-gild for them was not brought before the third sun.[6] And it should be rated equal, two lesser outlawries and one full outlawry.

Thorstein summoned him for no guilts in return; and a little later sent Thorstein men south to the Nesses.[7] Came they to Mossfell, to Grim's, and said there these tidings. Egil made as if he took small account of it, and yet quietly asked carefully about their dealings, Thorstein's and Steinar's, and so too about those men that had strengthened Steinar in this suit. And now fared the messengers home, and Thorstein deemed well of their journey.

Thorstein Egilson made great throng of men for the Spring-Thing, and came there a night before other men, and tilted their booths and his thingmen did the like, that there had booths. And when they had made things ready, then Thorstein let the company of his thingmen go to it and they made there great booth-walls; and now let he tilt a booth much greater than the other booths that were there. In that booth were no men.

Steinar rode to the Thing, and made great throng of men. There had Odd-a-Tongue rule over the company, and was all thronged about with men. Einar of Staffholt was likewise thronged about with men. They tilted their booths. The Thing was thronged with men. Men brought forward their suits. Thorstein bade no atonements for his behalf, but answered thus to those men who sought to bring about an atonement, that he was minded to let it abide judgement: said that it seemed to him the suits were little worth, those that Steinar fared withal touching the slaying of his thralls, but accounted Steinar's thralls to have wrought guilts enough for their slaying. Steinar bare himself big over his suits. It seemed to him his causes were lawful, and the strength to aid him enough to bring the law into force. Therefore was he eager in his suits.

That day went men to the thing-brent, and men spake forth their suits; but at evening should the courts fare out for the pleadings. Thorstein was there with his band. He had most rule there over the ordering of the Thing, because so had it been while Egil bare the priesthood and the oversight of men. They had of either party all their weapons. Men saw from the Thing that a band of men rode from beneath along Gorgewater, and there blinked there shields withal. And when they rode to the Thing, then rode there a man before them in a blue cape: had a helm on his head red with gold, and a shield at his side gold-bedight; in his hand a barbed spear: there was gold inlaid on the socket. He was girt with a sword. There was come Egil Skalla-grimson with eighty men, all well weaponed, as if ready for battle. That host was well picked. Egil had had with him the best bonders' sons from the Nesses southaway, them that he thought most like fighters. Egil rode with his band to that booth which Thorstein had let tilt and before was empty. Lighted they off their horses. And when Thorstein knew the faring of his father, then went he to meet him with all his band, and welcomed him kindly. Egil and his folk let bear in their faring-gear into the booth, and drive the horses to pasture. And when that business was done, went Egil and Thorstein with all the band up to the thing-brent, and sate them there where they were wont to sit.

And now stood Egil up and spake[8] on high: "Whether is Onund Sjoni here on the thing-brent?"

Onund said there he was: "I am right joyful, Egil, that thou art come. That will turn all to the better that which here standeth betwixt the suits of men".

"Whether is that by thy redes that Steinar thy son bringeth charges against Thorstein my son, and hath drawn together throng of men for this sake, to make Thorstein an outlawed man?"

"The cause is nowise in me", saith Onund, "that they be at ill accord. I have laid many words thereto and bade Steinar be set at one with Thorstein; because it hath been my wish at every turn to spare thy son Thorstein from dishonour, and the cause thereof is that old dear loving friendship that hath been betwixt us two, Egil, since we were bred up in the same garth."

"Shortly will that", saith Egil, "be made plain whether thou speakest this in sadness[9] or in vain falsehood, though that is the last thing I am minded to think. I mind me of those days when to either of us two it would have seemed unlikely, that we two should bring charges one against other, or not make our sons be quiet that they fare not with such foolery as I hear is here like to come about. That rede showeth good to me, whiles we two be alive and stood so near by to their strife, that we two take these suits under us and set them in order, and not suffer Odd-a-Tongue and Einar to set our sons a-biting each at other like fighting-horses:[10] let them have somewhat else from henceforth to make money by rather than take to such-like things."

Then stood Onund up and spake: "Right sayest thou, Egil, and that is ill-befallen unto us two, to be at that Thing where our sons strive together. And never shall that shame take hold upon us two, to be so empty of lordliness as that we set them not at one. Now will I, Steinar, that thou hand over unto me these suits and let me fare with them even as it likes me".

"I know not that," saith Steinar, "whether I will so cast down my suits, seeing that I have already sought me help from great men. I will now that my suits have such ending only as it shall like well Odd and Einar."

And now talked they, Odd and Steinar, between themselves;

said Odd as thus: "I will perform, Steinar, my bringing of help unto thee, even that which I promised, to get thee the law, or that ending of thy suits which thou wilt be willing to take upon thine hands. Thou wilt have most to answer for it, what is to become of thy suits, if Egil shall judge thereon".

Then spake Onund: "Nought need I to have these things from under the tongue-roots of Odd.¹¹ I have had from him neither good nor ill, but Egil hath done me many great good turns. Trust I in him much better than in others, yea and I shall rule in this: that will best behove thee, not to have all of us in thy teeth.¹² I have ere now had the ruling here for us two, and even so shall it be".

"Headstrong art thou in this matter, father; and oft, I am minded, shall we two repent us of this."

Therewith Steinar handed over to Onund the suit, and he should then pursue or settle it, so as the laws allowed. And straightway when Onund had the ruling in these suits, then went he to find out that father and son, Thorstein and Egil.

Then spake Onund: "Now will I, Egil, that thou alone shape and shear in these suits, even as thou wilt, seeing that I trust in thee best to set in order these suits of mine and all others".

And now took they hands together, Onund and Thorstein, and named them witnesses and that with the witness-naming, that Egil Skallagrimson should alone deal with these suits even as he will, and all unchallenged there at the Thing; and so these suits ended. Went men so home to their booths. Thorstein let lead to Egil's booth three oxen, and let hew them for his thing-victualling.

And when Odd-a-Tongue and Steinar came home to their booth, then spake Odd: "Now hast thou, Steinar, thou and thy father, had your way as to how your suits should end. Now count I myself loosed from my bond with thee, Steinar, touching that bringing of help which I promised thee; because so was it spoken betwixt us, that I should avail thee so far as that thou shouldst win thy suits, or bring them to that ending which pleased thee, howsoever shall seem to thee the award of Egil".

Steinar saith that Odd hath done well to him and manly, and their friendship shall now be much better than before: "I will call it that thou art loosed from thy bond with me touching that wherein thou wast bound".

About evening fared the courts out,[13] and it is not said that aught befell there to tell of.

CHAPTER LXXXII. OF EGIL'S AWARD IN THE SUITS BETWEEN STEINAR AND THORSTEIN.

EGIL SKALLAGRIMSON walked upon the thing-brent the day after, and with him Thorstein and all their band. There came then also Onund and Steinar: Odd-a-Tongue was also come there, and Einar and their folk. And when men had there spoken their law-business, then stood up Egil and spake as thus: "Whether are those father and son here, Onund and Steinar, so that they may understand my speech?"

Onund saith that they were there.

"Then will I open up mine award [1] betwixt Steinar and Thorstein. Take I up the matter there, when Grim, my father, came hither to the land and took here all the lands about the Myres and wide about the neighbourhood, and took to him homestead at Burg and appointed thereto demesnes, but gave, over and above this, choice of land unto his friends, so as they settled there since. He gave Ani homestead at Anisbrent, there where Onund and Steinar have hitherto dwelt. That know we all, Steinar, where the landmarks be betwixt Burg and Anisbrent, that there maketh Hafslech the boundary. Now that was not unwittingly, Steinar, that thou didst in grazing of Thorstein's land, and didst lay under thee his estate, and wast minded that he would be so great a shamer of his line as that he would be willingly thy robbing-prey (because thou, Steinar, thou and Onund, may know that, that Ani received land from Grim, my father); but Thorstein slew for thee two thralls. Now is that clear as day to all men, that they have fallen by their own act, and they are men not to be booted: yea more, though they had been free men, then would they yet have been men not to be booted. But because of that, Steinar, that thou bethoughtest thee that thou mightest rob

Thorstein, my son, of his land-holding, that which he took with my rede and that I took in heritage after my father, therefore shalt thou lose thine own land at Anisbrent and have no fee therefor. That too shall follow, that thou shalt not have homestead neither lodging here in the neighbourhood south of Longwater, and be gone from Anisbrent before the faring-days be passed, but fall unhallowed before all those men who will give aid to Thorstein, forthwith after the faring-days, if thou wilt not fare away or in any jot not hold to that which I have laid down for thee."

But when Egil sate him down, then named Thorstein witnesses of his award.

Then spake Onund Sjoni: "That will be the talk of men, Egil, that that award which thou hast made and spoken forth, is something askew.[2] Now is that to be said of me, that I have laid out mine whole self to bar these troubles; but from henceforth shall I spare nought that I have the might to do for the hurting of Thorstein".

"The rather am I minded", saith Egil, "that the lot of you two, father and son, will aye be the worse the longer we stand at strife together. I thought, Onund, that thou wouldst know that, that I have held my ground before such-like kind of men as ye two be, father and son. But Odd and Einar, that have dragged themselves so much into this case, have hereof gotten the honour they deserved."[3]

CHAPTER LXXXIII. HOW STEINAR SAT FOR THORSTEIN EGILSON BESIDE EINKUNNIR.

THORGEIR BLUND was there at the Thing, sister's son to Egil, and had done Thorstein great help in these suits. He bade that father and son give him somewhat of land out there on the Myres; he dwelt before to the south of Whitewater below Blundswater. Egil took that well, and urged Thorstein that he should let him fare thither. They set Thorgeir down at Anisbrent; but Steinar moved his homestead out over Longwater and sat him down at Leirulech. But Egil rode

home south to the Nesses, and that father and son parted with
blitheness.

That man was with Thorstein who was named Iri, than any
man else swifter-footed and of all men the keenest of sight. He
was an outlander,[1] and a freedman of Thorstein's, and yet had
he the minding of cattle, and that most, to gather the barren
sheep up to the fell in the spring-time and in autumn down to
the folds. But now, after the faring days, Thorstein let gather
those barren sheep that had been left behind that spring, and
was minded to let drive that to the fell. Iri was then at the sheep-
folds, but Thorstein and his housecarles rode up to the fell, and
they were eight in company. Thorstein let make a fence across
Grisartongue between Longwater and Gorgewater: he let many
men be at that work in the spring. And when Thorstein had
looked over the work of his housecarles, then rode he home; and
when he came over against the thing-stead, then came Iri running to meet them, and said that he will speak with Thorstein
apart. Thorstein spake that his companions should ride on,
whiles they talked.

Iri saith to Thorstein that he had fared up to Einkunnir that
day and seen to the sheep; "But I saw", saith he, "in the wood
above the winter-road[2] that there shone twelve spears and
certain shields".

Thorstein saith aloud, so that his companions heard it plain
so: "Why must he[3] be so set on meeting me that I may not ride
my ways home? And yet will Olvald think it unfair, that I should
deny him speech with me if he is sick".

Iri ran then the hardest he might, up the fell. Thorstein saith
to his companions: "Lengthened methinks now must be our
way, if we shall first ride south to Olvaldstead. Olvald sent me
word that I should go see him. And yet it will seem to him no
great return for the ox that he gave me last autumn, that I should
meet him, if it seemeth to him the matter presseth".

And now rode Thorstein and his men south along the marshes
below Stangarholt and so south to Gufa and down along the
river by the riding-roads. And when he came down from Vatn, then
saw they south of the river many beasts and a man near them;
there was a housecarle of Olvald's. Thorstein asked whether all

was well there. He said that there was all right well, and Olvald was in the wood a-hewing trees.

"Then shalt thou", saith Thorstein, "say to him, if he hath with me an errand of moment, that he may come to Burg; but I will now ride home."

And so did he. But that was heard say, though, later, that Steinar Sjonison had that same day sat up beside Einkunnir with eleven men. Thorstein made as if he had not heard of it, and that was let rest thereafter.

CHAPTER LXXXIV. OF THE END OF THE DEALINGS BETWEEN STEINAR AND THORSTEIN EGILSON.

A MAN is named, Thorgeir.[1] He was a kinsman of Thorstein's and the greatest friend of his. He dwelt in that time at Alptaness. Thorgeir was wont to have an autumn bidding every autumn. Thorgeir fared to find Thorstein Egilson and bade him to him. Thorstein promised to come, and Thorgeir fared home. But at the appointed day Thorstein made him ready for the journey, and there was then four weeks till winter. With Thorstein fared his eastman[2] and two housecarles of his. Grim was named a son of Thorstein's: he was then of ten winters, and fared too with Thorstein; and they were five in company and rode out to the force and there over Longwater, and so out as their road lay to Aurridawater.

But out by the river was Steinar at work, and Onund and housecarles of theirs; and when they knew Thorstein, then leapt they to their weapons and therewith after Thorstein and his men. And when Thorstein saw Steinar's faring after them, then rode they out of Longholt. There is a certain knoll, high and not wide: there light they down, Thorstein and his, from their horses, and hasten up on to the knoll. Thorstein spake that the boy Grim should fare into the wood and not be stood by at their meeting.

And straightway when Steinar and his come to the knoll, then set they on against Thorstein and his, and there befell a battle. Steinar and his were six in company, grown men, but the seventh

a son of Steinar's, ten winters old. This meeting saw those men
that were in the meadow-closes, from other farms, and ran to
it to part them. And when they were parted, then were Thorstein's housecarles both dead; fallen too was a housecarle of
Steinar's, and some wounded. And when they were parted,
searcheth Thorstein about, where Grim was, and they find him.
Grim was then wounded sore, and Steinar's son lay there beside
him, dead.

And when Thorstein leapt a-horseback, then called Steinar
upon him and spake: "Runnest thou now, Thorstein the
White!"3 saith he.

Thorstein saith: "A longer way shalt thou run, ere a week be
past".

And now rode Thorstein and his, out over the marsh, and had
with them the boy Grim. And when they came out into that
holt that is there, then dieth the boy; and they buried him there
in the holt, and that is called Grimsholt, but there is it named
Battleknoll, where they fought.

Thorstein rode to Alptaness that evening, as he had been
minded, and sat there at the bidding three nights, but thereafter
made him ready for faring home. Men offered to fare with him,
but he would not: rode they two in company.

And that same day, when Steinar knew it was to be looked for
that Thorstein would ride home, then rode Steinar out along the
sea. And when he came to those sandhills which are below
Lambistead, then sitteth he down there on the sandhill. He had
that sword that was named Skrymir,4 of all weapons the best;
he stood there on the sandhill with the sword drawn and turned
then but one way, because he saw then the riding of Thorstein
out along the sand.

Lambi5 dwelt at Lambistead, and saw what Steinar was a-
busied with. He walked from home and down to the bank, and
when he came to Steinar then grabbed he him from behind
under the arms of him. Steinar would tear himself free of him:
Lambi held fast: and fare they now off the sandhill down to the
level, but then ride Thorstein and his man by the lower road.
Steinar had ridden his stud-horse, and it galloped inland along
the sea: that saw they, Thorstein and his man, and wondered,

because they had not been ware of the faring of Steinar. Then struggled Steinar up again on to the bank, because he saw not that Thorstein had ridden by. And when they came to the brow of the bank, then Lambi kicked him down the sandhill; but Steinar was not on his guard for this: he raced down on to the sand, but Lambi leapt home. And when Steinar was come to his feet, then ran he after Lambi. But when Lambi came to the gate, then leapt he in, but slammed the door behind him. Steinar hewed after him, so that the sword stood fast in the wind-sheath.⁶ Parted they there. Steinar walked home.

But when Thorstein came home, then sent he, the day after, a housecarle of his out to Leirulech to say to Steinar that he should move his homestead beyond Burglava, but if not, he would use his vantage against Steinar in that he had the greater power in men; "And there will then be no chance for faring away". But Steinar made ready his journey, out to Snaefell-strand, and there set he up house where it is named Ellidi. And there endeth their dealings, betwixt him and Thorstein Egilson.

Thorgeir Blund dwelt at Anisbrent. He dealt unneighbourly with Thorstein all he might. That was on a time when they met together, Egil and Thorstein, that they talked much about Thorgeir Blund their kinsman, and all their talk came to the same thing betwixt them.

Then quoth Egil:⁷

> Erst I the lands with talking
> 'Ticed from hand of Steinar:
> Unto the heir of Geir
> Good work methought then wrought I.
> Scurvily doth my sister's
> Son, yet all bade fair then.
> Nought may he bind himself from bale,
> Blund.—And here I marvel.

Thorgeir Blund fared away from Anisbrent and fared south into Flokadale, because Thorstein thought there was no dealing with him, albeit he was willing to give way to him withal.

Thorstein was a man of no foxish tricks,⁸ and of righteous

ways and not overbearing with men, but held his ground if other men meddled with him, and indeed it came somewhat heavy for most men to try for the mastery with him.

Odd was then lord in Burgfirth to the south of Whitewater. He was temple-priest, and ruled over that temple that all men paid the temple-toll to this side of Skarths-heath.

CHAPTER LXXXV. OF THE LAST DAYS AND DEATH OF EGIL SKALLAGRIMSON.

EGIL SKALLAGRIMSON became an old man; but in his old age he began to be heavy of movement, and he was dull both of hearing and sight; he began withal to be stiff of leg. Egil was then at Mossfell with Grim and Thordis.

That was on a day that Egil walked out along by the wall and struck his foot and fell. Some women saw that, and laughed at it and spake: "Shent art thou now, Egil, altogether, sith thou fallest of thine own self".

Then saith goodman Grim: "Less mocked women at us two then when we were younger".

Then quoth Egil:[1]

> Like hobbled steed I stumble;
> Bald scalp I'm like to fall on;
> Woeful weak is leg-berg's
> Wimble; and hearing's gone now.

Egil became altogether sightless. That was upon a day, when the weather was cold in winter-time, that Egil fared to the fire to warm himself. The kitchen-wench talked of it, that that was a great wonder, such a man as Egil had been, that he should lie before their feet, so that they might not get their work done.

"Be content thou," saith Egil, "though I bake myself by the fire, and let us be kind and give place to one another."

"Stand thou up," saith she, "and get thee to thy place, and let us get our work done."

Egil stood up and gat him to his place, and quoth:[2]

> Blind toward embers turn I;
> Bid I the spear-care's goddess
> Pity the ill I bear in
> The balls that press mine eyelids.
> King that earth rang with name of,
> Who erst my words had game of,
> With words (but of the captain
> Of Hamdir's spear) advanc'd me.

That was yet another time when Egil gat him to the fire to warm himself, then asked a man of him whether he was cold in the feet, and bade him not stretch them out too near the fire.

"So shall it be," saith Egil. "But nought easy is it now for me to steer my feet, when I cannot see: and over-deaflike[3] 'tis, this loss of eyesight." Then quoth Egil:[4]

> Long meseemeth,
> Laid all alone,
> An old, old carle,
> Far from King's caring.
> Here's two cripples,
> Both bitter cold;
> And these women
> Need the warmth.

That was in the earlier days of Earl Hakon the Great, then was Egil Skallagrimson in the ninth ten-years of his age, and he was then a brisk man for all other sakes save loss of eyesight. That was in the summer when men made ready for the Thing, then asked Egil of Grim to ride to the Thing with him. Grim took that slowly; and when those two, Grim and Thordis, were a-talking together, then said Grim to her what Egil had asked for: "I will that thou find out what dwelleth under this asking".

Thordis went to speak with Egil her kinsman: it was then the greatest game to Egil to talk with her: and when she found him, then asked she, "Is that true, kinsman, that thou wilt ride to the Thing? I would thou wouldst say to me what might be in this rede-taking of thine".

"I shall say to thee", quoth he, "what I have thought on. Minded am I to have to the Thing with me those two chests that

King Athelstane gave me, that be full each one of them of English silver. I am minded to let bear the chests to the Hill of Laws, then when there is most throng of men there. And then I am minded to sow the silver: and methinks 'twill be wonderful if they all divide it well betwixt 'em. I am minded that there would be then kickings and buffetings, and it might come to that at last that all the Thing should be a-fighting."

Thordis saith, "This seemeth to me a rede indeed! and like to be talked of as long as the land is dwelt in". And now went Thordis to talk with Grim, and said unto him Egil's rede-taking.

"That shall never be, that he bring this to pass, so great a villainy!"

And when Egil came to talk with Grim about faring to the Thing, then Grim talked him off that altogether, and Egil sat at home through the Thing. Nowise liked him well of that. He was somewhat frowning.

At Mossfell they had hill-dairies, and Thordis was at the hill-dairy during the Thing. That was one evening, then when men made them ready for bed at Mossfell, that Egil called to him two thralls that belonged to Grim. He bade them take him a horse: "I will fare to the baths". And when Egil was ready, he gat him out, and had with him his silver-chests. He went a-horseback: and now fared down along the home-mead past a brent that was there, when men saw him last. But in the morning when men rose up, then saw they how Egil staggered about on the holt beyond the eastern garth and led after him the horse. Fare they then to him and fetched him home. But neither came back afterward, thralls nor chests; and there be many guesses, where Egil may have hidden his fee.

Beyond the eastern garth at Mossfell goeth a gill down out of the fell; but that hath come about to mark there, that in sudden thaws there is there a great waterfall, but after the waters have fallen away, there have been found in the gill English pennies. Some men say from this that Egil will there have hidden his fee. Below the home-mead at Mossfell are big fens and marvellously deep: many have that for true, that Egil will there have cast in his fee. To the south of the river are baths and a short way there-from big earth-holes; and some say from this, that Egil would there have hidden his fee, because thitherward is often seen howe-fire. Egil said that he had slain Grim's thralls, and so too, that he had hidden his fee; but that said he to no man, where he had hidden it.

Egil took a sickness the autumn after, that led him to his bane. And when he was dead, then let Grim put Egil in good clothes, and thereafter let flit him down into Tiltness and make there a howe, and Egil was laid therein and his weapons and clothes.

CHAPTER LXXXVI. OF THE FINDING OF EGIL'S BONES.

GRIM of Mossfell was baptized then when Christ's faith was brought into the law in Iceland. He let make a church there; and that is the saying of men that Thordis hath let flit Egil to church. And there is that for a token, that later, when a church was made at Mossfell and that church taken down at Bushbridge that Grim had let make, then was the church-yard there dug up, and under the altar-place then were found man's bones. They were much greater than other men's bones: men think they know from the sayings of old men that that would have been the bones of Egil.

There was then Skapti Thorarinson the mass-priest,[1] a wise man. He took up the skull of Egil and set it in the church-yard. The skull was wonderfully great; yet that seemed more beyond all likelihood, how heavy it was. The skull was all wavy-marked on the outside, like a harp-shell. Then would Skapti find out about the thickness of the skull. Took he then a hand-axe, great enough, and swung it with one hand at his hardest and smote with the hammer on the skull and would break it; but there where the blow came it whitened, but dented not nor split. And one may mark from such things, that that skull would be nought easy-scathed before the hewings of small men, while skin and flesh followed it.

The bones of Egil were laid in the outer part of the church-yard at Mossfell.

CHAPTER LXXXVII. OF THE MYRESMEN'S KIN THAT ARE
COME OF EGIL'S BLOOD AND LINE.

THORSTEIN EGILSON took baptism then when
Christ's faith came to Iceland, and let make a church at
Burg. He was a troth-fast man and a well mannered. He
became an old man, and dead of a sickness, and was laid to earth
at Burg at that church which he let make. From Thorstein is a
great line come, and a mort of great men, and many skalds; and
that is the Myresmen's kin, and so all that which is come from
Skallagrim.

Long held it in that line, that the men were strong and great
fighting men, but some wise of understanding. That was great
unlikeness of looks, whereas in that line have been bred up those
men who have been fairest in Iceland, as was Thorstein Egilson
and Kiartan Olafson, sister's son to Thorstein, and Hall Gud-
mundson, so also Helga the Fair, Thorstein's daughter, whom
they strove for, Gunnlaug the Wormtongue and Skald-Hrafn;
but the more part of the Myresmen were of men the ugliest.

Thorgeir, the son of Thorstein, was the strongest of those
brethren, but Skuli[1] was the biggest; he dwelt at Burg after the
days of Thorstein his father. Skuli was long a-viking. He was
forecastle-man to Earl Eric on *Ironbeak*, then when King Olaf
Tryggvison fell. Skuli had had a-viking seven battles.

TABLE I

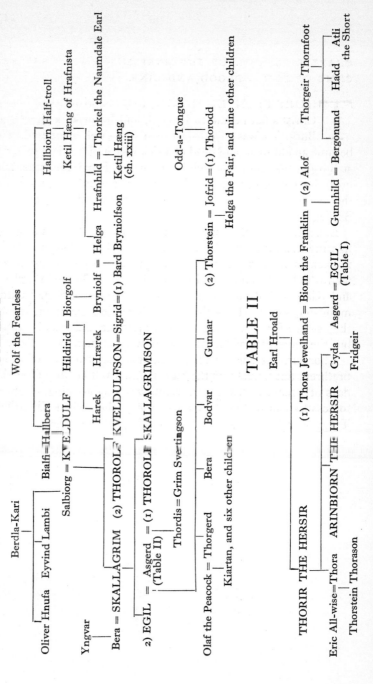

Wolf the Fearless

Berdla-Kari

Oliver Hnufa   Eyvind Lambi   Bialfi = Hallbera   Hallbiorn Half-troll

Yngvar   Salbiorg = KVELDULF   Ketil Hæng of Hrafnista

Hildirid = Biorgolf   Ketil Hæng = Thorkel the Naumdale Earl

Harek   Hrærek

Bera = SKALLAGRIM   (2) THOROLF KVELDULFSON = Sigrid = (1) Bard Bryniolfson

Bryniolf = Helga   Hrafnhild = Thorkel the Naumdale Earl

Ketil Hæng (ch. xxiii)

2) EGIL = Asgerd = (1) THOROLF SKALLAGRIMSON   (2) Thorstein = Jofrid = (1) Thorodd

(Table II)   Thordis = Grim Svertingson   Odd-a-Tongue

Helga the Fair, and nine other children

Olaf the Peacock = Thorgerd   Bera   Bodvar   Gunnar

Kiartan, and six other children

TABLE II

Earl Hroald

(1) Thora Jewelhand = Biorn the Franklin = (2) Alof

THORIR THE HERSIR   ARINBIORN THE HERSIR   Gyda   Asgerd = EGIL, (Table I)   Gunnhild = Bergonund

Thorgeir Thornfoot

Fridgeir

Eric All-wise = Thora   Thorstein Thorason

Thorgeir Thornfoot

Hadd   Atli the Short

TABLE III

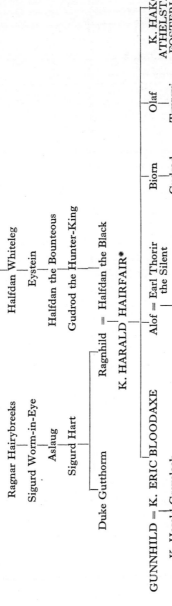
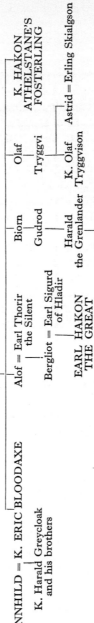

Olaf Tree-shaver
Halfdan Whiteleg
Eystein
Halfdan the Bounteous
Gudrod the Hunter-King
Ragnhild = Halfdan the Black
K. HARALD HAIRFAIR*

Ragnar Hairybreeks
Sigurd Worm-in-Eye
Aslaug
Sigurd Hart
Duke Gutthorm

GUNNHILD = K. ERIC BLOODAXE
K. Harald Greycloak and his brothers

Alof = Earl Thorir the Silent
Bergliot = Earl Sigurd of Hladir
EARL HAKON THE GREAT

Biorn
Gudrod
Harald the Grenlander
K. Olaf the Holy

Olaf
Tryggvi
K. Olaf Tryggvison

K. HAKON ATHELSTANE'S FOSTERLING

Astrid = Erling Skialgson

* Other children of K. Harald Hairfair not shown.

CHRONOLOGICAL TABLE

NOTE. The exact chronology is in dispute. I have in the main followed F. J.

LIST OF ABBREVIATIONS

A.S. Anglo-Saxon.

C.P.B. *Corpus Poeticum Boreale*. Vigfusson and York Powell. (Oxford Univ. Press, 1883: 2 vols.) Ref. by volume and page.

D. *Icelandic-English Dictionary*. Cleasby and Vigfusson. (Oxford Univ. Press, 1874.)

Eb. Eyrbyggja Saga. Ref. to Morris and Magnússon's transl. 'The Ere Dwellers' (Saga Library: Bernard Quaritch), by chapter.

Ed. Snorri Sturlason's Edda (the 'Prose Edda'). Ref. to Finnur Jónsson's ed. (Reykjavik, 1907) by page.

F.J. Finnur Jónsson's edition of Egils Saga Skallagrímssonar (Altnordische Saga Bibliothek, 1924). Ref. by page.

Gisl. Gísla Saga Súrssonar. Ref. to Dasent's 'Gisli the Outlaw' (Edmonston and Douglas, Edin. 1866) by chapter.

Glum. Víga-Glúms Saga. Ref. to Vald. Ásmundarson's ed. (Reykjavik, 1897) by chapter.

Grett. Grettis Saga. Ref. to Morris and Magnússon's transl. 'Grettir the Strong' (Longmans Green and Co., 1900), by chapter.

Gunnl. Gunnlaugs Saga Ormstungu. Ref. to Morris's transl. 'Three Northern Love Stories' (Longmans Green and Co., 1901), by chapter.

Hak. Hakon the Good's Saga. See Hkr.

Har. Gr. Harald Greycloak's Saga. See Hkr.

Har. Hfr. Harald Hairfair's Saga. See Hkr.

Hen-Th. Hen-Thorir's Saga. Ref. to Morris and Magnússon's transl. (Saga Library, vol. I: Bernard Quaritch) by chapter.

Hfdn. Halfdan the Black's Saga. See Hkr.

Hkr. Snorri Sturlason's Heimskringla. Morris and Magnússen's transl. (Saga Library: Bernard Quaritch). Ref. to vol. IV (which contains Notes, Indexes, etc.) by page; otherwise the ref. is to individual sagas by chapter (e.g. Har. Hfr. 1).

Icel. Icelandic.

Int. The Introduction to the present translation.

Korm. Kormák's Saga. Ref. to Vald. Ásmundarson's ed. (Reykjavik, 1893) by chapter.

Landn. Landnámabók Islands. Ref. to the Nordiske Oldskriftselskab ed. (Copenhagen, 1925) by paragraph.

Ld. Laxdæla Saga. Ref. to Vald. Ásmundarson's ed. (Reykjavik, 1895) by chapter.

Nj. Njáls Saga. Ref. to Dasent's 'Story of Burnt Njal' (Edmonston and Douglas, Edin. 1861) by chapter.

O.E.	Old English.
O.E.D.	*The Oxford English Dictionary.*
O.H.	Olaf the Holy's Saga. See Hkr.
O.N.	Old Norse.
O.T.	Olaf Tryggvison's Saga. See Hkr.
T.E.	The Terminal Essay to the present translation.
Vols.	Völsunga Saga. Ref. to Morris's transl. by chapter.
Yngl.	Ynglinga Saga. See Hkr.

TERMINAL ESSAY

SOME PRINCIPLES OF TRANSLATION

ENOUGH has been said of the spirit and style of the classical Icelandic saga to make it clear that for an Englishman to render the sagas into his own language is to labour under no alien sky and dig no inhospitable soil. More than that: the Old Northern tongue (called Icelandic because it is only in Iceland that it survives in its purity as a living language, and because it was Icelanders that built up its classic literature of prose and verse) more than any other language resembles our own. The two languages are akin in word, syntax, and idiom. Hundreds of words* are substantially the same in English and

* The following is a list of some of the more important: after, ale, all, back, bairn, bale, bane, bear, beneath, better, best, bid, bide, bind, blood, boot, broad, brother, burthen, busk, byrny, call, cast, chapman, cheap, choose, coal, cold, cost, dale, dare, day, deal, dead, deem, dirt, doom, draw, drift, drink, drown, dwell, earl, earth, east, eat, egg, eke, eld, elf, else, end, enough, errand, even, eye, fain, fair, fall, fare, fast, fat, father, fee, feed, fell, fellow, ferry, fetter, few, fey, fill, find, finger, first, firth, fish, fit, fleet, flit, float, flock, flood, fold, folk, follow, foot, for, force, fore, forgive, foster, fowl, from, frost, full, furlough, gab, gain, game, gang, garth, gem, get, gift, gill, gird, give, glad, goat, god, good, grass, gray, grim, grip, grit, ground, grow, guard, gush, hail, hair, hale, half, hallow, halt, hammer, hand, handsel, hang, hap, harbour, hard, harm, harry, harvest, have, haven, hause, hawk, hay, head, hear, heart, heath, heave, helm, help, hen, here, hew, hold, holm, holt, holy, home, honey, horn, horse, hound, house, how, ice, if, ill, in, iron, keel, kettle, kin, king, kirk, knee, knife, know, lamb, lame, land, lard, laugh, law, lay, lead, leap, leave, leet, leg, length, let, lie, life, like, linen, list, lithe, little, live, loan, loathe, lock, long, loose, lot, louse, lout, low, main, man, mark, may, meal, meat, meet, mere, mid, mild, milk, mind, mire, mirk, mis-, month, mood, moor, more, morning, mort, most, mother, mould, much, muck, murder, nail, name, near, neat, need, neighbour, ness, new, next, night, north, now, oak, oar, oath, of, off, oft, our, out, over, ox, oyce, quick, quoth, ransack, rash, raven, reave, red, rede, reek, rich, ride, right, rime, ring, rise, rive, rob, roof, room, root, row, rowan, rue, run, rune, ruth, sable, sackless, saddle, sail, sake, salt, same, sand, saw, say, scant, scathe, sea, seal, seat, see, seek, seethe, seldom, self, sell, send, set, shaft, shall, shame, shape, sharp, shear, sheathe, shield, shift, shine, ship, shoot, short, should, sick, side, sign, silver, sing, sister, sit, sith, skerry, skill, skin, slacken, slake, slander, slay, sled, sleek, sling, slit, slot, sly, small, smear, smith, snake, sneak, snick, snow, so, sodden, soggy, some, son, song, sore, sound, sour, south, spae, spar, spare, spear, spell, spew, spill, spurn, spurt, stack, staff, stall, stand, starboard, stark, stave, stead, steadfast, steal, steep, steer, stem, stepdaughter, etc., stern, stick, still, sting, stir, stock, stone, stool, stoop,

Icelandic, and among them great numbers of the simple basic words belonging to things that are close to the roots of all human thought and action. Thus there is likeness of spirit and likeness of language; and a good translation, a recognizable shadow that being looked on recalls the features and movements of its original without much degradation or distortion, is certainly no impossible thing. Yet there are few good translations of sagas: perhaps only two good translators, and all the rest mostly bad. And the reason is, what?

First, no doubt, there are the stubborn difficulties that stand in the way of all translation. The translator's problem is to say to us in our own tongue what has been said by someone else in another. If it be a proposition of Euclid, or an engineer's report on a mine, the difficulties are not serious, provided that the translator knows his two languages. Words are here simply instruments, or tickets denoting certain well-defined ideas: he need but choose his tickets aright, and his work is done.

But how if he have to translate, for example, this little quatrain of Sappho's:

δέδυκε μὲν ἀ Σελάννα
καὶ Πληίαδες, μέσαι δέ
νύκτες, πάρα δ᾽ ἔρχετ᾽ ὤρα,
ἔγω δὲ μόνα κατεύδω.

'The Moon has set, and the Pleiades, and it is middle night. And the hours go by. But I sleep alone.' Take, not my pedestrian prose, but the best translation you can discover or poet can make you. What is it beside the poetess's Greek?

This, it may be objected, is an extreme instance. Lyric poetry

storm, stour, strand, straw, stream, strew, string, strong, stud, summer, sunder, swain, swallow, swan, swarm, swart, sweat, sweep, swell, swim, swine, sword, tail, take, tale, talk, tame, tarn, tassel, teen, tell, thank, thane, that, thatch, thaw, their, them, then, there, they, thick, thief, thine, thing, think, thirst, this, thole, thorn, thorp, thou, though, thought, thraldom, thrall, threat, thresh, thrift, thrive, throng, thrush, thrust, thwaite, thwart, tide, tidings, till, tilt, timber, time, tit, toe, tongue, town, tread, tree, trough, trow, trust, turf, twin, un- (prefix; Icel. ú- *or* ó-), under, up, viking, wade, waggon, wake, wand, want, ward, ware, warm, warn, wax, way, weapon, weather, week, welcome, well, were, west, whale, what, wheat, where, white, why, wick, wide, wield, will, win, wind (n.), wind (v.), with, withstand, wolf, wonder, word, work, worm, worst, worth, wound, wrath, wreak, wreck, write, wrong, young.

of a high order must always be untranslatable. It expresses so intimately some individual moment in the poet's experience that it must be unique: rhythm, music of vowel and consonant, all the complex under-tones and over-tones of thought and feeling, are so bound up in the very words of the poet that the same thing can never be said again in another language. I had rather steer clear, though, of the too metaphysical, and say that great poetry and, in a lesser degree, all living speech, with all its play of expression, so personal, so elusively charming, is very hard to translate, and that in practice even the finest translations are but shadows of their originals. (It must be remembered that to translate is here taken to mean the saying of *the same thing* in another language: not the saying of something rather like it, as FitzGerald did in his lovely *Omar Khayyám*, or as Longfellow, perhaps, imagined he was doing in his *Saga of King Olaf*.)

The cardinal difficulty, then, of all translation is the difficulty of translating the living word. And the particular difficulty of translating the sagas is that, while they present this cardinal difficulty in a high degree, they give no warning to the unwary that any difficulty exists at all. The simplicity of the saga, the restraint of it, its homeliness, its stern objective outlook and ignorance of ornament, together with those likenesses between the languages, create a deceptive impression of ease that tempts the translator to his confusion. Mr Green, for instance, tells us in his preface that, "The prose of the Saga presents few difficulties to a translator. Icelandic prose, as regards order of words, is simple, and runs naturally enough into English. The sentences are mostly short and plain. In Egilssaga the style for Icelandic is pronounced by good authorities to be of the best; the translator can only hope that in its English dress it may not have lost all its attractiveness". In that hope he proceeds placidly along a path of which the following is perhaps a sufficient glimpse*: "These, when they were aware of the enemy, gathered themselves and advanced to meet them, expecting victory as heretofore. But, on the battle being joined, the Norsemen charged furiously forwards, bearing shields stronger than those of the Kvens; the slaughter turned to be in the Kiriales'

* Cf. p. 26 for this passage.

ranks—many fell, some fled. King Faravid and Thorolf took there immense wealth of spoil, and returned to Kvenland, whence afterwards Thorolf and his men came to Finmark, he and Faravid parting in friendship". The best translation is but a shadow. The worst, as here, traduces and defames the original, as if the ass should posture in the lion's skin. And that is a pure misfortune; seeing that those who cannot look on the lion's self, and who make small account of asses, may by such a spectacle be brought to the mistaken opinion that of lions also small account is to be made.

Indeed it is certain that the translation of the Icelandic classics is not a task well suited to the perfunctory efforts of well-meaning persons with a taste for history and archaeology but innocent of any feeling for language or style. A translator who with a more angelic caution approaches these quicksands will escape the grosser errors whereby the Icelandic is made to run so 'naturally' not into English but into the jargon of the schoolboy's crib. If he avails himself to the uttermost of the resemblances between the languages, it is within the bounds of possibility that he may succeed in producing an English version of a saga which shall convey in some degree the style and flavour of the original. If, from whatever motive, he ignores these resemblances, he is like a gardener who, wishing to grow rhododendrons and having a soil of sand and peat, digs up and throws away this suitable soil and at much pains substitutes chalk and clay. His translation will be as dead as the rhododendrons. But even supposing he uses all these advantages and avoids these errors, he will yet be fain to say at last (with Dasent, in the preface to his fine translation of *Njála*), "Even now, after all that has been done to make the rendering faithful, the translator lays it with dread before the public, not because he has any doubt as to the beauty of his original, but because he is in despair, lest any shortcomings of his own should mar the noble features of the masterpiece which it has been his care to copy".

Two translators of sagas stand above the rest: Sir George Dasent and William Morris. Their virtues and their weaknesses are complementary. Dasent, holding fast by the simple and natural, does not always escape the charge of colloquialism and prosiness: he has no great sense of the beauty and the living quality of words, and by that defect he loses in his versions some of the dignity and splendour of his originals. Morris, himself a poet, is drawn to an opposite error: his joy in words and their rhythm and music, while it enables him to produce a translation which has the life and freshness of an original composition and which preserves on the whole the very tone and accent of the saga, leads him astray sometimes into too great a smoothness of style and sometimes into a curiosity of archaism that has a sophisticated and literary effect quite alien to the works he is translating.

It would be interesting to compare Morris with Dasent in the same passage; but (fortunately, from other points of view) their work does not overlap. But the living quality of a good translation, which (like Morris's) is faithful word by word to the original and inspired with its spirit, is easily seen by placing a passage from his *Heimskringla* beside the same passage in the earlier translation by Samuel Laing. This is not to condemn Laing: he worked under difficulties unknown to Morris, many years before Dasent had set the example of bare simplicity or Vigfusson's monumental Icelandic Dictionary had smoothed the way for English scholars, and with no Icelandic collaborator to help him. Moreover he was interested rather as a historian and a student of institutions than as an artist. In his preface to his translation of the *Heimskringla*, with its long and valuable preliminary dissertation and its appendices and notes, he says, "The adventures, manners, mode of living, characters, and conversations of these sea-kings, are highly dramatic, in Snorro's work at least; and are told with a racy simplicity and truthfulness of language which the translator cannot flatter himself with having attained or preserved. All he can say for his work is, that any translation is better than none; and others may be stimulated by it to enter into the same course of study, who may do more justice to a branch of literature scarcely known among us". Laing's was a noble pioneering work, and it is with a deep respect for him, and in the spirit of his own words, just quoted, that I use his translation as a foil to the more perfect achievement of another Englishman who wrote half a century later.

The passage (*Heimskringla: Saga of Hakon the Good*, Ch. XVIII) reads in Morris* as follows:

"In the autumn at winter-nights was there a blood-offering held at Ladir, and the king went thereto. Heretofore he had ever been wont, if he were abiding at any place where was a feast of blood-offering going on, to eat his meat in a little house with but few folk, but now the bonders murmured at it, that he sat not in his own high-seat, where the feast of men was greatest; and the earl said to the king that so he would not do as now. So it was therefore that the king sat in his high-seat. But when the first cup was poured, then spake Earl Sigurd thereover, and signed the cup to Odin, and drank off the horn to the king. Then the king took it and made the sign of the cross thereover; and Kar of Griting spake and said: 'Why doeth the king thus, will he not do worship?' Earl Sigurd answers: 'The king doth as they all do who trow in their own might and main, and he signeth the cup to Thor. For he made the sign of the hammer over it before he drank'. So all was quiet that eve. But on the morrow, when men went to table, the bonders thronged the king, bidding him eat horse-flesh, and in no wise the king would. Then they bade him drink the broth thereof, but this would he none the more. Then would they have him eat of the dripping, but he would not; and it went nigh to their falling on him. Then strove Earl Sigurd to appease them, and bade them lay the storm; but the king he bade gape over a kettle-bow, whereas the reek of seething had gone up from the horse-flesh, so that the kettle-bow was all greasy. Then went the king thereto, and spread a linen cloth over the kettle-bow, and gaped thereover, and then went back to the high-seat; but neither side was well pleased thereat."

Laing† renders the same passage as follows:

"The harvest thereafter, towards the winter season, there was a festival of sacrifice at Lade, and the king came to it. It had always been his custom before, when he was present at a place where there was sacrifice, to take his meals in a little house by himself,

* Morris and Magnússon, Saga Library, *Heimskringla*, vol. I, pp. 169–70 (Quaritch, 1893).

† *The Heimskringla, or Chronicle of the Kings of Norway*, transl. Samuel Laing, vol. I, pp. 330–1 (Longmans, 1844).

or with some few of his men; but the bonders grumbled that he did not seat himself on his throne at these the most joyous of the meetings of the people. The earl said that the king should do so this time. The king accordingly sat upon his throne. Now when the first full goblet was filled, Earl Sigurd spoke some words over it, blessed it in Odin's name, and drank to the king out of the horn; and the king then took it, and made the sign of the cross over it. Then said Kaare of Gryting, 'What does the king mean by doing so? Will he not sacrifice?' Earl Sigurd replies, 'The king is doing what all of you do, who trust to your power and strength. He is blessing the full goblet in the name of Thor, by making the sign of his hammer over it before he drinks it'. On this there was quietness for the evening. The next day, when the people sat down to table, the bonders pressed the king strongly to eat of horse-flesh; and as he would on no account do so, they wanted him to drink of the soup; and as he would not do this, they insisted he should at least taste the gravy; and on his refusal they were going to lay hands on him. Earl Sigurd came and made peace among them, by asking the king to hold his mouth over the handle of the kettle upon which the fat smoke of the boiled horse-flesh had settled itself; and the king first laid a linen cloth over the handle, and then gaped over it, and returned to the throne; but neither party was satisfied with this."

This passage was chosen haphazard. It is by no means a good example of Morris, (indeed, it shows some of his more serious faults), nor a bad of Laing. To translate 260 words of Icelandic Morris has used 328 English words and Laing 337: there is nothing between them there. The capital difference is that Laing's version is heavy and lifeless, while Morris's is, by comparison, living human speech. Morris has the feeling and general effect of the original; he also follows it far more closely word by word. It is true to say that in every particular where he differs from Laing he is closer to the original.

This is not a matter of verbal accuracy or a matter of vocabulary, though both those have their importance. 'High-seat' is better than 'throne' for *hásæti*; 'first cup was poured' is better than 'first full goblet was filled' for *hit fursta full var skenkt*. 'Signed to Odin' is a translation of *signaði Óðni*, while 'blessed it in Odin's name' is a poor paraphrase; and the same is true of 'hold his mouth over the handle of the kettle' for *gína yfir kettilhödduna*, which is, simply and literally, 'gape over'. The real mischief, the reason why Laing's translation gives really no idea at all of the style of Snorri Sturlason, may be seen by comparing in the two versions the passage beginning, in Morris, 'But on the morrow' and ending 'nigh to their falling upon him'. The mischief is plain enough, and can be summed up in one word: Latinism.

Participial phrase and relatival and absolute constructions, so deeply rooted in the Latin language and by adoption grown not foreign to our own, are utterly foreign to the classical Icelandic. So repugnant are these constructions to the genius of that language that they kill it out of hand, completely, so that no flavour remains of the original in an English translation that makes free use of these idioms. There may be an Icelandic Gibbon or a Johnson or a Sir Thomas Browne: there is at any rate no whiff of him in the sagas. The point is so important, that it is worth while to give a literal translation of the passage just referred to, so that it may be seen on what a bed of Procrustes Laing has here laid and mutilated his original:

"The day after, when men went to table, then thronged the bonders about the king and bade him eat horseflesh; the king would for no sake do that. Then bade they him drink the broth; that will he surely not. Then bade they him eat the dripping, but the king will not that either (*vill hat ok eigi*). There was then made ready for a setting upon him."

Laing says they pressed him to eat of horseflesh—

"and *as he would* on no account do so, they wanted him to drink of the soup; *and as he would not* do this, they *insisted* he should *at least* taste the gravy; and *on his refusal* they were going", etc.

Morris has himself taken unnecessary licence in this passage. But Laing, no doubt quite unwittingly, has gone the whole hog, and lost touch with his original altogether.*

* In justice to Laing it should be said that he translated at second hand, through a Danish version.

Worse men than Laing have fallen into the same error and, unlike him, sought to justify it. Sir Edmund Head, in his translation of Viga-Glum, a saga told in an unusually rugged and primitive style, uses language like this: "It happened one summer, on his arrival in the Eyjafirth, that Arngrim did not invite him to his house, and though they met he did not speak to him, imputing to him that he had talked with his wife, Thordis, more than was proper; but the report of most men was that there was little or nothing in the matter". And in his preface he tells us: "I have adhered to the original as closely as was consistent with my desire of presenting to the English reader a translation that could be read without being very stiff and tiresome, but I am by no means sure that I have attained this object".

One thing is certain: no great work of human genius can be translated successfully by persons pre-occupied with the question how far they may safely follow their original and how far they would be well advised to alter, expurgate, adorn or rearrange it in order to recommend it to the popular taste of the moment. Pope,* in an auguster field, gives precedent here to Sir Edmund Head. In his *Essay on Homer*, prefixed to his translation of the *Iliad*, he expresses the view that many of Homer's compound epithets "cannot be done literally into English without destroying the purity of our language". Some, however, "may have justice done them by circumlocution; as the epithet εἰνοσίφυλλος to a mountain, would appear little or ridiculous translated literally *leaf-shaking*, but affords a majestic idea in the *periphrasis*:

The lofty mountain shakes his waving woods".

And later: "Upon the whole", he writes, "it will be necessary to avoid that perpetual repetition of the same epithets which we

---

* Two diverse examples of his practice:

Homer: γέγηθε δέ τε φρένα ποιμήν.
  Pope: The conscious swains, rejoicing in the sight,
    Eye the blue vault, and bless the useful light. (*Il.* viii, 559.)
Homer: τὸν δ᾽ ἀπαμειβόμενος προσέφη πόδας ὠκὺς Ἀχιλλεύς·
    Διογενὲς Λαερτιάδη, πολυμήχαν᾽ Ὀδυσσεῦ,
  Pope: Then thus the goddess-born, "Ulysses, hear". (*Il.* ix, 307–8.)

find in Homer, and which, though it might be accommodated...
to the ear of those times, is by no means so to ours: but one may
wait for opportunities of placing them, where they derive an
additional beauty from the occasions on which they are employed;
and in doing this properly, a translator may at once show his
fancy and his judgement".

So Mr Pope will go on avoiding "that perpetual repetition of
the same epithets" which is by no means accommodated to the
ear of persons of good taste, and Sir Edmund Head will go on
talking about people "assuming a high position in the district",
and "imputing" things, and saying, "on his arrival", where his
original says, stiffly and tiresomely, "when he came out". Meanwhile, those of us who would like to know something about
Homer and Viga-Glum's Saga must set to work and learn Greek
and Icelandic, or find a translator* who is not ashamed of his
original.

For, as translators, Pope and Head and their kind are deserving,
really, of no respect at all. They are ashamed of their mistresses,
that are of an infinitely greater worth than they; and for that, we
must call them ungallant coxcombs and send them to the Devil.
"Every Lover admires his Mistress", says old Robert Burton,
"though she be very deformed of her self, ill-favored, wrinkled,
pimpled, pale, red, yellow, tan'd, tallow-faced, have a swoln
juglers platter face, or a thin, lean, chitty face, have clouds in
her face, be crooked, dry, bald, goggle-ey'd, blear-ey'd, or with
staring eys, she looks like a squis'd cat, hold her head still awry,
heavy, dull, hollow-ey'd"—(the blemishes go on for another
twenty lines). He that proposes to introduce a saga, or any
other great old work in a foreign tongue, to a public that does
not know her, must be a true lover of his mistress, after that
kind. To "show his fancy and his judgement", as Pope counsels,
is a mere impertinence. He has to 'show' not anything that is
his, but his original. That will cost him all his pains, and try all
his powers.

For the translator, then, this is the commandment that
contains all the law: Thou shalt love thy Mistress. The sagas
took shape in the mouths of people who, as that great saga-

* We now have, for the *Iliad*, the version of Lang, Leaf and Myers.

lover W. P. Ker has said, have a self-conscious principle of style and good grammar: people who were the greatest story-tellers the world has ever seen. These prose epics have the qualities of great poetry: they are "simple, sensuous, and passionate".* They have the quality of what they spring from, the spoken word. The saga-man (simply, no doubt, as simple men enjoy good beer or sunshine) tasted and enjoyed every word: so must the translator, if his translation is to bear any likeness to his original. The strong and bare simplicity of the saga, so cosmically remote from all that is precious, bizarre, soulful, conceited, self-consciously self-important, or, in the popular sense, artistic, makes it hard on first acquaintance to grasp its essential quality. That quality is in fact pure *style*. And here, as in all art, style is life.

It may be useful in conclusion to refer briefly to two matters affecting the translation of the sagas: the first a matter of principle, the second of convenience.

(1) ARCHAISMS

Controversy has made itself heard from time to time on the question of diction, mainly in the form of attacks upon William Morris for using archaic words and phrases. Morris, as we have seen above, is open to the charge of employing sometimes a preciosity of expression that gives too literary a flavour to his versions; but the attack on the ground of his archaisms is misconceived. People who have never given much thought to the question are apt to take the view that old-fashioned language must be artificial and therefore devoid of life. They forget that the sagas themselves are written in what is, to us (and to Icelanders to-day, for that matter), old-fashioned language. The heroic age itself is old-fashioned to us to-day: it will seem not

* Passionate, in the sense that, for instance, Beethoven's greatest tragic works are passionate, or Webster's Italian tragedies, with a passion that makes itself felt through an iron restraint and concentration. In a sense, it can be said that the spirit of the sagas is beyond passion, if passion is thought of in its common and freer manifestations, examples of which abound in all regions, the highest and the lowest, from Wagner and Shakespeare to the products of the Keltic twilight and the inarticulate moans and shrieks of the untutored savage.

old-fashioned only but unreal and ridiculous if we attempt to galvanize it into a semblance of modernity by putting into its mouth the sophisticated parlance of our own very different times. The truth seems to be, indeed, the exact converse of the contention of these thoughtless critics: an archaic simplicity of speech is necessary in translating a saga (or Homer, or the Bible, or the *Arabian Nights*) if we wish to retain its spontaneity and vitality unimpaired.*

The reason for this is not far to seek. Much of our present-day language is *literary*, in the sense that it is a language no humane person speaks except in formal business, nor reads except because he cannot help it (e.g. in official documents or the newspapers). It is a written language, full of redundancies and pomposities and full of all manner of clichés and jargons. It is moreover highly abstract. And these ingredients and characteristics themselves carry associations foreign to the background of daily life under the old, simple, unmechanized civilizations. It is perhaps unnecessary to labour the point further, certainly in addressing a reading public who have welcomed Doughty's *Arabia Deserta*, a book which owes its effect of startling and breathing reality in an incalculable degree to the fact that it is written in a language framed by its author for the occasion in the greatest tradition of pre-Spenserian English. I will only add that that most vital and sparkling spring, the living water of Boccaccio himself, becomes flat and turbid at the touch of a translator who tries to make his version 'vivid' by making it modern. Let anyone who would test this read that most perfect of short stories (of Rinaldo d'Asti and the Widow Lady) first in John Payne's beautiful version, then in one of those which invite our preference (in one case at least) on the ground that Payne is heavy and dull. I think they will agree that the archaic version is the one that bubbles over with life and sprightliness, while the other is by comparison but a lame and out-of-fashion piece of vulgarity.

* Or, in a nutshell, as my friend George Rostrevor Hamilton has said it:

To a Translator of the Classics
They lived in a dead language: now, instead,
You in a living language make them dead.

Archaic language is not an end in itself. The end is, truth to the original. In the present version of *Egla* I have proceeded on a principle not unlike Doughty's: and my single aim has been to maintain, so far as the English language is capable of maintaining it, both generally and in detail, the style of my Icelandic original.

(2) PROPER NAMES

The treatment in English of Icelandic proper names, both personal and place-names, is chaotic. Pedants and cranks go their various ways in this matter, and revile one another; and the plain reader, for his part, is apt to be prejudiced in favour of the particular form in which a name or set of names first came to his knowledge. But it is tiresome and bewildering, especially to the plain reader, to find the same name served up in half-a-dozen different forms in as many books: Haraldr, Haraldur, Harald; Hairfair, Fairhair, the Fair-haired, Harfagri, Haarfagre, Harfager; Breiðifjörðr, Breiðifjörður, Breidifjordr, Breidifiord, Broadfrith, Broadfirth; Olaf Tryggvison, Olafr, Olafur, Olave, Tryggvi's son, Tryggvason, Tryggvesson.

It is time that a tradition was established and followed. Certain points are to be noted:

(*a*) The actual Icelandic names will not amalgamate with English: we cannot work in our own genitival inflexion -'s with the common masculine termination -*r* after a consonant, e.g. 'Haraldr's' or 'Thorolfr's'.

(*b*) The names are often extraordinarily closely related to English: *fjörðr* and *firth*, *dalr* and *dale*, *sker* and *skerry*, are the same words.

(*c*) The problem is purely a literary one, and is to be solved by practical good sense, ear and judgement, and not by some ridiculous system of rigid rules (e.g. to translate *everything*, or to translate *nothing*, or, most astounding inspiration of wrong-headed pedantry, to put it all into—Anglo-Saxon).*

---

* The distinguished editors of *Origines Islandicae* adopt this course, with grotesque results. Þórir becomes not Thorir but *Thore*; Steinarr, *Stan-here*; Herjólfr, *Hare-wolf*; Jörundr, *Eor-wend*; Önundr, *Ean-wend*; Böðvarr, not Bodvar but *Bead-were*; Broddi, *Brorde*; Skeggi, *Scegge* (which the reader will naturally call 'sedge'); Kolbeinn, *Colban*; and Ragnarr Loðbrók (Ragnar Hairybreeks) becomes *Ragn-here Lod-broc.*

Common sense suggests that, to establish a tradition, the best beginning is to base our practice broadly on that of translators whose works seem to have some chance of occupying a permanent place in English literature, viz. Morris and Dasent. This is what has been done in the present version of *Egla*. Where Morris and Dasent disagree, I have in most cases preferred to follow Morris. Is it unreasonable to suggest, in the interests of clearness and continuity, that future translators, and indeed all who write on these subjects in English, might sacrifice their pet pedantries and follow this practice?

NOTES

I. BOOKS FOR ENGLISH READERS

For the benefit of those who, having tasted, would have more, I name below a few sound vintages. Where particulars of publishers, etc., are not stated here, they will be found in the *List of Abbreviations*, p. 227 above.

(1) TRANSLATIONS OF SAGAS

The Story of Burnt Njal: G. W. Dasent (cheap edition now available, but without introduction, index, etc., in Everyman's Library).

The Saga Library (Bernard Quaritch): containing Morris's translations of *Eyrbyggja* (vol. II, 'The Story of the Ere-Dwellers'); the *Heimskringla* (vols. III–V); *Howard the Halt*, the *Banded Men*, and *Hen-Thorir* (vol. I).

The Story of Grettir the Strong: Morris's translation.

Three Northern Love Stories: Morris's translation (for *Gunnlaug the Worm-tongue's Saga*).

The Story of Gisli the Outlaw: Dasent.

The Faereyinga Saga: F. York Powell (David Nutt, 1896).

Cormac the Skald: W. G. Collingwood and Jón Stefansson (published by the Viking Club, Wm. Holmes Ltd., Ulverston, 1902): for *Kormak's Saga*.

The Völsunga Saga: Morris (The Walter Scott Publishing Co. Ltd., no date [? 1906]).

To the foregoing I add, with some misgivings, *Origines Islandicae:* Vigfusson and York Powell (2 vols., Clarendon Press, 1905), which contains texts and complete or partial translations of many sagas.

(2) BOOKS ON, OR BEARING ON, THE SAGAS

Epic and Romance: W. P. Ker (Macmillan, 1926).

Collected Essays: W. P. Ker (Macmillan, 1925); see vol. II, essays on 'Iceland and the Humanities', 'The Early Historians of Norway', 'Gudmund Arason', 'Sturla the Historian', 'Jón Arason'.

The Icelandic Sagas: W. A. Craigie (Cambridge University Press, 1913).

The Origin of the Icelandic Family Sagas: Knut Liestol (Williams and Norgate, 1930).

The Heroic Age: H. Munro Chadwick (Cambridge University Press, 1926).

II. BERSERK (berserkr): see ch. I, p. I.

O.E.D. gives no quotation earlier than Scott's *Pirate*, 1822. The derivation is in dispute: some say 'bear-sark', i.e. with bearskin shirt or kirtle; others 'bare-sark', i.e. without byrny. The latter is supported by the Yngl. 6: Odin's "own men went without byrnies, and were as mad as dogs or wolves, and bit on their shields, and were as strong as bears or bulls; menfolk they slew, and neither fire nor steel would deal with them: and this is what is called Bareserks-gang". In Thorbiorn Hornklofi's *Raven's-Song* the lady asks the raven about the berserks, "men battle-bold that stride among the folk"; and the raven says, "Wolf-coats they hight, they that in battle bear bloody shields". And in the same song, singing of the battle of Hafrsfirth, the raven says:

> Roared there the bareserks,
> Battle-wood was the host,
> Loud howled the Wolf-coats
> And clattered the iron.

Probably the biting of the shield-rim had a direct connexion with the roaring: cf. the bellowing (barritus) of Tacitus's Germans, "asperitas soni et fractum murmur, *objectis ad os scutis*".* So do little boys, banging their open hands against their mouths to give a broken, gobbling effect to their yells, 'ba-ba-ba-ba-bah'.

That this peculiar form of *furor athleticus* was no mere legend is proved by the fact that laws were made against it. Persons subject to it were called 'shape-strong', *hamrammr* (see below, p. 246), because they were thought to have the power of assuming bestial forms, as of wolf or bear. The fits left them strengthless, as we see in Kveldulf's case, ch. XXVII; cf. also the Eb. passage mentioned below.

It is not uncommon in the sagas to hear of berserks going about the countryside in Norway and challenging men for their women or goods; Grett. 40 is a *locus classicus*: the berserk "began to roar aloud, and bit the rim of his shield, and thrust it up into his mouth, and gaped over the corner of the shield". Grettir very adroitly kicked the tail of the shield so hard that the man's throat was riven asunder and his jaws fell down on his breast. Such bullies were much feared by honest folk, and their discomfiture was a stock exploit for a man of valour: see Glum. 4, 6, Gisl. 1, and Egil's dealing with Ljot the Pale in our own saga.

They were useful followers for kings and earls, but sometimes embarrassing to a private gentleman, as was found by Vermund the Slender (Eb. 25) when he induced Earl Eric to give him two such to take home to Iceland, because he deemed his brother, Slaying Stir, "lay heavy on his fortune, and dealt unjustly with him as with most others when he could bring his strength to bear on him. So he thought that Stir would deem it less easy to deal with him if he had such fellows" as these berserks were. The end of it was that they made

---

* *Germania*, ch. 3.

themselves so "big and rough with Vermund" that he had to pray his
violent brother to take them off his hands. Stir took them; employed
them to his satisfaction in some man-slaying business he had in hand,
but at length himself too found them "hard and high-minded", as
the earl had foretold, and in the end rid himself of them in a very cruel
and treacherous manner (Eb. 28). (See also following note on 'Shape-
strong'.)

III. SHAPE-STRONG (hamrammr): see ch. 1, p. 1.

Odin was Himself a shape-changer: "Lay then the body as if asleep
or dead, but He was then fowl or beast, fish or worm, and fared in the
twinkling of an eye to far-off lands on His own errands or other men's"
(Yngl. 7).

The classic instance is Sigmund the Volsung and his son Sinfjotli.
They "find a certain house, and two men with great gold rings asleep
therein: now these twain were spell-bound skin-changers, and wolf-
skins were hanging up over them in the house; and every tenth day
might they come out of those skins; and they were kings' sons: so
Sigmund and Sinfjotli do the wolf-skins on them, and then might they
nowise come out of them, though forsooth the same nature went with
them as heretofore; they howled as wolves howl, but both knew the
meaning of that howling; they lay out in the wild-wood, and each went
his way; and a word they made betwixt them, that they should risk the
onset of seven men, but no more, and that he who was first to be set on
should howl in wolfish wise....And when they were parted, Sigmund
meets certain men, and gives forth a wolf's howl; and when Sinfjotli
heard it, he went straightway thereto, and slew them all, and once more
they parted" (Vols. 8).

Landn. 14 tells how Dufthak of Dufthak's-holt "was exceeding
shape-strong, and so was Storolf Haengson; he dwelt then at Knoll;
there was strife betwixt them about grazing. That saw a man of second
sight at eventide about day-set, that a great bear walked from Knoll
but a bull from Dufthak's-holt, and their meeting was in Storolfsfield
and they went to it wrathfully, and the bear's might was the greater.
In the morning was that seen, that a dell was left there where they had
met together, as if the earth were turned up, and it is named there now
'Wavepit'. They were both outwearied".

Thrand the Strider, who helped Snorri the Priest in his attack on
the evil-doers at Ere in Bitter, "was said to be not of one shape whiles
he was heathen; but the devilhood fell off from most men when they
were christened" (Eb. 61).

The power seems to have come sometimes direct from the beast
itself. Odd Arngeirson of Lavahaven found his father and brother
slain by a white bear, and the bear lying there sucking their blood.
"Odd slew the bear, and brought him home; and men say that he ate
him all, and accounted himself then to have avenged his father when

he slew the bear, and then his brother, when he ate him. Odd was thereafter evil, and ill to do with. He was shape-strong so exceedingly, that he walked from home out of Lavahaven at evening and came the morning after into Thursowaterdale* to help his sister, that the Thursodalers were minded to stone to hell" (Landn. 306).

Kveldulf's evening-sleepiness was no doubt considered premonitory of the departure of himself in werewolf form while his body slept. The whole condition is closely allied to berserks-gang (see note, p. 244 above), and the verb *hamask* means to be seized with that *furor athleticus*: see the instance in ch. xxvii. Skallagrim inherited these propensities from his father, and Egil too shows signs of it in his fits of gloom and of fury.

That shape-changing was sometimes involuntary (and highly undignified) appears from some scoffs in the *Lokasenna* (*C.P.B.* vol. I, pp. 104–6); see also the flytings in the *Helgakviða* (*ibid.* pp. 136–7), and Sharphedinn's fatal taunt to Flosi, "Because thou art the sweetheart of the Swinefell's goblin, if, as men say, he does indeed turn thee into a woman every ninth night" (Nj. 122).

The belief is of course found in every age and land. In India the shape-changer becomes a tiger; in Japan a fox; in Africa a hyaena, less commonly a lion. The Greek word is λυκάνθρωπος. Herodotus, IV, 105, was told "that once every year each man of the Neurians becometh a wolf for a few days and then is turned again into the same shape as before. Yet am I not all persuaded when they say these things; but they say them none the less, and swear to what they say".

In Europe the shape is generally of wolf or bear. "Wolf-madness, when men run howling about graves and fields in the night, and will not be perswaded but that they are wolves. . . . Wierus tells a story of such a one at Padua, 1541, that would not believe to the contrary, but that he was a wolf. He hath another instance of a Spaniard, who thought himself a bear. . . . This malady, saith Avicenna, troubleth men most in February, and is now a dayes frequent in Bohemia and Hungary, according to Heurnius. . . . They lye hid, most part, all day, and go abroad in the night, barking, howling, at graves and deserts" (Burton, *Anat. Mel.* Part I, Sec. I, Mem. I, Subs. iv). The change was considered to be effected by "an oyntment which they make by the instinct of the devill, and putting on a certayne inchaunted girdle". Witches, who generally selected smaller and less harmful forms, as the cat, the hare, the crow, the weasel, sometimes used incantations, such as this (to take the shape of a hare):

> I sall goe intill ane haire,
> With sorrow, and sych, and meikle caire;
> And I sall goe in the Divellis nam,
> Ay quhill I com hom againe.

---

* I.e. from Thistlefirth in the far N.E. to near Hekla in the S.S.W., about 150 miles across the howling wilderness of the interior.

And, to resume her shape:

> Haire, haire, God send thee caire.
> I am in an haire's liknes just now,
> Bot I sall be in a womanis liknes ewin now.*

A fine modern story built on the theme of lycanthropy is Prosper Merimée's *Lokis*.

IV. GENERAL NOTE ON THE VERSES.

The stave on the wind at sea, p. 131, will serve as an example by which to explain very shortly and without technicalities the main features of the verse-form in which Egil's shorter poems are cast. The original reads as follows:

> Þel høggr stórt fyr stále
> stafnkvígs á veg jafnan
> út meþ éla meitle
> andœrr jǫtonn vandar,
> en svalbúenn seljo
> sverfr eirarvanr þeire
> Gestels ǫlpt meþ gustom
> gandr of stále ok brande.

Lit. "The furious (andœrr) giant (jǫtonn) of the wand *or* branch (vandar) still hews (jafnan høggr) the great (stórt) frost, i.e. 'ice-cold sea' (þel) out before the prow (út fyr stále) on the way (á veg) of the stem-bull (stafnkvígs) with chisel (meþ meitle) of storms *or* blizzards (éla); and (en) the cold-robed (svalbúenn) sallow-fiend (seljo gandr) sweeps (sverfr) pitiless (eirarvanr) that swan of Gestil (þeire ǫlpt Gestels) with gusts (meþ gustom) over prow and stem-post (of stále ok brande)".

I. Now first, as to form.

(1) The general movement is trochaic in feeling, with three beats in a line, thus: $- \cup - \cup - \cup$; but there is no definite rule as to the number of syllables in each line, and (as in English) there is a kind of counterpoint or cross-rhythm caused by the strong syllables coming sometimes off the beat; and it is on this cross-rhythm that the music of the verse largely depends.

(2) The lines in each couplet are connected by *Alliteration*: i.e. two stressed syllables in the first line must begin with the same consonant as the first stressed syllable in the second line (or with vowels—but *different* vowels—if it begins with a vowel); thus:

> Þel høggr *S*tórt fyr *S*tále
> *S*tafnkvígs, etc.

* R. Pitcairn, *Criminal Trials*, Edin. 1833, vol. III.

(3) *Within* each line is a system of internal *Rhyme* or *Consonance*, the precise rules of which vary. Thus:

> ÞEL høggr stórt fyr stÁLE.
> stAFNkvígs á veg jAFNan.
> sverfr EIRarvanr ÞEIRE.
> GESTels ǫlpt meÞ gUSTom, etc.

II. Secondly, as to content. Skaldic poetry (this is not true in quite the same way, or to the same extent, of the more ancient poetry of the *Elder Edda*, e.g. the *Helgi Lays*, the *Völospá*, the old mystical and didactic poems such as *Hávamál*, *Grimnismál*, the Volsung cycle, etc.) presents a violent contrast to classic Icelandic prose. The prose is simple, concentrated, direct, and clear: the poetry is complex, concentrated, indirect, and obscure. The one quality they share is the master-quality of concentration; economy of words, intolerance of the unessential.

Now the grand medium or vehicle of skaldic poetry is *Metaphor*. As Homer turned to simile for his great effects so (but far more constantly; indeed in line after line) the skald turned to metaphor. Always hesitate, in poetry, to call a king a 'king' (konungr): call him rather 'Flinger of gold', or 'All-wielder' or 'God of the byrny'. And if you call him 'Flinger of gold', do not too readily be content with the plain word 'gold'. Gold is a thing of splendour: it is *fire*: fire that burns even in the depths of the sea: it is the treasure of the dwarf Andvari coveted by the Gods, cursed with a curse: the treasure that the worm Fafnir slept on to guard it, till Sigurd the Volsung slew him. So (e.g.)—'Flinger of the *billow-fire*', rather than of plain 'gold'.

These metaphors are technically called 'kennings', and Snorri Sturlason in his *Prose Edda* gives elaborate lists of them based on the practice of the skalds. Court poetry had by his time (the thirteenth century) become 'conceited' and lifeless, and its demise was hastened no doubt by the freezing effect of such a system as this when once the inspiration of high poetry flagged and weakened. But it is vital to realize that, so long as inspiration held, the 'kenning' and the strict formalities of skaldic verse were not fetters or hobbles, but living organs of the Spirit.

In this particular stave of Egil's there are five kennings: (1) *stafnkvígr* (ship); (2) *éla meitill* (the chisel of the tempest); (3) *jötunn vandar* (the wind); (4) *svalbúinn selju gandr* (the wind); (5) *Gestils alpt* (ship). For the rest, for *svalr* (cold) cf. Swaledale. *Gestill* is the name of some sea-king. *Gandr* is a strange word, of uncertain derivation. Primarily it means a 'stick', and may have attained its ordinary sense of 'monster' or 'fiend' (*a*) from the riding of sorcerers on 'broomsticks', or (*b*) from the fact that sorcery deals with inanimate objects such as sticks and makes them ride. Cf. the terrible vision of the *gandreið* (which Dasent renders 'the Wolf's ride') described in Nj. 124.

The power of this highly artificial verse-form, as a vehicle not of frigid conceits but of poetry, will be apparent to anyone who cares to spend twenty minutes in informing himself of the meaning of this stave and getting it by heart (I mean, of course, in the Icel.).* Its grandeur, as a picture of the wind at sea, has not often been surpassed: cf. the plunging effect of the last line; the violent word *gandr* (a fiend or ride-by-night) which, owing to the suspension of its appearance for two lines after the governing words *svalbúenn seljo*, comes like the buffet of the wind itself, followed by the galloping anapæstic rhythm of *stále ok brande*. (For want of a *g*-word here, I have been reduced to unalliterative paraphrase.)

V. THE SCORN-POLE (níðstöng): see ch. LVII, pp. 130–1.

Níð is, technically, a scurrilous or obscene contumely, a libel, a shaming; in law, punishable by outlawry. There were two kinds of *níð* or 'scorn': the 'tongue-scorn' (tunguníð) by word of mouth; and the 'tree-scorn' (tréníð), by carving a person's likeness (query, in an obscene position) on a 'scorn-pole', with or without the additions, as here, of a horse's head and baneful runes.

For 'tongue-scorns' cf. (1) the mocking songs of Sigmund (dung-beards—beardless carle, etc.) against Njal and his sons, Nj. 44; (2) the story in Hkr. (O.T. 36) of the decision of the Icelanders that there should be made a scurvy rhyme on the Dane-King 'for every nose in the land' (i.e. for every man, woman, or child); one of these is quoted, based on a jest whose charms age, it seems, could not wither—the picture of the objects of the *níð* (King Harald Gormson and his bailiff) enacting their parts as stallion and mare under the public eye in the open countryside.

For 'tree-scorns' cf. (1) the insult laid on Slaying Skuta at the Althing, circ. 980, "that they should have Skuta's booth-tofts for a privy that summer, and withal he bade Thorgeir raise up there a beam (áss), and carve a man's head on the end of it" (*Reykdæla*, 25); (2) the close parallel to the present scene in the *Waterdale Saga*, where Jokull carved a man's head on the end of the post (sula) "and scored runes thereon with all that formular that was aforesaid. And now slew Jokull a mare, and opened her near the breastbone, and put her on to the post and let turn her homeward toward Burg" (*Vatnsdæla*, 34).

Professor Magnus Olsen has shown that a correct runic transcription of Egil's 'formular' carved on the *níðstöng* will give exact numbers of runes, repeated in such a way that they must necessarily have a magic meaning.

Possibly this use of dead horses originated from the desire to convey opprobrious suggestions of the kind referred to above. But, apart from this, the theory underlying Egil's procedure was no doubt that the ugly and ghastly spectacle of the horse's skull would frighten the

---

* See also note, p. 305, on Egil's stave lamenting the fall of Arinbiorn.

land-spirits into obeying the injunctions contained in the runes. Cf. Landn. where it is said that it was the beginning of the heathen law that men should remove (or cover up?) the dragon-heads on their ships when they came in sight of land, "and not sail to land with gaping heads or yawning snouts, so that the land-spirits should be frightened with it".

The *locus classicus* for land-spirits (who, it is to be noted, are properly of the gentle sex, in spite of instances below to the contrary) is O.T. 37: King Harald Gormson "bade a wizard shape for a skin-changing journey to Iceland....So he fared in the likeness of a whale. And whenas he came to the land he went west round about the north country; and he saw all the fells and hills full of land-spirits both great and small. But when he came off Weaponfirth he went into the firth, and would go up aland; but lo, there came down from the dale a mighty drake, followed of many worms and paddocks and adders, and blew venom at him. So he gat him gone, and went west along the land till he came to Eyjafirth. Then he fared up into the firth. But there came against him a fowl so great that his wings lay on the fells on either side, and many other fowl were with him, both great and small. So he fared away thence, and west along the land, and so south to Broadfirth, and there stood in up the firth. But there met him a great bull that waded out to sea and fell a-bellowing awfully, and many land-spirits followed him. Thenceaway he gat him, and south about Reekness, and would take land on the Vikars-Skeid. But there came against him a mountain giant with an iron staff in his hand, who bore his head higher than the fells, and with him were many other giants. So thenceaway fared the wizard east endlong of the south country".

The idea of *nið* is comparable with the legal idea of ὕβρις. Cf. one of Demosthenes's prosecutions where the offence charged was ὕβρις of an aggravated kind, the defendant having stamped on his prostrate enemies and flapped with his arms and crowed like a cock.

VI. EARL HAKON THE GREAT: see ch. LXXVIII, p. 200.

One of the greatest figures of his century in the North; son of Earl Sigurd of Hladir, of the great house of the Earls of Halogaland who claimed divine descent from Saeming, son of Odin. The sons of Gunnhild burned Earl Sigurd in his house in 962, two winters after the fall of King Hakon Athelstane's-fosterling, upon which Hakon was taken for earl and captain by the Thrandheimers. For three years he held Thrandheim against Gunnhild's sons, fighting many battles with them: then made peace, sharing Thrandheim with his enemies, "and now befell great love betwixt Earl Hakon and Gunnhild, though now and again they baited each other with guile". War broke out again, and Hakon at length fled to Denmark where he had good welcome from King Harald Gormson. From Denmark he stirred up rebellion against

Gunnhild's sons in Thrandheim. Gold-Harald, brother's son to King Harald Gormson, was minded at this time to claim a share of kingdom from the King his uncle: Hakon was in the confidence of both sides, and used the situation with Machiavellian skill to serve his own turn. He counselled the Dane-King to invite his fosterson, King Harald Greycloak, to visit Denmark, then betray him and satisfy Gold-Harald by giving him kingdom in Norway. King Harald Greycloak, after some misgivings, came with but three ships to the Neck in the Limfirth to meet the Dane-King his fosterfather. Here he was fallen upon by Gold-Harald with nine ships and slain with Arinbiorn and nearly all his men. But Earl Hakon in the meantime disclosed to the Dane-King a former saying of Gold-Harald's that he would slay the King his uncle, might but time and place serve, and so wrought upon the King that he gave Hakon leave to slay Gold-Harald and win Norway for the Dane-King. This agreed, Hakon fell upon Gold-Harald, defeated, captured and hanged him; after which King Harald Gormson sailed north and laid Norway under him, giving Hakon (as his earl) Rogaland and Hordaland, Sogn, the Firths, Southmere, Northmere, and Raumsdale. All pretence of vassalage came to an end when, after a great defence of the Danework against Kaiser Otto II, the Dane-King was forced to make peace with the Kaiser and took christening, and then "let christen Earl Hakon will he nill he". The King gave him priests and other learned men, and bade him christen Norway. But Hakon, when he saw his time, "cast up aland all those learned men", made offering to the Gods, and sailed home to Norway, where he ruled henceforth for twenty years (975–995), in everything but name a king. He restored the temples of the Gods, that were neglected during the time of civil war and famine under Gunnhild's sons, and in later years (date uncertain, but after 986) achieved his "crowning mercy", the victory over the Jomsburg vikings at Hiorungwick. On that occasion he is reputed to have offered up one of his sons to secure victory.

"Whiles Earl Hakon ruled in Norway was the year's increase good in the land. And good peace there was betwixt man and man among the bonders." But he made many enemies in his last years by his 'manner-less' dealing with women, which pleasant vice was made the instrument of his undoing; for Olaf Tryggvison landed in Norway at the happy moment when the bonders of Thrandheim were in open revolt against the Earl for an outrage of his upon the wife of one of them. On this tide of hatred against his great opposite, the young King rode into power, and the Earl ended his days murdered sleeping by a traitor's knife, in a pig-stye where he had been hidden for safety from King Olaf's men by Thora of Rimul, "a wealthy lady, and one of the Earl's best beloved".

Snorri says of Earl Hakon that "for many things was he worthy to be lord; first, for the great stock he was come of, and then also for the wisdom and insight wherewith he dealt with his dominion; for his high heart in battle and his good hap withal, for the winning of victory and slaying of his foemen....Most bountiful also was Earl Hakon. But most evil hap had such a lord in his death-day. And this brought it most about, that so it was that the day was come, when foredoomed was blood-offering and the men of blood-offerings, and the holy faith came in their stead, and the true worship" (O.T. 56).

For history, indeed, he stands mantled with the grandeur of sunset and of night; in his tragedy is gathered up the death of the old pagan North, the passage into darkness of the old Gods and the ancient way. It is characteristic of the historical genius of the Icelandic mind that Snorri's story of the Earl's life (Har. Gr. and O.T.) leaves us, if we follow it fairly, in no mood to take sides. It leaves us in a mood, rather, to look and reflect and pity; and to be aware perhaps of a divine Watcher at our elbow (grey-eyed Pallas, I suppose), to Whom these things are not so clear as they seemed to the people who "set up a whooping and stoned the heads [of Earl Hakon and the thrall who murdered him], crying out that there they fared meetly together, rascal by rascal". It is beside the great figure of the Earl that the virtues and heroics of the darling young herald of the new day who strode into power over his head, Olaf Tryggvison, can most soberly be measured: the old against the new.

MISCELLANEOUS NOTES

CHAPTER I

1 VIKING. Icel. has two words, *víkingr*, m., the practitioner; *viking*, f. (as here), the profession. This, the accepted occupation of a gentleman, was held in good esteem at home and in reprobation abroad. So to us, "The Unparalleled Exploits of Sir Henry Morgan, *our English Jamaican Hero*, who sacked Porto Bello, burnt Panama, etc."; but to the Spaniards our far more respectable hero, Sir Walter Raleigh, was "Guatarral, an English pirate".

For the derivation, *O.E.D.* hesitates between O.N. *vík* (creek, inlet, bay) and A.S. *wíc* (camp), thus tracing this martial name to quiet roots among longshoremen or villagers; just as the buccaneers are etymologically but cattle-hunters. *Vík* is probably right; as all beasts of prey have their lurking places from which they pounce, so the first vikings lurked in bays, and peaceable chapmen learnt to know what sort of men were likely to come out of these 'wicks'. In any case, the word has nothing to do with 'sea-king'. *O.E.D.* gives no quotation earlier than the nineteenth century. The pronunciation 'vicking' and spelling 'wicking' may be set down as pedantical affectations.

2 BERSERK (berserkr). See special note, p. 244.

3 OLIVER HNUFA (Ölvir Hnúfa). *Surnames of the United Kingdom* (Harrison, Morland Press, 1918) says, "Almost certainly Scandinavian

nomenclature has had its influence on the great vogue of Oliver—if not the common O.N. *Oleif-r* itself (Dan.-Norw. Olaf), at any rate the O.N. *Oelver*". *Hnúfa*: (?) 'snub'. By the old laws of Norway, if a female thrall stole the third time, "Then shall they shear off her nose; then is she named *stúfa* and *hnúfa*, and let her steal aye as she will" (D., s.v.).

4 A GREAT LADY (skörungr mikill). *Skörungr* is one of those words that make a translator despair. It is derived from *skara* (to jut out; poke the fire): used metaphorically both of men and women it carries the idea of prominence and of stirring, and refers both to character and disposition and to outward appearance. Cleopatra, Meredith's Diana of the Crossways, and Queen Elizabeth were *skörungar*; so were Don John of Austria, Hector, and Webster's Brachiano. Arinbiorn is called a *skörungr* (p. 161), where I have translated it 'lordly' man: so is Olaf the Peacock. Morris (Gunnl. 1) renders it 'a stirring woman', which misses the particular overtone of nobility: in Yngl. 32 he has "the greatest of noble women"; and (Eb. 28) 'stately' for Icel. *sköruligr*. Dasent (Nj. 13) has 'brave woman', which is unsatisfactory. Indeed, we have no word for it.

5 LANDED MAN (lendr maðr). Probably what is meant is that Kveldulf was a *hersir*.* In that time, before the uprising of King Harald Hairfair, there were, strictly speaking, no landed men in Norway and the titles of dignity were but three: KING, EARL, and HERSIR. These titles signified in ancient times degrees rather than distinct kinds of eminence. The hersir, the folk-king, and generally the earl, was each supreme in his own countryside, wielding the powers spiritual and temporal, war-lord and temple-priest. All three seem to have been commonly hereditary, and although the earl was sometimes definitely subject to a king, as Earl Hroald to King Audbiorn (ch. II), it seems likely that many of the earls mentioned in Landn. (notably the great line of earls of Halogaland whose seat was at Hladir) were independent sovereigns, differing from kings only in name. The hersir was bound to aid the king if he was attacked, but not necessarily to follow him to war outside his borders.†

When Harald Hairfair laid all Norway under him, these old rulers, whether kings, earls, or hersirs, had the choice of three things: fight, or flee the land, or become his men. The Landed Men were (*a*) those who, having become the King's men, held their old lordship at his hands: if kings, they might henceforth be styled earls (as befell in Naumdale, ch. III); if hersirs, they might retain their titles, as did Thorir the Hersir (ch. XXV); and (*b*) creatures of the King raised up by him to a new dignity, like Thorolf Kveldulfson. Snorri says that "they are named hersirs or landed men in the Danish tongue [i.e. O.N. or

---

* He is so called in Skallagrim's ditty made on the slaying of Hallvard and Sigtrygg (p. 52).

† See Kveldulf's attitude, p. 4.

Icel.] but *greifar* in Saxland and *barons* in England" (Ed. 226). In this new order, the hersir ranked below the earl; next came, apparently, the landed man proper; next the franklin (höldr), who was a freeholder by birth (óðalborinn); next the bonder (bóndi), plain farmer or gentleman; then the freedman (leysingi); last, the thrall (þræll).

6 SHAPE-STRONG (hamrammr). See special note, p. 245.

7 KVELDULF (Kveldúlfr). I.e. 'Evening-Wolf'.

8 THE YOUNGER, GRIM. Afterwards called Skallagrim (p. 37); Egil's father.

9 HOUSECARLES (húskarlar). As distinct from thralls: free-born retainers or servants, followers of their master (húsbóndi) as farm-men or fighting men as need might arise. So honourable a name was 'house-carle' in the old days that we find it as late as the eleventh century used of kings' courtiers.

10 LONG-SHIP (langskip). A 'ship of war', as distinct from the ship of burden or cheaping-ship (knörr, byrðingr, kaupskip). Long-ship is the generic term: drake (dreki), racer (skeið), snake-ship (snekkja), and cutter (skúta) are specific.

The *dreki*, or dragon of war, was named from the head and tail of that monster which stood at prow and stern. Magnússon (Hkr. IV, 431) thinks the terms *skeið*, *snekkja*, and *skúta* indicated decreasing order of size; the *skúta* beginning with 15 oars aside and going up to 20, the *snekkja* from 20 to 30, the *skeið* over 30. The *Long Worm*, King Olaf Tryggvison's famous ship, was a 34-bencher, and her length probably 180 feet. Viking ships have been found in varying degrees of preservation at Gokstad, Nydam and elsewhere.

The *karfi* (which I have called 'caravel') was a small ship, apparently comparable with the *skúta*, used probably by kings and great men as a private yacht. The specimen found at Oseberg a few years ago has been identified with some certainty as that of Queen Asa, mother of Halfdan the Black.

The long-ship was a galley, primarily built for rowing, with a sail to help. She was not meant for ocean voyages, and there is no record of a long-ship sailing to Iceland in the days of the settlement. Cf. the report by Harald Gormson's wizard, sent by him to spy out Iceland: "So great is the main betwixt the lands that all unmeet it is for long-ships" (ekki er þar fært langskipum) O.T. 37.

11 FEE (fé). *Fé* in Icel. is used indifferently of (*a*) cattle (in Iceland chiefly sheep), (*b*) wealth and goods in general, (*c*) money. 'Fee' in Old English has precisely these three meanings. I have rendered *fé* with 'fee' (which poets and the border ballads have made familiar in the vague sense of wealth, whether in money or goods) everywhere, except where the Icel. clearly meant cattle: in that sense the English word is dead past saving, and would sound awkward.

CHAPTER II

1 HIS EARL (jarl). See note, p. 253, above.

2 THE EARL'S SON THORIR. The first mention of Thorir the Hersir, a staunch friend of Kveldulf's family, and the father of Arinbiorn the Hersir, Egil's dear and lifelong friend.

3 EARL ATLI THE SLENDER and his sons were, according to Landn., the proximate cause of a momentous event—the first settlement by the Norsemen in Iceland. The three brethren were messmates with Ingolf Arnarson and Hiorleif his fosterbrother, until at a feast one autumn Holmstein made a strong vow that he would have to wife Ingolf's sister Helga, "or no woman else". Hiorleif misliked this; quarrels followed, in which first Holmstein and then Herstein were slain; and in the end Ingolf and Hiorleif had to give up their estates in Norway to Earl Atli as atonement for his sons. Then "those fosterbrothers made ready a great ship and fared to seek that land which Hrafn-Floki had found, which then was called Iceland" (Landn. 6).

4 AUTUMN-SACRIFICE (haustblót). By ordainment of Odin, "Folk were to hold sacrifice against the coming of winter for a good year; in midwinter for the growth of the earth; and a third in the summer that was an offering for gain and victory" (Yngl. 8). The feasts of blood-offering (blótveizlur) in Thrandheim in the days of K. Hakon Athelstane's-fosterling are thus described in his Saga: "It was the olden custom that when a blood-offering should be, all the bonders should come to the place where was the Temple, bringing with them all the victuals they had need of while the feast should last; and at that feast should all men have ale with them. There also was slain cattle of every kind, and horses withal; and all the blood that came from them was called Hlaut, but hlaut-bowls were they called wherein the blood stood, and the hlaut-tein a rod made in the fashion of a sprinkler. With all the hlaut should the stalls of the Gods be reddened, and the walls of the temple within and without, and the men-folk also besprinkled, but the flesh was to be sodden for the feasting of men. Fires were to be made in the midst of the floor of the temple, with caldrons thereover, and the health-cups should be borne over the fire. But he who made the feast and was the lord thereof should sign the cups and all the meat; and first should be drunken Odin's cup for the victory and dominion of the king, and then the cup of Niord and the cup of Frey for plentiful seasons and peace. Thereafter were many men wont to drink the Bragicup; and men drank also a cup to their kinsmen dead who had been noble, and that was called the cup of Memory" (Hak. 16). See also the account of Thor's temple at Thorsness in Iceland (Eb. 4). The editors of *C.P.B.* are probably right in regarding reference to idols as late interpolations based not on historic fact but on monkish fictions (*C.P.B.* vol. I, p. 401 ff.). Human sacrifices were not unknown but apparently very rare in the saga-time.

CHAPTER III

1 HARALD. Harald Hairfair (Haraldr Hárfagri). For a fuller account of the life of this great King, see his own saga (Hkr.). He took kingdom after his father in 860 at the age of ten, in the little realm of Westfold, east in the Wick (that part of Norway that surrounds the Oslofirth). It is told that he wooed a maiden "exceeding fair, and withal somewhat high-minded", who gave him this answer: "I will not waste my maidenhood for the taking to husband of a king who has no more realm to rule over than a few Folks. But that seems to me wonderful", she says, "that there be no king who will so make Norway his own and be sole lord over it, like as hath King Gorm in Denmark, or Eric in Upsala". Harald thereupon swore an oath never to let cut his hair or comb it till he should be sole King over all Norway. That oath he performed with the help of his mother's brother, Duke Gutthorm, and married the lady.* And when he had gotten to him all the land, "King Harald took a bath and then he let his hair be combed, and then Earl Rognvald sheared it. And heretofore it had been unshorn and uncombed for ten winters. Aforetime he had been called Shockhead [Lúfa], but now Earl Rognvald gave him a by-name, and called him Harald Hairfair, and all said who saw him that that was most soothly named, for he had both plenteous hair and goodly" (Har. Hfr. 23).

The best and shortest account that I have seen of Harald's policy and achievements is in the first dozen pages of ch. 11 of G. Gathorne Hardy's *Norway* (Ernest Benn, 1925).

2 THRANDHEIM (Þrándheimr). The countryside of the Trondhjem Fjord, divided into Outer and Inner Thrandheim, and again into eight folklands, viz. Orkdale, Skaun, Gauldale, Strind, Islesfolk, Spareby, Verdale and Stiordale. An open and fertile country, it was an early cradle of civilization, and later centred round the temple and seat of the great Earls of Hladir and, after Olaf Tryggvison's days, round his new town of Nidoyce (Niðaróss), a little further N.W., which is to-day (or rather was till yesterday) Trondhjem.

3 TUMBLED HIMSELF OUT OF KINGDOM (veltiz ór konungdómi). Literally, it seems: cf. the fuller account in Har. Hfr. 8 of this singular procedure: "King Hrollaug went on the top of the howe whereon the kings were wont to sit, and let array the kingly high-seat, and sat down therein; then he let lay pillows on the footpace whereon the earls were wont to sit, and tumbled himself down from the high-seat on to the earl's seat, and gave himself the name of earl".

4 THRALLS (þræll). Thralls were slaves: personal chattels, without the privileges of free men: probably as a rule outlanders, taken by war; cf. the references to Irish thralls *passim*. They were worked hard; cf. Eb. 37, "Arnkel was a great man for work, and made his thralls work all

* And many wives besides. The strife between his many sons broke up the realm after the great King's death.

day from sunrise to sunset". The great Erling Skialgson of Soli treated his thralls with kindness and consideration, a fact which is set forth at length as something noteworthy and strange (O.H. 22). Hiorleif, the landnama-man, was murdered by his thralls, apparently because he overworked them: "he had but one ox, and he let the thralls drag the plough" (Landn. 8). *Thrall* became a term of obloquy: 'a servile, mean fellow', and then 'a cruel, wicked wretch' (*D.* s.v.). Cf. the story in Hkr. (Hak. 13) of King Eystein the Evil, who in his oppression bade the Thrandheimers choose whether they would have for king over them his thrall or his hound.

5 THEM THAT SHOW SOMEWHAT OF FREE-BOARD IN THEIR SAILING, AND WILL BE MEN OF VALOUR (þeim er nökkurir eru borði ok kappsmenn vilja vera). Meaning, of course, that they have some self-respect and pride. Here, as often, the Icel. is unapproachable in terseness.

6 LET SHEAR UP THE WAR-ARROW (lét skera upp herör). Magnússon (Hkr. IV, 476) says it was of iron for circulation on the king's highways, but of wood for conveyance along by-ways; symbolical of the speed to be used in obeying the call to arms (*D.* p. 71): "In Iceland....a small wooden axe is still sent from farm to farm to summon people to the mantal-thing in the spring" (*ibid.*). Cf. the fiery cross of the Scottish clans.

7 LUCK (hamingja). Cf. also p. 208. The Icel. has properly a personal sense, of a guardian spirit. The *hamingja* at the hour of death left the dying person and passed into a dear son, daughter, etc. (*D.* s.v.): cf. Glum. 9, where Glum dreams "that he saw a woman walk inland up the countryside, and held thitherward, toward Thvera; but she was so great that her shoulders took even with the fells on either side. But it seemed to him that he walked out of the garth to meet her, and bade her to him. And therewithal waked he. All thought it wonderful, but he saith as thus: ''Tis a great dream and a notable, but so will I read it: that Vigfus, my mother's father, will now be dead, and that woman would be his *luck*, which walked higher than the fells. Ay, and was he before other men in most things as to worth, and his *luck* will be seeking her an abiding place thither where I am'. But in the summer, when ships came out, was brought tidings of the death of Vigfus".

The ancient mystical poem *Vafþrúðnismál* has a curious passage which seems to mean that as the Norns are to the ultimate power so are *hamingjar* to men on earth (*C.P.B.* vol. I, pp. 68, 479).

CHAPTER IV

1 HAKON THE EARL OF HLADIR. Grandfather of the great Earl Hakon, on whom see note, p. 250.

2 EARL ROGNVALD. Called Rögnvaldr Mœrajarl (the Mere-Earl); a beloved friend of King Harald, and father of Rolf the Ganger, Duke of Normandy. He was at last burnt in his house by sons of Harald, jealous

that the King gave them no rule; a misdeed that was horribly avenged on one of the princes by the Earl's son, Turf-Einar, Earl of the Orkneys (Har. Hfr. 30, 31).

3 SKALD (skáld). A poet. See note, p. 260 below.

4 ODAL RIGHTS (óðul). Under the original Norse principle of 'odal', the family was the owner of the land, which was inalienable. Later, the odal system was modified, and only gave members of the family a prior right of purchase or redemption of land which had been sold out of the family. Some authorities have contended that Harald Hairfair did not in fact take away the odal or make men pay land-tax; that what he did was merely to levy a personal tax on freeholders. But this, besides going against the written evidence (Hkr., Ld., and our own Saga), could hardly account for the bitterness aroused by Harald's policy. Gathorne Hardy's examination leads him to conclude that the sagas are right and that 'Harald's policy may be summed up in the words, *he applied for the first time in Norway methods already in existence for dealing with a subjugated people in foreign lands*' (*op. cit.* p. 40).

5 WAS FOUND ICELAND (fannz Ísland). When and by whom is not exactly known. The honour lies between Gardar, a Swede, who on his return "praised the land much and called it 'Gardarsholm'", and Naddod the Viking, presumably a Norseman, who also "praised it much", but called it 'Snowland'. The two extant versions of Landn. differ on the question who was first. Then Floki, 'a great viking', set sail from Rogaland to seek Snowland. He sailed by Shetland to the Faereys, and "Thence sailed he out into the deep with those three ravens that he had hallowed in Norway. And when he let loose the first, that one flew back over the stem: the second flew up into the sky and back to the ship: the third flew forth over the stem into that airt where they found the land". Floki called it 'Iceland' (Landn. 5). None of these stayed long in the new country. Nattfari, a shipmate of Gardar's, was accidentally left behind near Skialfandi Firth and seems to have settled there, but was driven away by a later comer (*ibid.* 294). It is however explicitly stated that Ingolf Arnarson was the first settler, *bygði fyrst landit*. See note, p. 258 on 'Ingolf'.

CHAPTER V

1 SOLDIERLY (garpligr). *Garpr*, like *skörungr*, is a heart-breaking word for the translator. It means something like a 'hero', but the word is homely, not magniloquent. *Hvat man garprinn vilja?* says Hrafnkel Frey's-priest when his horse Freyfaxi gallops home all mud and dirt: 'What does my bully want?' Two English ladies who a few years ago walked alone through Iceland, with a single horse to take their baggage, were admiringly called the *Göngu-garpar*, 'the walking garps'. *Reykdæla* 1 ends with the statement that that *enfant terrible* Vemund Kogur died of a sickness, "and yet men thought him the

greatest *garpr* while he was alive". Our English stock of synonyms are all too much soaked in moral sentiment to fit the clean-cut objectivity and strength of the Icelandic word.

2 COME AND SEE YOU (á fund yðvarn). 'You', 2nd per. pl., is generally used out of respect in speaking to the King, instead of the familiar 'thou' (þú); a practice found in many languages, including, at one time, English. The two forms (respectful plural and everyday singular) are often jumbled together in the same speech or even sentence, as the reader will observe *passim* from my translation. The same jumbling is frequent in Elizabethan English. Our modern idiom has turned heels in air, and while it accords the old formal 'you' to every mortal, man or beast, is content to *tutoyer* the Deity.

3 THAT WE, FATHER AND SONS, WILL GET NO LUCK WITH THIS KING. The first rumbling of the approaching tragedy.

CHAPTER VI

1 BODYGUARD (hirð). The 'King's men' or court in ancient times, kept by kings, earls, and other great men.

CHAPTER VII

1 The importance of this chapter to the main action will appear in the sequel (end of ch. IX, ch. XII ff.). In old Biorgolf's 'loose bridal' with Hildirid ill seed was sown, and an ill crop was to come of it.

2 BANQUET (gildi). There is no appreciable difference between *gildi* and *boð*, 'bidding'. *Gildi* originally, and rarely, had the sense of 'payment' (cf. weregild); meaning 'banquet', it is frequent in old poetry. Possibly this meaning arose from feasts to which each guest brought his own 'gild' or contribution. Later it meant 'guild' in the sense of a brotherhood or trades union: King Olaf the Quiet (1066–93) established the 'Great Gild' in Nidoyce 'and many others in cheaping-steads, but before there were turn-about drinkings (hvirfings-drykkjur)': Hkr. *Saga of Olaf the Quiet*, ch. 2.

3 TWO AND TWO (tvímenningr). To drink *einmenningr* meant you must 'floor the sconce' without assistance, instead of (as here) have a partner to help you. Cf. chs. XLVIII and LXXI.

4 CUTTER (skúta). See note on 'Long-ship', p. 254.

5 HALL (stofa). The homestead in the saga-time comprised a whole group of buildings of which the *stofa* was the chief. It was both sitting-room and dining-room, and served also as a guest-chamber both for sleeping in and for feasting. See Magnússon's full and admirable note on 'House', Hkr. IV, 353–63, especially pp. 356–8.

6 STRONG BEER (mungát). That which 'contents the heart'. *Öl* and *mungát* seem to be synonymous, whereas *bjórr* and *mungát* are distinguished (*D*. s.v.).

7 HILDIRID...BARE ALE TO THE GUESTS. High-born ladies waited upon their guests as a matter of honour, just as they do in Iceland to-day. Instances occur *passim* in the sagas; cf. Bergthora's carrying round water to wash her guests' hands, Nj. 35; and, in legendary days, Hildigunna, daughter of King Granmar, bearing ale to the vikings, Yngl. 41.

8 A LOOSE BRIDAL (lausabrullaup). The 'looseness' of this ceremony was sufficient to impair the legitimacy of the children. See p. 17.

9 AN OUNCE OF GOLD. The ounce (eyrir) is one-eighth of the mark (mörk). Dasent has a long note on money values in the saga-time (Nj. vol. II, p. 397 ff.). It is not generally realized how common, comparatively speaking, gold and silver were in the viking days: the 'fee' brought home by men of account from their summer harryings included luxuries and costly treasures of all kinds, and their fondness for magnificence is illustrated by countless instances in the sagas and by the constant reference in skaldic verse to the 'gold-scattering', 'ring-breaking' and 'treasure-flinging' propensities proper to a great man.

10 CALLED THE SONS OF HILDIRID. In the same way Egil's friend Thorstein Ericson (p. 148) was, when his father died, called Thorason, after his mother. Cf. Ld. 57: "Therefore was he called after his mother, because she lived longer than his father". Also cf. the case of the sons of the lady Fjorleif in *Reykdæla*, Vemund Kogur and his brothers. It was the common rule.

11 FINN-FARE AND FINN-SCAT (finnferð ok finnskat). I.e. the right of journeying into Finnmark (mod. Lapland) and trading with the Finns and collecting the scat (i.e. tribute) from them on the King's behalf. This seems to have been a royal monopoly, which before Harald Hairfair's days was held presumably by the kings of Halogaland.

CHAPTER VIII

1 THE KING'S STEWARDSHIP ON THE FELL (konungssýsla á fjalli). Explanatory of, and in apposition to, 'Finn-fare' (F.J.).

2 SKALDS. For the position of court-poets in Norway (who were after Harald Hairfair's time mainly Icelanders), see the note in Hkr. IV, 407-8, and references there quoted. Skalds were held in high esteem by their lords, for it was by their praise-songs that a king's fame was bruited abroad and the memory of his deeds handed down. They were men of action, often violent and overweening, like Egil, Gunnlaug the Wormtongue, Hrafn, Holmgang-Bersi, Kormak, Thormod Coalbrowskald, Hallfred the Troublous-skald and others. But Magnússon (Hkr. *loc. cit.*) well says that "The problem their art had to solve was, how to leave historical truth unobscured by professional eulogy, how to be true to this principle and dutiful to their patron at the same time. The school they had to go through for the solution of

this problem created them a class of independent, free-spoken, justice-loving men, influencing, when they have the opportunity, the king invariably in favour of justice and humanity ".

3 THORBIORN HORNKLOFI. A famous skald of King Harald's, whose 'Glym-Drapa' and 'Raven-song' have come down to us, though incomplete and corrupt.

4 SNAKE-SHIP (snekkja). See note on 'Long-ship', p. 254.

5 From this speech of Oliver's, and from many other examples, we gather the proper tone and attitude to be adopted in addressing the King. He must be approached as a wilful, and rather stupid, *child*, never forgetting, however, that he is a very *dangerous* child (as Skallagrim was to find, very nearly to his cost, some years later, ch. xxv).

6 MANY NOBLE KINSFOLK OF HIS. Both Bard and Thorolf were descended from Wolf the Fearless, the grandfather of Ketil Haeng of Hrafnista.

7 KINSMEN OF THEIRS BY BLOOD AND AFFINITY (frændr sína ok tengðamenn). The old word for 'connexion' as opposed to blood-relation was *sif*, 'sib' ('gossip' = god-sib).

8 A MIGHTY LORD (höfðingi mikill). Lit. a 'headman'. Icel. does not possess the English word 'lord' (A.S. *hlaford*).

CHAPTER IX

1 IN THE STEM (stafn). Or 'prow'. "*Stafn* seems to include the extreme space in the fore of a ship, when it does not signify the prow looked at from the outside" (Hkr. IV, 444). The *stafnbúar* were picked fighting men who bore the brunt of the fighting in a sea-battle (*ibid.* 448).

2 HAFRSFIRTH (Hafrsfjörðr). The generally accepted date for this decisive battle is 872, when King Harald was about 22 years old. For a slightly fuller account of Hafrsfirth see Har. Hfr. 19.

3 THOSE THAT IRON BIT NOT. Cf. Egil's difficulties with Atli the Short (ch. LXV). Also the case of Aslak Rockskull when he boarded Earl Eric's ship *Ironbeak* in the battle of the Jomsburg vikings against Earl Hakon: "Aslak was a bald man, by what is said, and yet hath he no helm on his head that day but battleth on with his bare pate. And 'tis clear sky and good weather and warm, and many men do off their clothes and have nought but their war-clothes only, for the heat sake. Now eggeth on Eric his folk against them, and now hew men at Aslak and upon his head both with swords and axes, and the blows fly off his pate like smoke and bite not on it. And this see they now, that he goeth hard forward, whatsoever be before him, and cleareth him his way; heweth ever on either hand. That is said, that Vigfus, Slaying Glum's son, took that rede that he grabbeth up a great anvil that lay there and driveth the neb of it into Aslak's head; and with that had he

nought to answer, but the anvil's neb sinketh in his pate so that it stood in his brain, and he straightway fell down dead" (*Flateyjarbók*; *Ólafs Saga Tryggvasonar*, ch. 153). Burton's *Anatomy of Melancholy* informs us that witches can make "stick-free's, such as shall endure a rapier's point, or musket shot and neu'r be wounded".

4 GIVE MY WIFE (gefa konu mína). Cf. Egil's taking to wife his brother's widow, ch. LVI.

5 LYKE-HELP (umbúnaðr). Lit. an 'arranging about' or 'putting in order', sc. in a decent manner of the corpse for burial.

6 TILTED. To 'tilt' (*tjalda*) is to pitch a tent; primarily, as here and *passim* in our saga, in the sense of rigging the awning of a ship, for Icel. is the language of vikings and seamen.

7 HAD BECOME FATHER AND SON-IN-LAW (mægð hafði tekiz með þeim S. ok B.). Lit. 'kinsman-in-lawship had come about between them'. A.S. has, but English has not, the equivalent of this general term *mágr*, which includes father-, brother-, and son-in-law.

8 BASTARD-BORN (frilluson). Lit. 'sons of a paramour *or* wish-wife'. *Frilla* is connected with *friðr*, 'peace *or* tranquillity', and in poetry has the meaning of 'mistress' (Lat. *amica*); but in prose with a slightly disdainful connotation, 'concubine'.

CHAPTER X

1 THE FELL (fjall). I.e. the highlands of Finnmark. *Fjall* (mountain) is generally used of a bigger thing than *fell* (hill).

2 SCAT (skattr). The general term for tribute; see our saga and Hkr· *passim*.

3 KYLFINGS (Kylfingar). Query, from some part of Garthrealm (*Garðaríki* = Russia).

4 COD-FISHERIES (skreið-fiski). *Skreið* = 'a shoal of fish', particularly a shoal of *spring cod*. It has also come to mean '*dried* fish' (cod, codling, haddock, etc.).

5 A HUNDRED (hundrað). Here, as always, the old 'long' hundred, 120; still used in Iceland for counting sheep in a flock or a fisherman's share in a catch.

At this point we stand at the highwater-mark of Thorolf's fortunes:

"Prosperity doth bewitch men seeming cleere,
But seas doe laugh, shew white, when Rocks are neere".

CHAPTER XII

1 Harek is a past master in the art of making the better appear the worse, of slanderous innuendo.

2 THERE SHOT TERROR INTO THE BREASTS OF THESE BONDER-LADS
(búandkörlum skaut shelk í bringu). *Skelkr* (cf. Engl. 'skulk') is
etymologically connected with the idea of slavery, and has a contempt-
uous connotation: 'funk'.

3 BIDDEN AND BOUN (búnir ok boðnir). One of those alliterative
formulas not uncommon in Icel.: cf. ''twixt fell and foreshore'. Harek
plainly overreaches himself here, and a less jealous mind than King
Harald's might have observed it.

CHAPTER XIII

1 SHIP OF BURDEN (byrðingr). A merchant-ship as opposed to a
war-ship.

2 GREY-WARES (grávara). "Calabar skins, skins of the squirrel as
distinct from beaver and sable" (Hkr. IV, 344).

3 BEAVER-SKINS (bjórskinn). Beavers, common enough in Europe,
and even in England, at one time, are so far exterminated that the name
naturally suggests to-day the American species.

CHAPTER XIV

1 KVENS (Kvenir). These dwelt on either side of the Gulf of Bothnia;
held by some to have been of Swedish stock, but F. J. points out that
the king's name, Faravið, does not sound Norse.

2 KIRIALS (Kirjálar). Kirialaland is mod. Karelia, in east Finland.

3 THE KEEL (Kilir). Mod. Kjölen; the massif that forms the water-
shed between Norway and Sweden. There is a riddle, "Why is it that
Norway cannot sail and Sweden cannot swim?" "Because Norway
turns the Keel upward, and Russia took the Finns away from Sweden".

CHAPTER XVI

1 GIFTS OF REMEMBRANCE (minningar). 'Keepsakes.' Cf. Skarphedinn's words to Gunnar Lambison at Njal's burning, "Here now is
a keepsake (minjagripr) for thee", as he took out of his purse the jaw-
tooth which he had hewn out of Thrain (G.'s uncle), and threw it at
G. and struck him in the eye so that it started out and lay on his cheek
(Nj. 129).

2 THAT THEY SHALL GET THAT THEY CAME TO MARKET FOR (at þeir
komiz þar at keyptu). I.e. they will get the bargain they deserve, and
little to their liking.

CHAPTER XVII

1 VAGAR (Vágar). In the Lofoten Islands, mod. East and West
Vaagö; still a great place for cod-fishing (F.J.).

2 THEN CAME THOROLF THERE WITH A HUNDRED MEN. A plain lie, for Thorolf was in Kirialaland (see p. 30). But the King is ready to swallow all their slander now.

CHAPTER XVIII

1 SIGTRYGG SHARP-FARER. *Snarfari* means lit. 'swift-farer'; 'sharp' in the sense of 'brisk': cf. our colloquial 'look sharp'. I have rendered it 'sharp-farer' to preserve the assonance of the brothers' by-names *snarfari—harðfari*.

2 WESTFOLD (Vestfold). Harald's ancestral kingdom, W. of the Oslofirth.

3 THE KING'S ERRANDS (sendiferðir konungs). F.J. says that these brethren were so-called *gestahöfðingjar*, captains of the 'guests'. As to these 'guests' he quotes *Konungsskuggsjá*, which shows that they were housecarles, members of the King's bodyguard, and so called because they "take guesting at many men's houses, and not altogether as a matter of friendship". Their duty was "to hold espial through all the King's realm and be ware if he have any unfriends in his realm....And if the King appoint guests to any of his unfriends, and it so betide that they are slain to whom the guests were appointed, then have the guests for their trouble a share of their fee": in brief, these 'guests' were an organized service for committing murder and robbery in the King's name. Olaf the Holy had 30 guests "and assessed them wages and gave them laws" (O.H. 55).

4 THE KING SAW...THAT THAT WAS NO LIE. Very delicate irony.

5 SET TO WED (veðsetti). The O.E. term for 'mortgage', an exact counterpart of the Icel.

CHAPTER XIX

1 SO AS ONLY THE HILL TOPS SHOWED OVER THE SEA'S BOURNE (svá at sjór var í miðjum hlíðum). Lit. 'so that the sea was in the mid slopes'; with the result, of course, that he was hull-down and probably out of sight altogether to people spying from the shore.

2 EASTAWAY (í Austrveg). All the lands east of Sweden were *Austrvegr*: generally, the eastern shores of the Baltic.

3 THE ERE-FLEET (Eyrarfloti). The great gathering of merchant-ships that came together at an appointed time every year at Eyrr (Skanör) in Denmark (F.J.).

4 BAILIFF (ármaðr). Lit. 'year's-man'. His duty was to get in everything which must be collected for the sustenance of the King and his court when travelling about the country. In time they came to be more and more powerful as their tax-gathering duties grew (F.J.). Their unpopularity as 'King's thralls' with inconvenient powers is well shown by the story of Seal-Thorir and Asbiorn Seal's-bane (O.H.

122–8); cf. the saying of the great Erling Skialgson: "I bow the neck of a good will to thee, King Olaf; but this shall I deem a troublous matter, to lout before Seal-Thorir, who is thrall-born through all his kin, although he be now your steward, or to bow to other such as are his peers of kindred, although you lay honour on them" (*ibid.* 122).

CHAPTER XX

1 His only child. This is a slip. Thordis, another child of Yngvar's, is mentioned at the beginning of ch. LVIII, and also in Landn.

2 Bald-headed (sköllóttr). Skallagrímr = 'Bald Grim'. Egil, too, was early bald (pp. 111, 116), an inconvenience which he shares with other famous men, e.g. Scipio Africanus and Julius Caesar.

CHAPTER XXII

1 By Skarnsound....Elda-eid. Skarnsound is the waterway that connects this firth with the more northerly Beitsjór (mod. Beitstadfjord); Eldueið, the isthmus that parts the Trondhjemsfjord from the Namsenfjord. King Harald took the way that goes to-day from Fosnaes over Elden to Rödhammer (F.J.).

2 Bade go out women, etc. This was the gentlemanly procedure when the terrible expedient of 'burning in' was adopted; cf. Njal's burning (Nj. 128), where Flosi was ready to let the women and children and housecarles, and Njal himself, go out; and even in the bitter wars of the Sturlung age a like mercy was shown, e.g. at the burning of Flugumyri. It was not so, however, when a low fellow like Hen-Thorir was in charge of the business: "Blundketil and his folk awoke not before the house was ablaze over them. Blundketil asked who had lighted that hot fire, and Thorir told who they were. Blundketil asked if aught might get him peace; but Thorir said: 'There is nought for it but to burn'. And they departed not before every man's child therein was burnt up" (Hen-Th. 9).

3 Shield-burg (skjaldborg). Formed by men of his bodyguard standing about the King with shields interlocking; commonly used by kings in battle, e.g. by King Hakon Athelstane's-fosterling and Eric's sons at Fitiar in Stord (*Hákonarmál*, Hak. 32, p. 190); by Earl Eric in the great sea-fight at Svold (O.T. 116); by King Olaf the Holy at Sticklestead (O.H. 218). See also the breaking of King Brian's shield-burg by Brodir the Viking (Nj. 156). Cf. the Roman *testudo*.

4 Eyvind Skaldspiller. Great-grandson on the distaff side of King Harald Hairfair. His *Haloga-Tale* (*Háleygjatal*) and *Hakon's-Song* (*Hákonarmál*) are extant, the one in praise of the family of the Earls of Hladir composed for Earl Hakon the Great, the other in memory of the last battle, victory and death of King Hakon Athelstane's-fosterling. His by-name of *Skáldaspillir* doubtless meant that he stole

from the older skalds; like some other nicknames (e.g. Audun Ill-skald—'Poetaster'), given originally in spite, it stuck without any sense of dishonour. That it was justified is demonstrated by the poems just mentioned, so far at least as form is concerned.

CHAPTER XXIII

1 THERE FELL HILDIRID'S SONS. A perfunctory, but perhaps adequate, dismissal of these schemers.

2 INGOLF AND HIORLEIF. Ingolf Arnarson was the first settler (landnámamaðr) in Iceland; both Landn. and Ari's *Islendingabók* say that he dwelt at Reykjarvík (mod. Reykjavík, now the capital of Iceland). The reason for his journey (see note, p. 255, on Earl Atli the Slender) was more respectable than that of another famous discoverer, Eric the Red, whose discovery of Greenland followed upon manslayings which had made first Norway and then Iceland too hot to hold him. A statue of Ingolf by Einarr Jónsson, as of Cortés staring from his peak in Darien, stands on the little green hill at the foot of the Hverfisgata in Reykjavík, looking north over the ships and the harbour and the waters of Faxa Flow. For Hiorleif's fate, see note on 'Irish Thrall', p. 298.

3 This is the country of *Njal's Saga*.

4 LITHEND (Hlíðarendi). The seat of Gunnar of Lithend, the hero of the earlier part of *Njal's Saga*. Baug was Gunnar's great-grandfather.

5 LAND-TAKE MEN (landnámamenn). Hence the title of the *Land-námabók*, the great book of settlements and generations, which has been called the foundation of all exact history, political or social, of the North.

6 WEATHERLID (Vetrliði). When King Olaf Tryggvison's militant missionaries, Thangbrand and Gudleif, were preaching christianity in Iceland in 999, "they fared to Fleetlithe.…There Weatherlid the Skald, and Ari his son, spoke most against the faith, and for that they slew Weatherlid" (Nj. 98).

7 SPEAKER OF THE LAW (lögsögumaðr). The highest office-bearing person in the Icelandic commonwealth; for his duties and powers see Nj. vol. I, p. lvii, and other references given s.v. in the index to that book.

CHAPTER XXIV

1 STAVE. 'Thunder-Lord'—Odin. 'Thing of Odin's shield-mays', assembly of the Valkyries—i.e. *battle*. (For general note on the verse-form of these 'staves', see note, p. 247.)

2 PAY BOOT (bæta). Atonement, weregild. For a general discussion of the ways open to free men under the old law to obtain redress, see Dasent's Introduction, Nj. vol. I, pp. cxl–cxlii. Friendly atonement by way of 'paying boot', when accepted and carried out, had the effect of

complete reconciliation, and in theory at least put an end to the blood-feud. Overbearing men sometimes made it a point of pride to do as they pleased and make atonement to no man; e.g. Slaying Stir, the father-in-law of Snorri the Priest, who "was a masterful man in the countryside, and had a many folk about him; he was held guilty at many men's hands, for that he wrought many slayings and booted none" (Eb. 18); Thorbiorn the Priest: "It is well known, Howard, that I have slain many men, and though folk called them sackless, yet have I paid weregild for none" (*Howard's Saga*, ch. 5); and Hrafnkel Frey's-priest, who "stood much in single combats and paid no man fee, so that none gat of him no boot, whatsoever he might do" (*Hrafnkel's Saga*, ch. 1).

CHAPTER XXV

1 LEARNED IN WIZARDRY (fjölkunnigr). 'Full knowing'; the word used *passim* of those reputed to know all there is to be known, both what they ought and what they ought not to know, i.e. art magic.

2 SIT-BY-THE-FIRE (kolbítr). Lit. 'a coal-biter'. An idle lout that sits all day in the kitchen; but sometimes turns into a hero in later life.

3 GARTH (garðr). (1) The primary meaning is a 'yard', an enclosed space; generally when used alone *garðr* means a 'hay-garth *or* stack-yard'; (2) a court and premises; (3) esp. in Norway, Sweden and Denmark, a 'house *or* building' in a town or village (cf. mod. use of *gaard* in Norse); (4) a very common use in Icel., a 'fence': *túngarðr*, the 'fence *or* wall round the home-mead'.

4 THORIR HROALDSON. See note, p. 255 above.

5 ROUND-SHIP (knörr). A big ocean-going ship, used for warfare over the high seas, where long-ships could not go; also used as cheaping-ships (Hkr. IV, 427–8).

6 SOLUNDS (Solundir). Mod. Indre and Ytre Sulen, at the mouth of the Sogn Firth.

CHAPTER XXVI

1 DUKE GUTTHORM (Gutthormr). Pronounced 'Gutt-horm'. For more of him see IIkr., Hfdn. 5; also Har. Hfr. 1, 2, 4, 18, 21, 28, 29.

2 TUNSBERG (Túnsberg). Mod. Tönsberg, an ancient cheaping-stead in Westfold.

CHAPTER XXVII

1 GANGWAY HEAD (bryggjusporðr). I.e. where the gangway touched the land or the jetty.

2 BYRNY-TROLL (bryntröll). Probably a double-edged axe (cf. F.J., note *ad loc.*): a fanciful name, like the Fr. 'miséricorde' and Engl. 'morning-star' or 'holy water sprinkler'.

3 STAVE. Whether or not this is in fact Skallagrim's composition, it is a masterpiece of condensation. 'Hersir'—Kveldulf. 'Yngling's bairns'—Gutthorm was of royal descent both by his father's and mother's side.

4 REEKNESS (Reykjanes). The extreme S.W. peninsula of Iceland, forming the southern horn of the great bay of Faxa Flow. Looking N. from Reykjavík in ordinary weather you can see in the clear Icelandic air the two-eared white dome of the Snæfells Jökull, the culminating point of the northern horn of the bay, eighty miles away across the sea. Reekness still 'reeks' with the smoke of hot springs, and it is a rough point to round if the weather is at all stormy.

5 THAT NESS THAT WAS THERE. I.e. Digraness; mod. Borgarnes.

CHAPTER XXVIII

1 WIDE WOODS. There are none now. But there is no reason to doubt that this treelessness is of comparatively recent date. Cf. the references in the sagas to charcoal-burning which implies woods, e.g. by Vigfus at Drapalithe (Eb. 26); and the constant references to 'woods' where the context clearly requires substantial trees. Snorri the Priest and Arnkel would not have quarrelled about Crowness "and the wood thereon, which is the best possession in the countryside" (*ibid.* 31) if it had been, as it now is, mere scrub not reaching to your heel as you ride through it; and there is detailed reference to the cutting, piling, seasoning, and loading of timber in that wood (*ibid.* 35). Either the farm-stock has eaten down the young growths so that the woods have perished, or (as is not unlikely) there has been a definite climatic change since the saga time. The rowan-trees in the parson's garden at Þingvellir, some 15 ft. high, are to-day quite a feature in the countryside.

2 A GREAT FIRTH. I.c. Burgfirth.

3 HVANNEYRI. On the S.E. shore over against Burg, with a panorama of firth and fell, including, close at hand, the grand mountain wall of Skarðsheiði. Here is to-day the agricultural college of Iceland, with fine buildings and a big model farm.

4 ANDAKIL. *Önd*, 'a duck' (gen. pl. *anda*), and *kill*, 'a creek *or* inlet'.

5 SKALLAGRIM GAVE LAND, etc. This, the usual procedure, determined the fundamental character of the Icelandic commonwealth: a republic of aristocrats surrounded by their 'thing-men', towards whom they stood in the double relation of chief and temple-priest. Cf. the account of Thorolf Mostbeard's settlement of the Thorsness country, in the opening chapters of Eb., and remarks in Int. p. xx–xxi on 'Priest'.

6 ONUND SJONI. A shipmate of Egil's in later years. For the dealings of him and his son Steinar with Egil's son Thorstein, see chs. LXXX–LXXXIV.

7 WHITEWATER. The Hvítá is extraordinarily white; but the statement that Skallagrim and his men had never seen glacier-water is very strange: possibly a gloss by a copyist who thought the land of Jotunheim and the Jostedalsbrae possessed no glacier streams. Or it may be true. For while the saga is curiously vague about the locality of Kveldulf's family seat, merely placing it in the Firdafylke, there are certain indications (including this passage) that it was in the Dalsfjord, a neighbourhood which is in fact without glacier rivers.

CHAPTER XXIX

1 THORD THE YELLER. A great lord in the western dales, who dwelt at Hvamm. For his by-name 'Gellir', cf. Hen-Th. 13: "He was come from Broadfirth out of the west country who alone was able to answer Odd-a-Tongue, and whose voice and speech were as the roaring of a bull". He is a frequent figure in the sagas, and was responsible for the constitutional reforms which in 964–5 led to the dividing of the land into Quarters and the setting up of Quarter-Courts at the Althing.

CHAPTER XXX

1 WHEN OTHER MEN WENT TO SLEEP. See p. 76 and note 3 to ch. XL.

2 STAVE. 'Wind's weeds'—*bellows*. 'Viddi's brother'—the *wind* (but it is not known who Viddi is). 'Gold of Beam-enjoyer', gold of the fire—i.e. the glowing *metal*. 'Stirring cots that swallow the storm-blast'—*bellows*.

CHAPTER XXXI

1 SPRINKLED WITH WATER. The old pagan custom.

2 STAVE. Not Egil's, but a later fabrication. 'Glittering ling-thong' —*the snake* or *worm* (draco); the worm's bed (cf. the Volsung story of Fafnir) is *gold*. 'Light-encircled worm-lands' is another kenning for *gold*.

3 STAVE. 'Herdsman of the wound-fowl'—*a warrior* (who, by plying his trade, gathers together ravens, etc. to feast on the carrion). 'Surf-dogs'—*the sea-snail shells*; query, so called from some children's game on the sea-shore. 'Sea-steed'—*ship*. 'Beck-partridge'—*duck*; the 'bed' of it—its *egg*. This stave, too, is not genuine, but belongs to the twelfth or thirteenth century.

CHAPTER XXXII

1 BIORN AND THORA JEWEL-HAND. This little idyll (chs. XXXII–XXXV) is no adventitious ornament. The importance, in Egil's career, of Biorn's wedding with Thora will appear later.

CHAPTER XXXIII

1 EARL SIGURD. Son of Eystein Glumra, and brother of Rognvald the Mere-Earl. King Harald Hairfair, when he had cleared out the vikings "West-over-sea", gave Earl Rognvald the Orkneys and Shetland. "But Rognvald straightway gave both the lands to Sigurd his brother, who abode behind in the West. And the king or ever he fared back east gave the earldom to Sigurd. Then there joined him to Sigurd, Thorstein the Red, son of Olaf the White and Aud the Deeply-wealthy, and they harried in Scotland, and won to them Caithness and Sutherland all down to the Oikel-Bank. Now Earl Sigurd slew Tusk-Melbrigda, a Scottish earl, and bound his head to his crupper; but he smote the thick of his leg against the tooth as it stuck out from the head, and the hurt festered so that he gat his bane therefrom, and he was laid in howe in Oikel-Bank" (Har. Hfr. 22).

2 MOSEYBURG. Presumably the Broch of Mousa, for a description and photograph of which see p. 44 of Dr Brøgger's *Ancient Emigrants* (Clarendon Press, 1929). These brochs are probably Pictish and date from remote antiquity.

3 A FIRTII WONDROUS GREAT. I.e. Faxa Flow.

4 A FIRTH WAS BEFORE THEM. I.e. Burgfirth.

5 A CERTAIN NESS. The Ness is Digraness (mod. Borgarnes), and the isle Brakarey, and the sound Brak's Sound, see ch. XL. Biorn seems to have anchored where the little steamer *Suðurland* anchors to-day that plies between Reykjavík and Borgarnes.

CHAPTER XXXVI

1 ERIC BLOODAXE (Eiríkr Blóðöx). This best loved son of King Harald Hairfair succeeded him, as will be seen later (ch. LVII), as King of Norway, but after a stormy year or two was forced to flee the land, yielding the throne to his half-brother Hakon. Eric's mother was a Danish princess, Ragnhild, daughter of the King of Jutland (Har. Hfr. 21). His career after he was turned out of Norway, and the date of his death (and indeed that of his turning out), are not exactly known. This much is certain, that he was a great sea-king in his youth, and also in later life: that he was sometime king in York (this is confirmed from English sources): that he was finally driven out of Northumberland, and fell (probably in 954) in a great battle in an attempt to win back that kingdom: see Hak. 3 and 4, where it is said that there fell in that battle King Eric and five kings with him and two sons of Earl Turf-Einar of the Orkneys. He was "a big man and a fair; strong and most stout of heart; a mighty warrior and victorious, fierce of mind, grim, unkind, and of few words" (Har. Hfr. 46). A great soldier but a poor statesman, he was steered, like Ahab and Macbeth, by the masculine will of his wife. The rich inheritance, painfully created by

his father's genius during so many years, of an undivided realm of Norway, survived for Eric but a few months, and then fell to pieces in his rude and unskilful hands. See also note, below, on Gunnhild.

2 CARAVEL (karfi). See note on 'Long-ship', p. 254.

3 MANY SUMMERS. Circ. from 905 to 918 (F. J.).

CHAPTER XXXVII

1 BIARMALAND (Bjarmaland). The land of the Perms, round the basin of the White Sea (Hkr. IV, 241).

2 GUNNHILD. For the full story of Eric's finding her in Biarmaland, dwelling with two Finnish wizards of hellish powers, under whose tuition she was studying art magic, see Har. Hfr. 34. She is described (*ibid*. 46) as "the fairest of women, wise and cunning in witchcraft; glad of speech and guileful of heart, and the grimmest of all folk". In our saga she is the most implacable of Egil's enemies; partly, it would seem, on the principle of *odi quem læseris*, for her first act is an attempt, on small provocation, to poison him (ch. XLIV). This great Queen appears in the sagas in a baleful light, an instance of those many glorious women who, being "fam'd for masculine vertue, have bin vitious". In her widowhood she appears as insatiable as the great Catharine in her taste for personable young men (see Nj. and Ld. for her relations with Hrut and Olaf the Peacock): a taste that is hinted at in our own saga (Thorolf Skallagrimson, Bergonund), but with no suggestion that it was indulged to an inconvenient extreme during Eric's lifetime. Pride is her great spring of action: she cannot away with the old Norse conception of a king as but *primus inter pares*, and is for ever driving on her lord towards greater show of autocratic power and formality. Thus in her hatred of 'this great Egil' is incarnate the theme (fundamental in this saga) of the strife for power between the king and the great houses; and an impartial reader can hardly help feeling throughout the scene in York (chs. LIX, LX) that there is a very great deal to be said in principle for the Queen's point of view.

There are reasons (not, I think, conclusive) for thinking that Gunnhild was not, as the sagas make her, the daughter of Ozur Toti, but a Danish princess, daughter of King Gorm the Old of Denmark. Two of her sons are named Gorm and Gamli (i.e. Old), and there are many instances of Danish support lent to her interests and those of her sons. Still, since Ragnhild, Eric Bloodaxe's mother, was a Dane, it is not necessary to make Gunnhild a Dane to supply the connexion. Professor Nordal pointed out to me that, even supposing her to have been King Gorm's daughter and the sagas therefore wrong in point of fact, it is interesting to note that they are still right in their broad historical view of the Queen, expressed by making her a foreigner brought up among Finns with magic powers. For the essential matter is that, whether she came from the cot of her Finnish tutors or from the highly developed court of Denmark, the Norse ways were strange and jarring to her, with their informal ideas about kings: "Who ever heard tell of such-like doings to a King-man?" Dasent has an admirable note on Gunnhild, Nj. vol. II, pp. 377–96.

3 BERGONUND. A personage of some importance to Egil's career: see ch. LVI ff.

CHAPTER XXXVIII

1 A NEEDFUL ERRAND. Presumably to get leave from Asgerd's kinsfolk for his wedding with her; see ch. XLII.

2 WE SHALL NOT MEET. As usual, this foreboding is fulfilled. Cf. Kveldulf's foreboding of the fall of the elder Thorolf, ch. XIX; Egil's in ch. LIV; Bergthora's saying (Nj. 126): "Now shall ye choose your meat to-night, so that each may have what he likes best; for this evening is the last that I shall set meat before my household", and many similar passages in the sagas, which well illustrate Keyserling's profound saying (Int., p. xxvii) that the belief in predestination is always grandiose in effect where its disciples possess proud souls.

3 STAVE. 'Switch's care-bed' (sveigar kör)—*axe*, which chops down the brushwood (switch) and so is its 'death-bed'. 'Wound-wolf'—*axe* again, from another point of view. 'Muck-horn' (arghyrna): *arg* is a term of the foulest opprobrium, see *Lokasenna* and notes thereon, *C.P.B.* vol. I.

CHAPTER XXXIX

1 REEKDALE (Reykjadalr). Mod. Reykholtsdalur. Reykholt was the seat of the great Snorri Sturlason. Riding from Burgfirth past White-water-meads you can see to-day, at ten miles' distance, the 'reek' of the hot springs as if the land was burning. At Deildartunga (and I believe at other farmsteads in the neighbourhood) they bake their bread by the heat of the springs. Snorri's bath is still shown to visitors, a circular well rimmed round with stones. In the river some miles below Reykholt is a 'water volcano', a small rock islet in midstream which, from several holes in its surface, continually throws out boiling water into the cold river that surrounds it.

2 BLUND-KETIL. Burnt in his house by Hen-Thorir, according to Hen-Th. and Landn.; but Ari in *Íslendingabók* says it was Thorkel that was burnt, the son of Blund-Ketil.

CHAPTER XL

1 BALL-PLAYS (knattleikar). A game of bat and ball, often mentioned in the sagas. Antiquarians have not succeeded in reconstructing its rules with any certainty (see F.J.'s note *ad loc.*). It was played by sides, and with a bat and ball: apparently one player hit the ball with

the bat, and the opponent tried to catch it: if he missed it there seems to have been a general scrimmage for the ball.

The one clear thing about the game is that it was very rough. Cf. Gisl. 8: "Those brothers-in-law, Thorgrim and Gisli, were very often matched against each other, and men could not make up their minds which was the stronger, but most thought Gisli had most strength. They were playing at the ball on the tarn called Sedgetarn. On it there was ever a crowd. It fell one day when there was a great gathering that Gisli bade them share the sides as evenly as they could for a game.

"'That we will with all our hearts,' said Thorkel, 'but we also wish thee not to spare thy strength against Thorgrim, for the story runs that thou sparest him; but as for me I love thee well enough to wish that thou shouldst get all the more honour if thou art the stronger.'

"'We have not put that yet to the proof,' says Gisli, 'may be the time may come for us to try our strength.'

"Now they began the game, and Thorgrim could not hold his own. Gisli threw him and bore away the ball. Again Gisli wished to catch the ball, but Thorgrim runs and holds him and will not let him get near it. Then Gisli turned and threw Thorgrim such a fall on the slippery ice that he could scarce rise. The skin came off his knuckles, and the flesh off his knees, and blood gushed from his nostrils. Thorgrim was very slow in rising.... Gisli caught the ball on the bound, and hurled it between Thorgrim's shoulders so that he tumbled forwards, and threw his heels up in the air.... Thorkel jumps up and says: 'Now we can see who is the strongest or is the best player. Let us break off the game'."

2 STAVE. Almost certainly genuine Egil.

3 AFTER SUNSET. Skallagrim's 'shape-strength', like his father's, affects him in the evening. Cf. his feat of strength by night related in ch. xxx.

4 KING OLAF. Olaf the Quiet, reigned 1067–93; son of King Harald Hardrada who fell at Stamford Bridge, 1066.

CHAPTER XLI

1 FRANKLIN (Höldr). An untitled person who takes rank in the social scale above the *bóndi*, and is a freeholder by birth (óðalsmaðr, óðalborinn), Hkr. IV, 338. The word is not derived from *halda* to hold, but is identical with A.S. *hæleð*, Germ. *held* (hero). For Biorn's attitude, cf. the story in the *Fornmannasögur* version of *King Harald Hardrada's Saga*, ch. 62, where the king offers one Hogni the title of landed man but Hogni begs to be excused from taking the honour, "Because I know that that will be said (as true it is), then when landed men be come together, 'There shall Hogni sit outermost; he is the

E S   18

least among landed men, for that he is of bonder's kin'; then will the name of landed man be in no wise to mine honour, rather a thing to laugh at. Now will I rather be named bonder, that I have the birth for. There will be rather somewhat of honour for me in that talk, that then it will be said (though it amount to little), wheresoever bonders be come together, that Hogni is of them the foremost".

2 TAKEN IN THANKFUL WISE. See pp. 72, 73. Thorolf was plainly a man of tact.

3 ARINBIORN. This is the beginning of a deep and lifelong friendship. Arinbiorn is mentioned also in Landn. and in Hkr.

CHAPTER XLIII

1 CURDS (skyr). Doubtless the *lac concretum* of Tacitus (*Germania*, ch. 23). *Skyr* is a staple article of food in Iceland to-day; many foreigners find it unattractive at first, but the taste for it grows with use. It is thick and pasty, with a clean, sour flavour. Served (as it is) with cream and sugar, it is a dish for kings.

CHAPTER XLIV

1 BLOOD-OFFERING UNTO THE GODDESSES (Dísablót). Dame Bertha Phillpotts (*Cambridge Medieval History*, vol. II, p. 486) thinks that the *Dísir*—'(supernatural) female beings'—probably covered both the Valkyries and the Norns. There was a great 'Hall of the Goddesses' at Upsala through which, when he 'happed to be at a sacrifice to the Goddesses' King Adils rode his horse; "and the horse tripped his feet under him...and the king fell forward from off him, so that his head smote on a stone, and he brake his skull, and the brains lay on the stones, whereby he gat his bane" (Yngl. 33). Earl Hakon the Great had a private Goddess, Thorgerd Shrine-bride,* to whom he is said in the *Jómsvíkinga Saga* to have offered up his son in order to escape defeat in his battle against the Jomsburg vikings in Hiorungwick; the Jomsburgers were overborne by foul weather and a great hail-storm, and thought they saw a woman on Earl Hakon's ship, "and it seemed to them as if arrows flew thick and fast from every finger of her, but every arrow was the bane of a man" (*Fornmannasögur*, I, 176). Dame Bertha Phillpotts (*op. cit.*) observes that the Dísir are "too capricious to be called guardian spirits. Those of one family, provoked at the coming change of faith, are credited with having killed one of its representatives. We see the reasonableness of the attitude taken up by a would-be convert, who stipulates that the missionary shall guarantee him the mighty archangel Michael as his 'attendant angel' (fylgju-engill)". The sad case referred to is that of a son of Hall of the Side, mentioned (Nj. 95) as *Þiðrandi, sá er Dísir drápu*—'whom the

* Hǫlgabrúðr, i.e. the bride (wife) of Hǫlgi, another form of Helgi.

Goddesses slew'. Thidrandi's death is related at length in the so-called *Olaf Tryggvison Saga Major*, a work much diluted and marred with monkish additions: Dasent summarises the curious story in his introduction (Nj. vol. I, p. xx).

2 This episode in Atley should be compared with the Rabelaisian scene in the house of Armod Beard, pp. 170–3.

3 STAVE. 'Shatterer of helm-bane ogress' (brjótr herkumla sverre-flagþa)—shatterer of the *axe*, e.g. by using it too violently, as Skallagrim did with King Eric's gift, ch. XXXVIII; so *warrior*. 'Sword-saplings'—*men*.

4 CUP-MAID (ölselja). F.J. recalls that in Valhalla the Valkyries pour out the ale for the heroes of bliss (Einherjar).

5 RUNES (rúnar). The ancient runic alphabet of 24 letters is found in inscriptions, generally on stones, all over the North. Sophus Bugge, and Prof. von Friesen of Upsala, have shown that it is derived from the Greek (not, as formerly supposed, the Latin) alphabet. "Once on a time the self-same speech was spoken by every 'Gothic' tribe from Roumania to Norway. As separate tribes were isolated, this language split of course into different tongues", *C.P.B.* vol. I, p. 573. The language of the runes is thus the oldest 'Northern Tongue', going back to about 300 A.D.

Runes were held to be magic mysteries of Odin's invention. In *Hávamál* He says: "Runes shalt thou find and staves to read, most great staves, most steadfast staves, which Fimbul-þulr drew, and the High Gods made, and Hroptr of the Powers scored: Odin among Æsir, but for Elves Dainn, and Dvalinn for Dwarves, Alsviðr for Giants. I Myself scored some" (*C.P.B.* vol. I, p. 25).

For Egil's powers with runes, cf. also ch. LXXII.

6 STAVE. 'Root of the fierce beast's ear-tree' (óþs dýrs viþar róta)— *the root* (i.e. part nearest the head) *of the horn* (ear-tree) *of the aurochs*: in short, the upper part of the drinking-horn. 'Ale that Bard did sign' (ǫl þats Bárøþr signde); the cups were 'signed to the Æsir' (i.e. the Gods) after ancient wont, O.H. 113.

7 STAVE. 'Wild-ox's bill-drops' (atgeira úra ýring), lit. 'the rain-drops of the bill *or* halberd of the aurochs'; the aurochs's 'bill' is its horn—*a drinking horn*: the 'rain-drops' of that—*beer*. The last couplet is

> rigna getr at regne
> regnbjóþr Hǫars þegna.

The 'rain of Hoar's thanes' (Odin's thanes; i.e. the Gods) is *poetry*. Egil thus says, 'I am making a poem' (F.J.): a somewhat gratuitous and pointless piece of information. Personally, I do not doubt (in view of the immediate sequel) that a double meaning is intended, and the suggestion called up by *oddský* (spear-sky) in the previous line is carried into this last couplet: the Gods can rain not poems only, but swords of vengeance on poison-mixing ale begrudgers such as Bard.

8 RANSACK. 'Rannsaka' is the regular legal term for a domiciliary search, whether for a criminal or for stolen goods. Cf. the ransacking at Mewlithe (Eb. 18, pp. 33–4), and Arnkel's ransacking for Odd Katlason (*ibid.* 20, pp. 44–7).

CHAPTER XLV

1 WHEN THE SEARCH-PARTIES...SHIP (er leiti bar í milli þeira ok skipsins). Lit. 'When a slope *or* rising brow was brought *or* came between them and the ship'; i.e. the ship lay in what was 'dead ground' for them. Cf. p. 121, where a similar phrase is used.

2 STAVE. 'Listland', mod. Lister, a district in West Agdir: here it stands, as *pars pro toto*, for *Norway*. 'Hlökk's rowan'—*King Eric* (Hlökk being a Valkyrie).

3 THE KING'S DOOM (dóm konungs). Thorir offered the King 'self-doom' or the right of laying down his own award, the most honourable terms that could be offered to the other side in a blood-suit.

CHAPTER XLVI

1 A HALF-MONTH'S PEACE. The matter-of-course way in which this arrangement (first do your trading, then make war—apparently on your customers) is recorded, is illuminating.

2 TORTURING. The collocation of ideas, *skemtan* (amusement, entertainment) and *kvelja* (to torment; cf. Engl. 'quell') is to be noted. The amusement was (or was believed by the Norsemen to be) popular among barbarians such as the Kurlanders and the Wends; cf. O.T. 38, where Earl Sigvaldi, then captain of the Jomsburgers, kidnapped King Svein Twi-beard (later the conqueror of England) and forced him to make peace with the Wend-king, "'Either else would the earl', said he, 'deliver King Svein to the Wends'. Now King Svein knew full well that then would the Wends torment him to death" (kvelja hann til bana).

It may seem curious that instances of refined cruelty in the North are characteristic not of the old heathen days but of the time after the introduction of christianity. The Northman is by nature "a dog that killeth clean rather than a cat that patteth and sporteth with her prey". But the religion of Love reached Europe, unhappily, from the East, well imbued with the spirit of Anti-Christ, intolerance, and the stake. The admired young missionary king, Olaf Tryggvison, dealt with refractory cases in a way of which neither Torquemada nor Philip II (nor even the Calvinist inventor of the 'dormouse torture') need have been ashamed; cf. O.T. 83, "Then let the king bear in a hand-basin full of glowing coals and set it on Eyvind's belly, and presently his belly burst asunder"; and (*ibid.* 87), "Raud cried out at him, saying that he would never trow in Christ, and blasphemed much; and the king waxed wroth, and said that Raud should have the worst of deaths. So he let take him and bind him face up to a beam, and let set a gag between his teeth to open the mouth of him; then let the king take a ling-worm and set it to his mouth, but nowise would the worm enter his mouth, but shrank away whenas Raud blew upon him. Then let the king take a hollow stalk of angelica, and set it in the mouth of Raud, or, as some men say, it was his horn that he let set in his mouth; but they laid therein the worm, and laid a glowing iron to the outwards thereof, so that the worm crawled into the mouth of Raud, and then into his throat, and dug out a hole in the side of him, and there came Raud to his ending". Cf. also the treatment of Brodir the Viking after Brian's battle (Nj. 156). King Olaf the Holy also "taught men right manners"; and if they were slow to learn, he let "maim them of hand or foot, *or sting their eyes out*" (O.H. 72). I will add to these instances the account of the vengeance taken upon Sigurd Slembi-deacon, an able adventurer and claimant to the throne of Norway in the chaotic years that followed the death of King Sigurd Jerusalem-farer. "They brake his legs asunder with axe-hammers, and his arms withal. Then they stripped him of his clothes, and were minded to flay him quick, and they ripped the scalp off his head; but they might not do it, because of the blood-rush. Then they took walrus-hide whips and beat him long, so that well nigh was the hide off, as if it were flayed. But sithence they took a stock and shot it at the backbone of him, so that it went asunder. Then they dragged him to a tree and hanged him, and hewed off his head sithence" (Hkr. *Saga of Ingi, son of Harald*, ch. 12). This gives us a christian standard, some two centuries nearer our own time, by which to measure such roughness as we may find in Egil and elsewhere under the old dispensation.

3 SHIELD-WAINSCOT (skjaldþili). Probably because of the custom of hanging shields and weapons on the wall; cf. ch. XI.

4 MADE SLAVES OF (þjáðir). Cf. *þ́r*, 'a bondwoman'. The same word is used of King Harald's 'enslavement' of Norway, pp. 3 and 6.

5 THAT SHAME. Egil's moral scruples had an unfortunate effect so far as his late captors were concerned. He is shocked at the idea of an unavowed theft, but with an easy conscience puts it right by owning up, and at the same time burning the whole houseful, men and all.

CHAPTER XLVII

1 HARALD GORMSON. King of Denmark circ. 936–86. The chronology of the saga seems at fault here (F.J.). For his support of Gunnhild and her sons, and later betrayal of King Harald Greycloak: his relations with the great Earl Hakon: his defence of the Danework against Kaiser Otto: his forced christening by the Kaiser: and his death in war against his rebellious son Svein Twi-beard, see Hkr. (Hak., Har. Gr. and O.T.). *Jómsvíkinga Saga* gives a shocking but perhaps not very reliable account of his end, at the hands of Palnatoki, the famous captain of the Jomsburg vikings.

2 STAVE. 'Stainer of the wolf's teeth' (úlfs tannlitoþr)—*warrior*; addressed to Thorolf. 'Dalefish-bounty's season' (dalmiskunn fiska; lit. 'dale-mercy *or* bounty of fishes', by transposition for 'dale-fishes' mercy *or* bounty'), an elaborate 'double-decked' kenning for *summer*, the season that extends mercy or bounty to the *snake*, which is commonly called poetically 'fish' of the dale, etc., cf.

> Fish of the wild-wood,
> Worm smooth-crawling,
> With wolf-meat mingled,
> They minced for Gutthorm. (Vols. 30.)

3 TREE-BURG (tréborg). A fence or palisade of wooden stakes or logs.

CHAPTER XLVIII

1 PEACE-LAND (friðland). Finding that the burglar is not intent on *your* spoons and forks (because you haven't got any), you ask him to stay to supper. Normandy was *friðland* to Norse vikings (O.H. 19).

2 STAVE. 'Wound-partridge' (benþiþorr)—*the raven*. The last couplet is bloodthirsty enough—

> létom blóþga búka
> í borghliþe sœfask.

3 GOING ON THE FLOOR AT EVERY HEALTH. I.e. men stood up from their seats on either side of the hall and drank to one another over the long fires that went down the middle. Cf. King Athelstane's reaching the ring across to Egil on his sword point, ch. LV.

4 This conversation between Eric and Gunnhild is an instance of the concentrated character-drawing of which the sagas are full.

5 TO DRAG ON (draga framm). The ordinary sense is to 'breed up, rear'. F.J. says it is here ironical, "to allow Skallagrim's sons to live until", etc. Or it may mean to "show favour" to them. I have followed F.J.

CHAPTER XLIX

1 EYVIND BRAGGART AND ALF. Cf. the account in Hkr. of the battle of Fitiar in Stord, some 35 years later: "The brethren [Gunnhild's sons] had there a great host from out of Denmark; and there were in their company their mother's brethren, Eyvind Braggart and Alf Ashman, both strong men and stout, and the greatest of man-slayers....King Hakon [Athelstane's-fosterling] was easy to know above other men, for his helm flashed again when the sun shone on it....Then took Eyvind Finnson a hat and did it over the king's helm. But forthright Eyvind Braggart cried out on high: 'Doth now the king of the Northmen hide? or is he fled away? where is gotten the golden helm?' Forth then went Eyvind and Alf his brother with him, smiting on either hand, and making as they were mad or raging. But King Hakon cried on high to Eyvind: 'Keep thou the road wherein thou art,

if thou wouldst find the king of the Northmen'....But little was the while to bide ere thither came Eyvind and hove up sword and smote on the king; but Thoralf thrust forth his shield against him, so that Eyvind staggered; and the king took his sword Quern-biter in both hands, and smote down on Eyvind's helm and clove helm and head down to the shoulders. Therewith Thoralf slew Alf Ashman....And anon therewith fell terror and fleeing among the folk of Eric's sons" (Hak. 29, 31). For Alf's later appearance in our Saga, see ch. LVI. On the question whether he and Eyvind were really the Queen's brothers, see note on 'Gunnhild', p. 271.

2 GUNNHILD'S TONGUE...THE KING'S MIGHT. Cf. the somewhat similar phrase used by Arinbiorn, p. 162.

3 HAD SLAIN IN THE SANCTUARY (hafði vegit í véum). *Vargr í véum*, a 'wolf in the sanctuary'; a law-phrase, metaph. *an outlaw*, who is to be hunted down as a wolf and is declared accursed for having committed a crime in a holy place (*D*. s.v. *vargr*).

4 STAVE. 'From back of wave-steed' (af unnar heste)—*off his ship*.

CHAPTER L

1 PRIME-SIGNED. *Prímsigna* is to give the *prima signatio* or *signaculum crucis*.

CHAPTER LI

1 OLAF THE RED. See general note on 'Winaheath', p. 280.

2 RAGNAR HAIRYBREEKS (Ragnarr Loðbrók). The history of this great Danish king is clouded with legend. There is a mythical *Ragnars Saga*, some passages in Saxo's chronicle, a *þáttr* (or short tale) of Ragnar's sons, and some poems, notably the *Krákumál* dating from the twelfth century; these seem all to be connected with the lost *Skjöldunga Saga* (the lives of the Kings of Denmark). For the viking expeditions of Ragnar and his sons, see *Cambridge Medieval History*, vol. III, pp. 318–19, 329–31. His end (first half of the ninth century) was that, being minded to bring England under him, he was shipwrecked on the Northumberland coast, and taken alive by King Ella who "set him in a worm-close". Here, like Gunnar of old, he died singing, and the *Krákumál* purports to be his death-song. His sons, Sigurd Worm-in-Eye, Biorn Ironside, Ivar the Boneless, and Whitesark, made conquests and ruled in many lands. They avenged their father by what seems to have been the approved method, viz. by cutting 'an erne' on Ella's back: cf. Har. Hfr. 31, where Earl Turf-Einar cut an erne on the back of Halfdan High-leg, the slayer of his father Earl Rognvald, "in such wise, that he thrust his sword into the hollow of the body by the backbone, and sheared apart all the ribs down to the loins, and thereby drew out the lungs". The names of Ragnar and his sons are frequent in genealogies.

CHAPTER LII

1 STAVE. Second couplet, lit. 'I learn that prince is thing-hard'; i.e. an unpleasant person at a meeting (poetical *meiosis* for the 'Thing of weapons', or battle).

Third couplet,

> Glapstígo lét gnóga
> Goþrekr á mó troþna;

lit. 'Godrek let tread stray-paths enough on the moor', i.e. let (himself) tread the path of death. Cf. Völospá, *troða halir hel-veg*, 'men tread the way of hell'. 'Alfgeir's land' is, of course, Northumberland.

2 HAZEL A FIELD (hasla völl). I.e. stake it off with hazel-poles as a field for battle. Cf. Hak. 24; O.T. 18.

3 WINAHEATH (Vínheiðr). Much has been written in the attempt to identify this place and this battle. There are serious difficulties about the chronology of the English episodes. According to the saga, Egil helped King Athelstane in a great battle against Scots and others at Winaheath. In that battle Thorolf fell, and a year (or two years) later Egil married his widow, and went home to Iceland where he remained several years. He came back to Norway and strove with Bergonund at the Gula-Thing the year before Eric Bloodaxe was driven out of Norway. The year after that event (i.e. in 936) he sailed for England again, fell into Eric's hands in York, and once more visited Athelstane.

The description of the battle of Winaheath agrees with what the Anglo-Saxon Chronicle and other sources tell us of the battle of Brunanburh (which, it should be noted, is in one place called 'Wendune'). Except the saga, there is no authority for the battle of Winaheath, nor is there any record of any great battle of Athelstane's against the Scots except Brunanburh.

Can we, then, identify Winaheath with Brunanburh? The objection is the date. Brunanburh was fought in 937, Eric fled from Norway in 936. We should thus (a) upset the whole order of events, (b) leave room for scarcely any interval between Egil's two visits to England (Athelstane died in 939), and (c) postpone Egil's marriage by some ten years to a date that does not fit in with the known ages of his children. The better opinion inclines to-day to identify the two battles, correcting the whole chronological system of the saga accordingly. Still, the truth may yet be that Egil and Thorolf took part in a smaller and little-known battle in or about the year 927, to which the saga has mistakenly attributed the setting and importance of Brunanburh. If the *Höfuðlausn* episode did in fact take place in York in the year of Brunanburh (i.e. a year later than the date given by the saga), Egil might well have been the first to bring news of that battle to London. The saga's account of Winaheath must in any case be traced ultimately to Egil's own reminiscences; and he might easily (perhaps not unwillingly) in later years have fallen into a confusion which might persuade himself and others that Winaheath was indeed Brunanburh, and that he had helped Athelstane to victory not in some forgotten fight but on that field of worldwide renown.

4 WHAT TRICKSTERS THESE ENGLISH BE (at yðr mundu þeir reynaz brögðóttir, enir ensku). A Welsh turncoat as long ago as the tenth century, exclaiming against 'perfide Albion'.

CHAPTER LIII

1 SWORD CALLED 'LONG'. Egil's sword (8 lines below) was called *Nadder* (naðr, 'an adder'). Egil had another sword given him later by Arinbiorn, called *Dragvandil* (p. 146). For pet-names of weapons, cf. Skarphedinn's axe *Ogress of war* (Rímmu-gýgr, 'war's-ogress'), Nj. 45, etc.; King Hakon Athelstane's-fosterling's sword *Quern-biter* (Kvernbítr), Har. Hfr. 43; Gisli's sword (later reforged as a spear) *Graysteel* (Grásíða) and Skeggi's *Warflame* (Gunnlogi), Gisl. 1, 3, etc.; Steinar's sword *Skrymir* (p. 217), also mentioned in *Kormak's Saga*, a story which is rich in named weapons, viz. Bersi's sword *Whitting* (Hvítingr) 'with a life-stone to it' (a precious stone set in the hilt that would heal wounds given by the blade), and Midfirth-Skeggi's sword *Sköfnung*: "There is a pouch to it, and that thou shalt let be. Sun must not shine on the pommel of the hilt. Thou shalt not bear it until fighting is forward, and when thou comest to the field, sit all alone and then draw it. Hold the edge toward thee, and blow on it. Then will a little worm creep from under the hilt. Then slope thou the sword over, and make it easy for him to creep back under the hilt". But Kormak was "hot and hasty" and the sword "cold and slow"; he did not heed his instructions, "and the little worm came, and was not rightly done by"; and the good of the sword was spoilt, and it came groaning and creaking out of its scabbard (Korm. 9; I have followed, in the main, Collingwood's transl.).

2 FEATHER (fjöðr). I.e. the blade.

3 BYRNY-TWISTER (brynþvari). *Brynja*, a 'byrny'; *þvari* (þverr-, 'across, transverse'), 'a cross-stick'.

4 NEITHER HAD A BYRNY. Coats of mail were costly luxuries; even so, it is remarkable that captains like Thorolf and Egil should go without them. Query, is this connected with the 'bare-sark' tradition?

5 WOOD-WROTH (óðr). This seems to be berserks-gang.

6 LAND-TENTS (landtjaldar). *Tjöld* to the Northman, who is born a sailor, means naturally a *ship's* 'tent' (the tilt or awning for use at night, etc.; cf. our saga *passim*). For landsmen the primary suggestion is just the other way, and we feel the distinctive word 'land' unnecessary.

7 AND ADILS. This, however, was a false report: see below.

CHAPTER LIV

1 LET THE KING HAVE HIS WAY. Thorolf is 'fey'. Cf. Njal's fata counsel, before the burning of Bergthorsknoll, that men should go into the house and defend it from within instead of meeting the enemy in the open. "'Let us do', said Helgi, 'as our father wills; that will be best for us'. 'I am not so sure of that,' says Skarphedinn, 'for now he is "fey"; but still I may well humour my father in this, by being burnt indoors along with him, for I am not afraid of my death'" (Nj. 127).

2 AT OPEN SHIELDS (í opna skjöldu). A manœuvre common in ancient warfare: to take your enemy on his right flank, where (because the shield is on the left arm) he is at a disadvantage if thrown on the defensive. Cf. Thucydides, v, x, where the success of Brasidas's victorious sally from Amphipolis was helped by the incompetence of the Athenian general, τὰ γυμνὰ πρὸς τοὺς πολεμίους δούς, "offering his unshielded flank (lit. 'naked') to the enemy"; i.e. Kleon allowed his right wing to be taken by Brasidas 'at open shields'.

3 THERE FELL KING OLAF. But see general note on 'Winaheath', p. 280.

CHAPTER LV

1 EGIL CLASPED A GOLD RING, etc. It may be doubted if either the noble stave that follows or the queer dumb antics in King Athelstane's hall afford such convincing evidence of his grief as does this simple renunciation of solid treasure.

2 STAVE. 'Went forth' (gekk snarla), lit. 'walked swiftly, keenly', sc. 'forward in the battle'. 'Earth greens' (jǫrþ grœr), 'the sod grows again over his howe'. 'Brother', the word used is a poetic one, *barmi*, connected with *barmr* (breast); a brother nourished at the same breast. The original stave is very fine.

3 STAVE. Last couplet:

> Helt, né hrafnar sulto,
> Hringr á vápna þinge.

The 'weapon-thing' is, of course, *battle*.

4 PERSONAL DESCRIPTION. F.J., in his introduction, well notes the masterly way in which the moment is selected for this vivid portrait: the moment when the sitter is torn with conflicting passions arising from victory and bereavement. If the picture is grotesque, it is also living and unforgettable.

5 EYEBROWS JOINED IN THE MIDDLE (skolbrunn). D. says the exact sense of *skolbrunn* is uncertain. F.J. says it usually means 'with brown eyebrows', but prefers the interpretation I have adopted.

6 STAVE. 'Byrny's god' (brynjo Hǫþr)—*warrior*, i.e. King Athelstane. 'Gleaming thong of paw-tongs' (hrynvirgel hrammtangar)—*arm-ring*. 'Hawk-trod...Vingi'—*arm* or *hand*. 'Spear-storm fish'—*sword*; the 'gallows' of that—the *hand*. 'Snare of red gold' (rauþmeldrs gelgja), lit. 'snare of red meal' (i.e. gold)—*gold ring*. Last couplet: the King, by his gift, encourages me to praise him again.

7 GLAD OF HIMSELF. The simplicity of his mind, with its violent contradictions of nobility and graspingness, is most disarming. There are many other instances.

8 STAVE. 'With pulling of an arm-string.' *Armsíma* (*síma* is used to-day of telephone wires) is the gold ring. The poet's mind is playing with the figure of the cord of gold having power to lift the huge crags of his grief-bent brows. For the evident pleasure he derives from the thought of his dark and rugged features, cf. *Arinbiorn's Lay*, p. 196, and staves on pp. 114, 145, 146, and 175.

9 DRAPA (drápa). Derived from *drepa*, either in the sense of 'striking' the chords of an instrument (*D.* s.v., but this seems very doubtful), or (better, F.J.) in its ordinary sense of 'slay': 'a battle-song'. The drapa is a heroic laudatory poem with a burden or refrain. Egil's great *Höfuðlausn*, given in full on pp. 141–5, is a drapa.

10 STAVE. 'He that rouseth Our Ladies of the Battle-din' (faldgnáar hjaldrsnerrande). *Gná* is a Valkyrie; cf. 'The Sword-God wakes Our Lady of Sakes' in the *Höfuðlausn*. 'Ella's scion' (Ella, king of Northumberland: cf. note, p. 279, on 'Ragnar Hairybreeks')—*Athelstane*. 'Kings' head-stem' (harra hǫfoþbaþmr), i.e. main shoot of the family-tree of kings—*Athelstane*. 'Flinger of the billow-fire' (hyrjar hrann-brjótr), lit. 'breaker of', etc.; lavisher of gold—again, *Athelstane*.

11 BURDEN. 'Reindeer-way' (hreinbraut)—*mountains*. Athelstane is king of all the land, even to the mountain-tops.

CHAPTER LVI

1 BERGONUND. See above, p. 71.

2 STAVE. 'Young hawk-cliff's goddess' (ung haukaklifs Hlín): 'hawk-cliff' = arm: Hlin of that—a *lady*. The playing upon words in the last four lines is like a Shakespeare sonnet, and quite untranslatable:

Verþk í feld, þás foldar
faldr kømr í hug skalde
bergóneres brúna
brátt miþstalle hváta.

Brúna miþstallr, the thing standing up between (and below) the brows, is the *nose*. *Bergóneres foldar faldr* cannot be understood; but it conceals the name of Asgerd (query, *faldr*, 'clothing', part of which is *gerðr*, 'girdle', giving the second syllable of the name *Ás-gerðr*?); further

F.J. extracts a reference to the first syllable (*Ás*, 'a God') from *bergóneres*. With my 'When-*As girdle*' I have tried, clumsily enough, to give some indication of this obscure punning.

3 STAVE. Suttung is a giant. The 'beer' (feast-fare) of the giant—*poetry*. 'Sea-fire goddess'—*lady*: but some of the words here are corrupt. 'Dighters...Valkyries'—*warriors*. 'Fount (lit. beverage—*veig*) of the Lord of Strife', i.e. of Odin—*poetry*. Meaning, the poets will be able to unravel his obscure puns and find out his mistress's name, because they know the tricks of the trade.

4 BIORN THE HITDALE CHAMPION. He has a saga of his own, not (so far as I know) translated into English.

5 ILLUGI THE BLACK. Of Gilsbank; famous as the father of Gunnlaug the Worm-Tongue; see Gunnl., and also Eb. 17, and the *Heath-slayings Saga* (translated in same volume of the *Saga Library* as Eb.).

6 MANY WINTERS. 927 to 932 (F.J.).

7 WITH GUNNHILD. The Queen had, in her later years at any rate, a taste for personable young men: see the account of her scandalous proceedings with Hrut (Nj. 3, 6, and 7; Dasent has, perhaps pardonably, drawn a decent veil of paraphrase over one or two passages) and with Olaf the Peacock (Ld. 21); but there is nothing to suggest that her friendship now, in Eric's lifetime, with Thorolf Skallagrimson (pp. 71, 94), and later with Bergonund, went to these lengths.

8 VERY LOUD AND SAUCILY (snelt mjök). Cf. 'the wind blows sharp and snell'. D. says (*ad loc.*), 'harshly, in a high-pitched voice'.

9 THE GULA-THING. Magnússon (Hkr. IV, p. 461) says it was "held on the shore of the bay of Gula, or rather of its off-shoot inlet Eyvind-wick, which cut into the southern side of the broad peninsula which bounds from the south the mouth of Sognfirth. It represented the folklands of South Mere, Firthfolk, Sognfolk, Valdres, Haddingdale, Hordfolk, Rogaland, and Agdir; and all these districts, when collectively spoken of, went under the territorial designation of Gula-Thing laws (parts)".

10 BONDWOMAN. The circumstances on which Bergonund based this charge were, of course, the runaway match related in chs. XXXII–XXXV. As to the substance of the charge, cf. the contentions on both sides, pp. 119–120.

11 A STEEP THING (örðigt). F.J. says the meaning is not (as commonly), 'difficult', but 'hostile, contumacious' (feindlich, widersetzlich): "it seems to me too strong, and almost as if you would treat me as an enemy". *Örðigr* primarily means 'erect, upright, rising on end' (*D.*), and at the risk of being accused of slang, I have used an idiom that precisely corresponds.

12 ODAL-BORN (óðalborin). See note on 'Odal', p. 258.

13 NOBLE-BORN (tíginborin). I.e. descended from kings or earls (referring, no doubt, to Asgerd's grandfather, Earl Hroald, see ch. 11).

14 Bergonund's speech is a flawless masterpiece, ending, as it were with a thunderclap, with the proposal that the lady shall not only lose her case (quite wrongfully, as it appears), but be herself adjudged the King's bondwoman!

15 UNSPOKEN. Reading *ómælt*: not, as F.J., *ómæt* (without might).

16 STAVE. First couplet:

> Þýborna kveþr þorna
> þorn reiþ áar horna.

'Þorna þorn', which might stand for a general kenning for a *man*, is pointedly used of Bergonund, the son of Thorgeir *Thornfoot*. *Reiðr áar horna* is the 'bearer of the river of horns' (i.e. of ale)—a *lady*. 'Spear-brandisher' is addressed to Bergonund, as is also 'rich man'. I have preserved as far as I could the rhymes and assonances of the original.

17 ASHMAN. Alf Ashman, her brother. See note, p. 278.

18 HOLMGANG. See note, p. 292.

19 PICK AND CHOOSE. Aimed, not obscurely, at the King. Cf. p. 123, where the spear that slew Ketil was clearly meant for his master.

20 This 'banning' of Egil's amounts to a serious *nið* or 'Scorn' against the King himself; cf. special note, p. 249 on 'Scorn-pole'. Cf. also the *Waterdale Saga*, ch. 33: "But if any come not [to holm, when challenged], then shall be raised a Scorn (nið) against them, with this formular: That he shall be every man's dastard (níðingr), and be never in the fellowship of good men, and have the anger of the Gods and the name of truce-dastard".

21 STAVE. The first two couplets are stuffed with consonances and playings on the word *arfi* (heir):

> Erfinge ræþr arfe
> arfljúgr fyr mér svarfa,
> mœtek hans ok heitom
> hóton, Þyrnefótar.

The last two couplets are corrupt and of doubtful meaning. I have been driven to a somewhat free rendering. 'Stock's sorrows syth'd of earth' makes no sense: neither does the original (though Ernst A. Kock, *op. cit.* in note on p. 304, has amended the text and got some meaning from it). 'Earth-dweller's bed', i.e. the worm's bed (the Worm Fafnir) —*gold*.

22 HOUSE-THING (húsþing). Cf. Engl. 'husting'. A council summoned from the immediate followers of a king or earl, usually to deal with some matter of immediate urgency.

23 STEERED HER HIMSELF. The whole sentence reads, *hann sagði leið fyrir honungs skipinu, en hann stýrði sjálfr.* F.J. is probably right in saying, "*en hann*, i.e. King Eric". In the sequel (same page) Ketil was steering, and Egil mistook him for the King, probably both because of the likeness and because it was known that the King usually steered himself.

24 RUDDER...LOOPS. *Stýristöng*, which I have translated 'rudder', is properly 'rudder-pole *or* rudder-stave'. We say 'starboard' (Icel. stjórnborði) of the right-hand side of a ship because that was where the rudder was in the viking time. See Hkr. IV, 445 for a full and interesting note on rudders. *Loops* (hamla) are used for rowlocks in Norway and Iceland (and elsewhere) to-day.

25 STAVE (1). 'Thunder-lord...heart' (þrymrǫgner vígelds þrótt-harþr)—*Eric.* 'Wound-salmon' (sárlax)—a *sword*: the 'Sýr' (a by-name of Freyja) of that—a *Valkyrie*: the 'quivering thorn' (bifþorn) of the V.—*a spear*.

26 STAVE (2). Lit. 'So should the Gods pay him for robbing of my fee: Let the Binders sweep the king from the land: wroth be the Rulers, and Odin. Let the oppressor (lit. mower) of the folk flee from the lands, O Land's-God. Frey and Niord, loathe Ye the people's plague who hurteth the holy places'. This curse was no doubt held to have had its due effect next year, when Eric had to flee from Norway (p. 134).

CHAPTER LVII

1 BARE GUNNHILD A SON. Harald Greycloak, King of Norway, 961–970. He was fostered by Arinbiorn, who followed him into exile about 955 (ch. LXIX) and was his right-hand man till their death together at the Neck in the Limfirth.

2 ROGNVALD. Elsewhere only mentioned in the list of the sons of Eric Bloodaxe in *Flateyjarbók.* F.J. thinks this is because he died so young. Some reject the whole story about Rognvald.

3 THE BEACONS (Vitar). F.J. says they are an unidentified group of skerries. *Aldi* he identifies with the mod. island of Alden in the Firdafylke.

4 STAVE. 'When young.' He is now about 32 or 33.

5 CARAVEL (karfi). See note on 'Long-ship', p. 254.

6 A BEAR. Common enough in Norway in ancient times, and fairly common in certain parts (e.g. in Jostedal) comparatively recently, but now rare. See the stories about bears in Mr Cecil Slingsby's *Norway, the Northern Playground*, ch. xx.

7 NEBS OF WOOD (skógarnef). I.e. straggling 'noses' of wood and undergrowth jutting out from the main forest.

8 BUSINESS. They asked *hvat hann hefði syslat*. *Sysla* is the regular word for a job or piece of business. Its use here has the characteristic grim humour of *meiosis*.

9 STAVE. 'Bough...ling-firth mackerel' (lyngs fjarþǫlna ljósheims bǫrr), 'ling's firth'—*land*; 'mackerel' (ölun) of that—a serpent or *worm*; the 'shining home' (ljósheim) of that—*gold*; the 'bough of gold'—a *man*. 'Bedfellow of Bor's Son' (beþja Bors niþjar), i.e. of Odin: His 'bedfellow'—the *earth*. 'I have given the earth a bloody head-dress.'

10 ALL WRATHFUL (allreiðr). The berserk rage, probably. The violence of this scene is immeasurably enhanced by the tense quietude of the narrative.

11 STAVE. 'War-flame' (vígleiptr)—*sword*. 'Saplings of ocean-moon' (þollar lagar mána), i.e. of 'ocean-brightness', i.e. of *gold* (cf. the familiar Rheingold story, which is based on the far older Volsung story, *C.P.B.* vol. I, p. 31)—*men*.

12 SCORN-POLE (níðstöng). See special note, p. 249.

13 STAVE. See special note, p. 247.

CHAPTER LVIII

1 This little conversation between father and son is highly illuminating and diverting to the onlooker.

2 SKALLAGRIM'S DEATH. Cf. the similar incident in Eb. 33, of Arnkel's burial of his wicked old father, Thorolf Haltfoot: "Now Arnkel went into the fire-hall, and so up along it behind the seat at Thorolf's back, and bade all beware of facing him before lyke-help was given to him. Then Arnkel took Thorolf by the shoulders, and must needs put forth all his strength before he brought him under. After that he swept a cloth about Thorolf's head, and then did to him according to custom. Then he let break down the wall behind him, and brought him out thereby, and then were oxen yoked to a sledge, and thereon was Thorolf laid out, and they drew him up into Thorswater-dale". Magnússon in his note on this (Eb. p. 282) says, "It would seem that in those times it was customary to teach him who was supposed to be likely to walk again a way to the house which did not lead to the door of it, but to the obstructing wall—a custom which seems to trace its origin to the imagination that ghosts being brainless were devoid of initiative". Skallagrim's grave was excavated some years ago by the late Síra Einarr Friðgeirsson, the learned parson at Borg. No human remains were found (they had probably been shifted to consecrated ground after the change of faith), but horses' bones and other relics were dug up, and Síra Einarr showed me a tooth which no doubt belonged to Skallagrim's horse, who, as the saga tells us, was buried with him.

CHAPTER LIX

1 HAKON ATHELSTANE'S-FOSTERLING. Also called Hakon the Good, a name which he seems to have deserved: reigned 934–60. He was privately a christian, and tried to christen Norway, but without success (Hak. 15–20). For the story of his birth and fostering with King Athelstane, see Har. Hfr. 40–43. He fell, *æt. circ.* 40, in the moment of victory, at the battle of Fitiar in Stord.

2 ERIC BLOODAXE IN NORTHUMBERLAND. There is disagreement as to the date of Eric's rule in Northumberland, and some will have it not earlier than 948. There are reasons (see note, p. 280 on 'Winaheath') for putting Egil's visit to York in 937. That Eric ruled in York, and that the events here narrated are substantially historic, there is no reason to doubt.

3 FASHION OF A LITTLE MAN. Icel. 'lítilmannligt'.

4 GARTH. See note, p. 267.

5 STAVE. 'Rope-core of Harald's hard-spun line' (snarþátt Haralds áttar), lit. 'the hard-spun cord of Harald's line' (*ætt*—family).

6 NIGHT-SLAYINGS ARE MURTHERS (náttvíg eru morðvíg). Cf. *D.* s.v. *morð*, where it is explained that in ancient times *murder* (morð) and manslaying (víg) were distinguished. To slay a man and give notice of the fact forthwith was *víg*, and might (if those in charge of the resulting blood-feud were willing) be atoned for by paying boot. But stealthy and secret killing was murder, and the doer of it became 'morðvargr', 'murder-wolf', and was out of the pale of the law.

7 A MAN TO BE MOCKED AND TEASED (ertingamaðr). From *erta*, 'to taunt, tease, provoke'.

8 BRAGI. F.J. says he is the earliest historic Norse skald we know by name: fl. circ. 800–50. He was Arinbiorn's great-grandfather on the mother's side.

9 SHAPE-CHANGER (hamhleypa). Or 'skin-leaper'; one who leaps from his (or her) own human skin into that of, e.g., a *swallow*. Cf. note on 'Shape-strong', p. 245.

CHAPTER LX

1 HÖFUÐLAUSN. The rush and tumult of this great war-song can hardly be attained by a translation: unless indeed we find a poet to translate it who is, in a manner of speaking, Egil born again. I give the first stave as it reads in the original, with a literal translation, so as to help the reader to form an idea of the metre and movement of the poem and (as one compares a portrait with the sitter) to gather the

principle underlying the present version and the mark it has aimed at
but never fully attained:

Vestr komk of ver,	West came I over sea
en ek Viþres ber	And I bare Vidrir's
munstrandar mar,	Wish-strand's ocean:
svá's mítt of far;	So is my (way) of faring;
drók eik á flot	Drew I oak afloat
viþ ísabrot,	With the breaking of the ice;
hlóþk mærþar hlut	Loaded I with booty of praise
munknarrar skut.	My wish-ship's keel.

The stave consists of four couplets; within each couplet the lines
rhyme and are also related by alliteration. The structure of the poem
is symmetrical: 16 eight-line staves, like the above, arranged thus:
5 : 2 : 2 : 2 : 5; and 4 four-line verses which, coming in at the divisions
(:), form a changing burden.

St. 1. 'West over sea'; the British Isles were still 'West over sea'
to Icelanders, who still looked at the world with their mind's eye
pointing from Norway. 'God's wish-strand's spray'—*poetry*.

St. 2. 'Odin's drink'—*poetry*.

St. 4. Last four lines:

> Þar heyrþesk þá,
> þaut mækes á
> malmhríþar spá,
> sús mest of lá.

Lit. 'There was heard then the song of the iron-storm, the sword-
river whistled (þaut), which ran most in spate'. *Mestr of liggja* of a
river in spate is idiomatic in Icel. to-day.

St. 5. Last four lines:

> þars í blóþe
> í brimels móþe
> vǫllr of þrumþe
> und véom glumþe.

Lit. 'The field of the seal thundered in wrath under the banners, there
where it wallowed in blood'.

St. 7. Third couplet:

> œxto under
> jǫfra funder.

I have throughout this book translated *jöfurr* 'war-lord'. Its primary
(but very rare) meaning is a 'wild boar': its metaphorical and common
meaning, in poetry, probably arises from kings and lords in early
times wearing boar's-head helms.

St. 8. Second couplet:

> beit bengrefell,
> þat vas blóþrefell.

Blóðrefill is a curious word. It means the point of a sword; query, with original reference to its coming out at the other side of your enemy after a good thrust. (*D.* says, "Does 'refill' here mean a *snake*?") 'The sword-belt's ice' (fetelsvell)—i.e. the *sword*. 'Odin's oaks'—*men*.

St. 9 (*Burden*). Original:

> Þar vas odda at
> ok eggja gnat.
> Orþstír of gat
> Eiríkr at þat.

St. 10. 'Night-hags' horses' (flagþs gote); cf. Thorvald Hialtison's stave on the battle of Fyrisfield where Styrbiorn the Strong fell in 983:

> Fari til Fyrisvallar folka tungls hverr es hungrar,
> verðr at virkis garði vestr kveld-riðo hesta.

'Fare to Fyrisfield whosoever of the moon-folk (i.e. wolves) hungereth: food at the western garth for *night-riders' stallions*' (*C.P.B.* vol. II, p. 62).
Last couplet:

> Traþ nipt Nara
> náttverþ ara.

Lit. 'Nari's sister (i.e. the Goddess Hell) trod the night-meal of eagles'.

St. 12 (*Burden*). Text is obscure in first couplet. I read:

> Kom gnauþar læ
> á Gjálfa skæ.
> Bauþ ulfom hræ
> Eiríkr of sæ.

'Gjalfi', a sea-king; his 'steed'—a *ship*. Last couplet, lit. 'Eric offered wolves carrion by sea'. Sea-fights were commonly fought near enough to land to enable the wolf to enjoy the leavings.

St. 13:

> Lætr snót saka
> sverþ-Freyr vaka,
> en skers Haka
> skíþgarþ braka,
> brusto broddar
> en bito oddar,
> báro hǫrvar
> af bogom ǫrvar.

Lit. 'Frey of the Sword (i.e. *Odin*, God of Battles; or, possibly, by a not uncommon poetic licence, *Eric*) lets wake the Lady of Sakes *or* Quarrels (i.e. the Valkyrie), and lets break the wooden fence (i.e. *bulwark*) of the skerry of Haki (i.e. of the *ship*, Haki being a sea-king)'; etc. This stave and the next bring the battle-picture to its climax, where the rush of imagery, borne up by every technical device of which the metrical form is capable, makes the poetry like a leaping flame.

St. 15 (*Burden*). 'Wound-bees' (unda bý)—*arrows*.

St. 16. The second half of this stave is obscure, and probably corrupt:

> Verpr ábrǫndom
> en jǫforr lǫndom
> heldr hornklofe,
> hann's næstr lofe.

The meaning of *Hornklofi* is conjectural. I have taken it as meaning the raven, and referring to Eric's banner.

St. 17. 'Wristglow' (bógvite)—*gold rings*. 'Hawk-strand'—*the hand*; 'ore' of that—*gold*. 'Frodi's flour' (Fróþa mjǫl), lit. 'meal'; again—*gold*; F.J. quotes the story of Frodi, the Dane-King, and his magic mill.

St. 18. 'Spear-guard' (broddflǫtr)—*shield*. 'Seat of rings'—*hand*. Last two couplets:

> Þróask hér sem hvar,
> hugat mælek þar,
> frétt's austr of mar,
> Eiríks of far.

St. 19. 'Odin's sea'—*poetry*.

St. 20. 'Words' measure', etc. meaning, 'I know when to stop'. 'Hold of cheer' (hlátra ham), lit. 'skin of laughter'—i.e. the *breast*.

CHAPTER LXI

1 STAVE. 'Helm-crag' (hjalma klett)—*head*. 'Lofty-minded son' is Eric: the 'all-wielding' father, Harald Hairfair.

2 STAVE. Hugin is one of Odin's two ravens: the raven's 'rest-day' (várar, pl.) is lit. his 'pledge' or 'peace'—when he is gorged and so perforce rests from his banquet; the 'hastener' (mǫgnoþr, lit. 'one who makes strong with a spell') of that satiety—a *warrior*. The 'hereditary stool of the hat of Ali' (Ála hattar arfstóll), i.e. of the hat of the sea-king, i.e. of the helm—is the *head*. 'Lord of battle-adders' (rógnaþra reginn)—the *King*.

CHAPTER LXII

1 AFTERWARDS CALLED THORASON. See note, p. 260.

CHAPTER LXIII

1 A STONE BEYOND THY STRENGTH. Icel.: *at þú, Egill, munir hafa kastat steini um megn þér.*

CHAPTER LXIV

1 HOD...BLINDHEIM. F.J. notes this as one of the very few inaccuracies of *Egla* in Norse topography: Blindheim is not in fact in the island of Hod but in the island of Vigr.

2 STAVE. 'Land-hankerer' (landbeiþoþr); he who seeks or desires the land (? Norway)—*King Eric.*
Second couplet:

> Syngrat gaukr, ef glamma
> gamm veit of sik þramma.

Lit. 'Sings not cuckoo if he knows vulture of yelping (*glamma*—properly a tinkling, or noise generally) lumbers along (þramma; cf. *D.*) after him'. Another reading is 'sigrat' (*sinks* not) for 'syngrat', meaning the cuckoo does not settle. F.J. remarks, with justice, that it is very difficult to understand, but seems to embody a proverb. 'Bear of eagle's stall-stone' (arnstalls sjǫtolbjǫrn), a pun on Arinbiorn's name—'Biorn of the Hearth'. The text of the last couplet is obscure and possibly corrupt, but the meaning is fairly clear.

3 This little episode is related in the characteristic method of the sagas: appearances are noted in their order as they appear to the onlooker, without explanation or comment, and (as in real life) their significance is revealed only when the different threads are suddenly gathered together and the fact drawn up to daylight, as here in Gyda's speech to E. on the following page. The dramatic effect is very great. It demands attention, it is true, on the part of the reader or listener; but some will think it reasonable, in the presence of a masterpiece, that they should be required to attend.

4 LJOT THE PALE. Ljótr ('Ugly') is not uncommon as a proper name, and more particularly as a name of a *berserk*. Cf. the late and unreliable *Svarfdæla Saga*, where a berserk is called Ljot the Pale. Some critics have on this ground thrown doubt on the present episode, but the natural inference is that *Svarfdæla* borrowed from *Egla.*

5 HOLMGANG (hólmganga). Lit. 'a walking on the holm, *or* isle'; ('Tybalt, you rat-catcher, will you walk?'): the Northern variety of the wager of battle found in so many early systems of law. The present passage is a *locus classicus* in the subject, as are also ch. LXV, Korm. 10 and 12, and Gunnl. 14. Magnússon in a valuable note (Hkr. IV, pp. 349–51) gives reasons for thinking most of these instances, with their elaborate rules about 'hazelled fields' (the hazel never grew in Iceland), not holmgangs at all; he holds the holmgang proper to have been a purely Icelandic (as distinct from Norse) institution. It took its name

from the 'holm' or islet in the little river Axewater which runs through the Thingfields in Iceland. The right to challenge your opponent in a law-suit to single combat on that little isle dates probably from the foundation of the Althing in 930, and lasted until 1006, when Gunnlaug the Worm-tongue and Hrafn fought. "On the second day after this it was made law in the law-court that, henceforth, all holmgangs should be forbidden; and this was done by the counsel of all the wisest men that were at the Thing; and there, indeed, were all the men of most counsel in all the land. And this was the last holmgang fought in Iceland, this, wherein Gunnlaug and Hrafn fought" (Gunnl. 14).

The preparations for Kormak's fight with Holmgang-Bersi are thus described: "That was the holmgang-law, that there shall be a cloak five ells in the skirt, and loops in the corners; there should there be set pegs with heads on one end; that was named *tjösnir*. He that made it ready should walk to the *tjösnir* so as he might see the heaven betwixt his legs while he held the lobes of his ears, with that formular which since is followed in that blood-offering which is called *tjösnublót*. Three borders shall be round about the cloak, of a foot's breadth. Out from the borders shall be four poles, and that is named *hazels*; that is a hazelled field that so is made. A man shall have three shields, but when they are spent, then shall [the men] go upon the cloak though before they should by chance have left it; then shall they shield themselves with their weapons thenceforth. That one shall hew [sc. the first blow] who was challenged. If one be hurt so that blood come on the cloak, they are not bound to fight longer. If a man step with one foot out beyond the hazels 'fareth he on heel', but 'runneth' if he step with both. His own man shall hold shield before each of them that fight. That one shall pay holm-ransom who is the more wounded: three marks of silver" (Korm. 10).

6 BERSERKS-GANG (berserksgangr). See notes on 'Berserk', p. 244 and 'Shape-strong', p. 245.

7 STAVE. 'Quickener of Gondul's storm': Gondul is a Valkyrie; her storm—*battle*: the quickener or 'whetter' of that—a fighting man, i.e. *Ljot*. There seems to be little point in stating that Ljot 'does blood-offering unto Powers' (blótar bǫnd), unless it is meant as a reproach. This meaning it could only carry if the stave is (as F.J. believes it is) a late (christian) fabrication, and none of Egil's. The 'ring-god' (Æger bauga), Ægir of rings, an open-handed man—and so a *man* simply. 'Eyes all-fey' (alfeigom augom); a 'fey' man is one *death-bound*, fated to die.

8 STAVE. 'Quivering sprout of byrny'—*spear*.

9 STAVE. 'Shield's moon'—*sword*. The last couplet is:

> Kyrrom kappa errenn
> (Kome ǫrn á hræ) jǫrnom.

10 STAVE. That Ljot 'fares somewhat ahead' is said in mockery. 'Flood-fires' flinger'—*man*; (addressed to Fridgeir). 'Treasure-hankerer'; cf. 'woe-hankerer' below; Ljot desires treasure for himself and woe for others. 'Dart-storm's staff' (fleindǫggvar stafr), the staff of the rain (*or* dew) of javelins—a *man*. 'Bald-head' (rotinn skalli), lit. 'rotten bald-pate'; *rotinn* is used especially of a hide where tanning has made the hair fall off (*D.* s.v.). Egil is never tired of his personal peculiarities, his bald pate, black brows, swarthy looks, etc.

11 STAVE. 'Feaster of wolves' (ulfgrenner), lit. 'wolf-battener'. 'Breaker of lowe of sea-loch' (lóns logbrjótanda), 'fire of sea-loch'—*gold*; he who breaks that (i.e. breaks up gold rings and gives the bits among those who have deserved well of him), is the bounteous man—here, *Fridgeir*.

Last couplet:

> jafn vas mér gnýr geira
> gamanleik viþ hal bleikan.

Lit. 'Even with (i.e. equal to) a game of play it was to me, the din of spears with the pale man'.

CHAPTER LXV

1 THE SWORD BIT NOT (beit ekki sverðit). Atli had 'deaved the edge of it'—see note 3 below, on Egil's stave on the subject. Generally on 'not biting', see note, p. 261.

2 BIT ASUNDER HIS WEASAND (beit í sundr í honum barkann). F.J. quotes a parallel from the Franco-Prussian war.

3 STAVE. 'Deaved' (deyfa), i.e. blunted, sc. with his deadly glance. The last couplet—

> jaxlbróþor létk eyþa
> [ek bar sauþ] af nauþom—

is lit. 'I let gag-tooth's brother waste *or* destroy [words in square brackets are corrupt and untranslatable] at need'. 'Gag-tooth' should be properly 'jaw-tooth', a molar: its 'brother', an incisor, or canine.

For the power of a wizard's eye on weapons, cf. Grim Droplaugson's coming to holm with two swords because his foe 'knew how to deave edges' (*Droplaugarsona Saga*, at end). Odin Himself in the old mystical poem *Hávamál* says:

> Edges I deave of Mine adversaries:
> Bite not their weapons, as wands.

CHAPTER LXVI

1 NO FEW WINTERS. I.e. from 938 till 954 (F.J.).

2 THORSTEIN. Youngest, and also the most famous. See below.

CHAPTER LXVII

1 ONUND SJONI. See note, p. 269.

2 YULE (Jól). The great heathen festivity of the winter season, held at Midwinter-night (12th Jan.) for three days. King Hakon Athelstane's-fosterling, who was privately a christian before he dare be so publicly, 'made a law that Yule should be holden the same time as christian men hold it, and that every man at that tide should brew a meal of malt or pay money else, and keep holy tide while Yule lasted' (Hak. 15).

3 STAVE. 'Arinbiorn hath the warding withal of a lord's unpitying might' (Arenbjǫrn of hefr árnat eirarlaust oddvita ríke), lit. 'Arinbiorn withal hath served (F.J. subdued) without pity, *or* without sparing (sc. himself), a leader's might'. The sense is obscure: I have taken it to be that Arinbiorn has had a difficult job between his friend Egil and his liege-lord Eric.

CHAPTER LXVIII

1 Egil's insufferable greed of money is well displayed in this chapter.

2 HARALD ERICSON. Harald Greycloak: see note, p. 286.

CHAPTER LXIX

1 SHIELD-BURG. See note, p. 265.

2 LIMFIRTH...THE NECK. This was to be later the scene of Arinbiorn's death; cf. note, p. 251.

3 BUT IT WAS BY MUCH THE GREATER PART...THAT FOLLOWED ARINBIORN (en hitt var meiri hluti liðs miklu, er fylgði Arinbirni). The Icel. *hitt*, 'that other', is sharply distinctive, and there is no ambiguity (as there is—short of long-winded explanation—in English) as to the meaning, viz. that most of them went with Arinbiorn to Denmark.

4 WITH BLITHENESS AND FRIENDSHIP. It was their last parting.

CHAPTER LXX

1 HIGHWAYMEN. Icel. *stígamenn* (path-men).

2 FOR-SENDING (forsending). 'A sending one to certain death, a dangerous mission' (D. *ad loc.*). For once, I fear I have used an English word of doubtful authority.

3 TO FOLLOW THE KING. Cf. the similar view expressed by Kveldulf, p. 4.

CHAPTER LXXI

1 ARNALD. The sequel gives ground for thinking that this 'friend of ours' was a Mrs Harris.

2 SNOW-SHOES (skíð). Modern Norse *ski*: a word which everyone knows to-day and most people mispronounce.

3 CURDS (skyr). See note, p. 274.

4 STAVE. 'Hild of Hornés' (Hildr horna), the Hild (a Goddess) of the drinking-horns—i.e. a *woman*.

5 THAT THEY SHOULD SWIFTLY DRINK. The reader must keep constantly in mind (as Egil obviously did) the probability that Armod meant to make Egil and his men helpless with drink, and then murder them. There is a Rabelaisian gaiety in the following scene (from here to end of ch.) which, if we will but shake off for the moment our modern squeamishness, is very delightful.

6 STAVE. The first two couplets:

> Títt erom verþ at vátta,
> vætte berk at hættak
> þung til þessar gǫngo,
> þinn, kinnalǫ minne;

of which the literal translation appears to be: 'I am eager to testify to thy victuals; I bear heavy testimony that in this walk [sc. across the floor] I hazarded my cheek-surge'.

7 STAVE. 'Ekkil's...bestrider' (Ekkels eykríþr), lit. 'rider of Ekkil's [a sea-king's] draught-horse', a sailor, and so simply—a *man*. 'Song-god' (bragar Ulle)—a *poet*. 'Horn-mere' (hornasund), lit. 'horn-sound' (sea)—*ale*. 'Froth-mash tarn' (hrosta tjǫrn): *hrosti* is the mash of malt for brewing; cf. *Sonatorrek* (p. 192), where Aegir, the brewer of the Gods, is called 'Judge of the Froth-mash'.

The last couplet has a rousing swing:

> hrosta tjǫrn í horne
> horns, til dags at morne.

8 SLEPT THROUGH THE NIGHT. It is to be presumed, in all the circumstances, that somebody kept watch.

CHAPTER LXXII

1 STAVE. 'Giver of arm-snakes' (ýter armlinns), i.e. of *rings*: a bountiful man (doubtless ironical). 'Terror-eker (ógnar hvesser), 'whetter of terror', warrior—i.e. *Armod*. The last two couplets are very obscure. F.J. interprets them as meaning, 'I hold it unworthy to stand such treatment from this man; still, we will go our ways'— meaning, I suppose, that it was hardly decent not to kill Armod. My own reading is, ' *You* may think you have not been paid properly for the drink you gave me [with double meaning—(*a*) that I should have respected my host, or (*b*) that your proper payment would have been that I should slay you]; still, we will go our ways'.

2 A SICK WOMAN. For the sequel to this little episode, see p. 182. As to Runes, see note, p. 275.

3 STAVE. 'A mirk stave' (myrkvan staf), i.e. an obscure one. 'Leek-linden' (lauka lind), 'lime-tree of the leek'—a *woman*. The leek, or garlic, is used poetically and metaphorically of sleek, taper-formed things, and so of an elegant woman.

CHAPTER LXXIII

1 STAVE. 'Red snicking-knives of Din-God' (roþnom hneiteknífom hjaldrgoþs)—*swords*. F.J. considers this stave decidedly not genuine; partly, it appears, because the estimates submitted are too modest for such a hero as Egil, and partly because it contains late words (e.g. *hneite*) which could not have been used by Egil. He thinks it is merely a fabrication based on Egil's stave on a similar theme on p. 200. *C.P.B.*, on the other hand, who go in general to the extreme in rejecting as spurious the vast bulk of the shorter verses in *Egla*, print this among the few they are disposed to accept as genuine. Those who incline to the *C.P.B.* view can urge that modesty is perhaps as good an argument for as against genuineness: that the late words may have crept in later, and in any case some of the readings are doubtful: and, finally, that the stave has intrinsic merit, and the reference to 'black-browed me' (svartbrúnom mér) is characteristic.

CHAPTER LXXIV

1 MAN-GILDS (manngjöld). Engl. 'weregild'. See note on 'Boot', p. 266.

2 EACH NAMED WOLF. F.J. quotes parallels for this inconvenient practice.

3 SPLASHED THIS UP IN OUR EYES (jós slíku í augu oss upp). Lit. 'sprinkled such-like (things) up in our eyes'.

CHAPTER LXXV

1 FAIRY-BABES (hégómi). Cf. 'All the bugbeares of the night, and terrors and *fairybabes* of tombes', etc. (Burton, *Anat. Mel.* Part 1, Sec. III, Mem. 2, Subs. iii): it is really 'fear-babes', and has in this context exactly the feeling of Icel. *hégómi*, something that is false to the touch or taste, an empty imagining ('leere einbildung', F.J.). Cf. p. 211, where I have translated it as 'vain falsehood'.

2 TO BE PICKED UP LIKE FORFEIT GOODS (uppnæmir). *Uppnæmr* (adj.) means one who can be 'uptaken', taken away, got the better of, brought to heel: then, as a law term, seizable, forfeitable property. It is of course impossible to say whether the technical sense was in Egil's mind: in modern Icel. it has, I believe, entirely vanished, and *uppnæmr* in every-day use means simply 'helpless'.

3 A GREAT FLAT STONE (hellustein mikinn). There is a parallel in the *Waterdale Saga*, ch. 41, for this singular breastplate, which must have been as ponderous to fight in as the armour of Tweedledum and Tweedledee as portrayed by Tenniel.

4 SPAN NEW. Icel. *spánýir*.

CHAPTER LXXVI

1 IN HIS SAGA AND...IN THOSE SONGS. F.J. quotes Hak. 8, "Then went he east-away beyond Gautland and harried there, and gat great tribute from the land", and the half-stave preserved in that chapter from Gutthorm Cinder's *Hakon's Drapa*:

> Shielded by skirt of Odin
> He won scat of the Gautfolk;
> Gold-hewer the all-bounteous
> Won spear-storms in that faring.

2 Egil gave his long-ship to Thorstein partly, no doubt, because he could not take her to Iceland; cf. note on 'Long-ship', p. 254.

CHAPTER LXXVII

1 IRISH THRALLS. These were not uncommon, but there is no sound reason for thinking there was any important admixture of Keltic blood among the Icelanders. Of the 400 landnámamenn, or settlers, it has been estimated that 50 at most came from the Hebrides, Ireland, Caithness, and England. Of those 50 some were vikings who happened to be sojourning in those parts, but some were, no doubt, of mixed blood. Queen Aud, who settled Laxriverdale, was the widow of Olaf the White, Norse King in Dublin: she had Irish thralls. Olaf the Peacock was himself the son of an Irish princess taken in war and bought for a concubine by his father. Certain names, e.g. Kjallakr, Kjartan, Dufþakr, Njáll, betray a Keltic origin. For the murder of Thord Lambison by these Irish thralls, cf. the story of Hiorleif's fate, Landn. 8: "But in the spring he would fain sow. He had but one ox, and he let the thralls drag the plough. But when Hiorleif and his were at the hall, then counselled Dufthak that they [i.e. the thralls] should slay the ox, and say that a bear of the wood had slain it; but then should they set upon Hiorleif and his when they sought for the bear. After that, said they unto Hiorleif these things. But when they fared to seek the bear, and drifted apart in the wood, then slew the thralls every one his man, and murdered them all to an even number with themselves. They fled away with the wives of them and their farmstock and the boat. The thralls fared to those islands that they saw in the sea in the south-west, and made their dwelling there awhile... Ingolf fared west to Hiorleifs-head. And when he saw Hiorleif dead, then spake he: 'Little befitted it here for a good fellow, that thralls should be his bane; and I see that so it betideth unto everyone who will

not do worship'". Ingolf followed the thralls to the Westmen-Isles and slew them all: and place-names were named after them, including the name of the isles themselves—Vestmannaeyjar.

2 LAMBI. For the amusing episode between him and the furious Steinar, see pp. 217–218.

3 GRIM SVERTINGSON. Speaker of the Law 1002–3. Egil in his old age went to live with this son-in-law: there is more of him in ch. LXXXV.

4 SKAPTI THORODDSON. Speaker of the Law 1004–30. He plays a prominent part in Nj. and Grett.

CHAPTER LXXVIII

1 OLAF THE PEACOCK. Comes into several of the sagas, e.g. Ld., in which he plays a big part, and Nj. He was a man of much magnificence and show, and one of the great men in the Western Dales, of royal kin on both sides.

2 VERMUND. Vermund the Slender, son of Thorgrim Kiallakson the Priest, dwelt at Bearhaven on the N. side of the Snaefellsness peninsula. His brother was Slaying Stir, 'very masterful and exceeding in wrongfulness', the father-in-law of Snorri the Priest. Vermund himself was peaceful and respectable; see Eb. *passim*.

3 SLAYING BARDI. The hero of the *Heath-slayings Saga*.

4 THE MEADS (Vellir). There is a farmstead to-day at Hvítárvellir on the south bank where the river Hvítá (Whitewater) opens into Burgfirth. The conditions of wind and tide here are apt to be dangerous precisely in the way described in the saga. I crossed in a heavy open boat from Hvanneyri to Einarsness on an evening of late summer of an unforgettable beauty, at the turn of the tide after a stormy day, when the whole countryside was bathed in the golden light of the low-swinging sun, and the vast ramparts of Skarðsheiði and the Heiðarhorn seemed to be built not of rock but of heavenly topaz and sapphire, because of the sunset glory on their new snows and the blue and amethystine shadows in the gullies. A few weeks later two farm-lads from Hvanneyri were drowned by a cruel accident very like that which cost the life of Bodvar Egilson.

5 SHUT-BED (lokrekkja). These were bedrooms for the heads of the household, made by partitioning off parts of the passage that ran round the hall behind the long benches (cf. p. 133); the way into the 'shut-bed' was by a door opening into the main body of the hall from behind the high seat. Thorkel Foulmouth had his 'deeds of derring do' carved over his shut-bed (Nj. 118). Cf. also Eb. 25, where it is said of Thorbiorn Jaw that, "A lock-bed he had made exceeding strong with beams of timber, but the Bareserks brake that up, so that the naves outside sprang asunder; yet was Stir himself the bane of Thorbiorn Jaw"; and the slaying of Thorgrim the Priest by Gisli Surson, Gisl. 9.

6 NONES (nónskeið). The canonical hour of nones (3 p.m.). This is of course an anachronism.

7 AT FREYJA'S. The old poem *Grimnismál*, st. 13, describing the mansions of the blest, says:

> Folk-vangr es inn níundi, enn þar Freyja ræðr
> sessa kostom í sal:
> halfan val hon kýss hverjan dag,
> enn halfan Óðinn á.

'*Folk-mead* is the ninth, and there Freyja ruleth the choice of seats in the hall. Half the slain She chooseth every day, but half Odin hath.' *C.P.B.* think *halfan val* must mean the one half of mankind—i.e. *women*. This interpretation is supported by this passage in *Egla*, but by no other evidence. *Valr* is usually translated the 'slain', but it is quite possibly connected with *velja*—to *choose*; (*Valkyrja*, a 'chooser of the slain', or 'chooser of the chosen'). If Freyja has half the 'chosen dead' that half may well be women, and *Folk-vangr* Her private Valhalla for ladies.

8 DULSE (söl). "An edible species of seaweed, *Rhodymenia palmata*, having bright red, deeply divided fronds. In some parts applied to *Iridæa edulis*" (*O.E.D.*).

9 SCORE IT ON A ROLLER (rísta á kefli). An anachronism interpolated in the text in the thirteenth century (F.J.).

10 NOTES ON SONATORREK. The *Sonatorrek* was probably composed about 960.

The measure is the same as that of the *Arinbjarnarkviða*: unrhymed alliterative verse of a slower movement than the wind-rushing short rhymed couplets of the *Höfuðlausn*. My rendering has kept the alliterations wherever possible, has aimed at faithfulness to the original, word for word and line by line, but above all has sought to model itself (by ear) on the beat and music of the original. The first stave reads:

> Mjǫk erom tregt
> Tungo at hrœra
> Með loptvétt
> Ljóþpundara.
> Esa nú vænlegt
> Of Viþors þýfe,
> Né hógdrœgt
> Ór hugar fylgsne.

Lit. 'Much is it for me difficult tongue to move with air-weight of lay-balance. 'Tis not now hopeful of Vithor's theft, nor (is it) easy-drawn out of heart's hiding place'.

St. 1. 'Odin's plunder' (Viþors þýfe), the gift of song or skaldship, stolen by Odin from the Giants.

St. 2. 'The fair thing found of Frigg's kinsfolk' (fagnafundr Friggjar niþja), skaldship. *Frigg*, Odin's wife.

St. 3. 'Faultless', etc., referring (cf. st. 24) to the gift of skaldship. (The first four lines are very corrupt, and various guesses have been made at their meaning.)

'Giant's wound-stream' (Jǫtons háls under), lit. 'wounds of the Giant's neck'—the *sea*.

St. 4. 'Maples' (hlyner). Doubtless the big Norse maple, *acer platanoides*.

St. 7. 'Ran' (Rán), Aegir's wife, Goddess of the sea.

St. 8. 'The Ale-smith' (Qlsmiþr), Aegir, the God of the sea, and brewer to the Gods.

'The fierce storm's brother' (hroþa vábrœþr), lit. 'the storm's baleful brother'—*Aegir*.

St. 10. 'The way of bliss' (*munvegr*), i.e. to Valhalla.

St. 13. 'Light wind of the Moon's bride' (byrvind Mána brúþar), a kenning for the *mind*, or *thought*.

'Hild' (Hildr), Goddess of War.

St. 15. 'In Iceland dwelling.' This is paraphrase and guess-work. Egil says *Elgjar galga*, 'the Elk's gallows', which has been explained as a kenning for *ice* (the hunted elk perishing in the ice-hole); hence 'the folk of the elk's gallows' means 'the folk of Iceland'. I agree with *C.P.B.* that this is far-fetched. *C.P.B.* amends *Yggjar galga*, 'Ygg's gallows' (i.e. the Ash, or World-Tree, of Yggdrasill). The text may be corrupt.

St. 16. The rest of the stanza is lost.

St. 18. *C.P.B.* shuffles and divorces the lines of this stanza (in my opinion, most unhappily), and moreover renders the first four lines in a sense which seems to misconceive their whole bearing. The stanza as it stands is very moving and very true in its swift and unprepared change of key: the scornful and self-sufficient pride of the first four lines suddenly softening to the wistful sadness of the last four.

'Where the bee's path beareth' (býskeiþs bœ), lit. 'the dwelling of the bee's race *or* swift course'.

St. 19. 'Judge of the Froth-mash' (fens hrosta hǫfundr)—*Aegir*.

St. 21. 'He which holdeth converse with men' (Gauta spjalle), lit. the 'speller', or converser, with the Goths—*Odin*.

St. 22. 'Lord of Spears...Ruler of Wains...Awarder of Vict'ry' (geirs dróttenn...vagna rúne...sigrhǫfundr)—*Odin*.

St. 23. 'Vilir's Brother...Mimir's Friend' (bróþor Víles...Míms vinr)—*Odin*.

St. 24. 'God of Battles, Great Foe of Fenrir' (Ulfs báge víge vanr), lit. 'Wolf's Foe, to battle wont'; the Foe of the Wolf Fenrir, with whom He must fight at the Twilight of the Gods—*Odin*.

St. 25. 'The Wolf's right Sister—All-Father's Foe's' (Tveggja bága njǫrva nipt), lit. 'Tveggi's foe's near (i.e. proper, not half-) sister', the Goddess of death—*Hell*. Tveggi is probably a name of Odin. The ness is Digraness (modern Borgarnes), where Kveldulf and Skallagrim, and now Egil's sons Bodvar and Gunnar, are laid in howe.

11 FITIAR IN STORD. See the account of this great battle in Hkr. (Hak. 28–32), where there is also a translation (but, like all Morris's translations of skaldic poetry, unsatisfactorily smooth and 'literary') of Eyvind Skaldspiller's *Hákonarmál*, with its grand overture:

Göndul ok Skögul sendi Gauta-Týr
at kjósa of konunga:
hverr Yngva ættar skyldi með Óðni fara
í Valhöll at vesa.

'Gondul and Skogul the Goths'-God sent to choose of the kings'; the Valkyries of the God of Hosts halting their steeds beside the dying but victorious king, to summon him home.

12 NOTES ON ARINBJARNARKVIÐA. Unluckily the text of this third great poem of Egil's is corrupt and mutilated.

The measure is the measure of the *Sonatorrek*. The first two staves say in effect, 'I am a proud man, and I speak my mind'. St. 3–10 recount the episode of the *Höfuðlausn* in York. St. 11 is almost lost. The rest is praise of Arinbjorn's nobility, truth, and generosity, ending in the last stave with the proud Horatian theme, "Exegi monumentum ære perennius".

St. 3. 'The Hersir'—*Arinbiorn*.

St. 5. The grandeur of this justifies quotation:

Vasa tunglskin
tryggt at líta
né ógnlaust
Eiríks bráa,
þás ormfránn
ennemáne
skein allvalds
œgegeislom.

St. 6. 'Bolster-hire' (bolstrverþr), the price of a night's lodging, paid in this case in the form of the *Höfuðlausn*. 'Him that is make of the fish of the wildwood' (maka hœings markar), lit. 'make *or* equal of the forest-trout', i.e. of the worm or serpent—*Odin* (from a story in Ed. of His becoming a snake and in that form discovering the art of poesy). 'Ygg's cup'—*skaldship* (Ygg, a by-name of Odin).

St. 7. 'Knob of hats' (hattar staup). Egil is never tired of this theme.

St. 8. 'Noddle', Icel. *tira*, which F. J. says is ἅπ. λεγ. of unknown meaning; query, 'head' or 'gift'. Last two couplets:

> ok sá muþr
> es mína bar
> Hǫfoþlausn
> fyr hilmes kné.

St. 10. 'Of kempés foremost' (knía fremstr), i.e. 'of champions'; for 'kempe' or 'kempery-man', see the border ballads *passim*.

St. 13. 'Offspring of Hersirs'—*Arinbiorn*.

St. 15. 'Bear of the Table of Birches' Dread' (bjǫrn bjóþa birkes ótta). An elaborate pun on his friend's name—another unfailing attraction to the poet. 'Birches' dread' is *fire*; the 'table' of that, the *hearth* (Icel. arinn); 'Hearth-bear', 'Arinn-björn'.

St. 16. 'Bear of the Stone' (Grjótbjǫrn); the same joke.

St. 17. The first two couplets are corrupt. The text I have taken reads as follows:

> En Hróalds
> at hǫfoþbaþme
> auþs iþgnótt
> at alnom sifjar.

'Hroald's head-stem' (cf. 'Kings' head-stem' in the drapa on Athelstane, see note, p. 283), the head of the family sprung from Earl Hroald, Arinbiorn's grandfather. 'The wind-bowl's wide bottom', that bowl whose brim is the horizon, and its contents the land we dwell in.

St. 18. The text is again obscure. The authority I have followed reads the first couplet:

> Hann drógseil
> of eiga gat,

filling up with the word 'eiga' the lacuna in F.J.'s text. 'Draw-rope unto hearing-baskets', a cord to draw men's *ears* to hearken to him. 'Vethorm' F.J. thinks may be an unknown friend of Arinbiorn's; others say it means 'one who spares the temples', i.e. a god-fearing man. In my translation I have not ventured to judge between these interpretations. 'Weaklings' defender' (veklinga tøs). *Tøs* is a kind of axe or hatchet always kept at hand and used daily.

St. 19. The idea in the last two couplets seems to be: Bountiful men are far to seek, and it is a weary way from one such house till you find another such; and it is not every bountiful man who can be all things to all men and be loved of all sorts and conditions of men, as Arinbiorn is.

St. 20. 'Long-built bedstead-ship' (legvers lǫngom knerre)—a curious kenning for a *house*. 'Dwelling-stead of spear'—*hand*.

St. 21. 'He who dwells in the Firths', Arinbiorn, who was lord of the Firthfolk. 'Draupnir's scions' (Draupnes niþja); Odin's ring, named Draupnir, gave birth in one night to eight others each as heavy as itself (F.J., quoting Ed.). This stave is simply a set of variations on the thought of the bountiful man smashing up his bits of gold and flinging them as largesse among his friends and followers.

St. 22. Something is lost here.

St. 23. 'The mews'-path, much beridden of Rokkvi's steed' (máskeiþ ramriþen Rǫkkva stóþe)—the *sea*. (Rokkvi is a sea-king.)

St. 24. This is the original:

> Vask árvakr,
> bark orþ saman
> meþ málþjóns
> morgenverkom,
> hlóþk lofkǫst
> þanns lenge stendr
> óbrotgjarn
> í bragar túne.

The 'servant of speech' is the *tongue*. 'Bragi's mead', the *tún*, or home-mead, of 'Bragr', which doubtless here means of 'poetry' (cf. *D.* s.v. *bragr*).

13 EINAR JINGLE-SCALE (Einarr Skálaglamm). Our saga is the chief authority for the life of this famous skald of Earl Hakon's. His brother Osvif's daughter was Gudrun of Laxriverdale, the heroine of *Laxdæla*. His most famous poem was 'Gold-lack' (*Vellekla*), mentioned on p. 201, a drapa on Earl Hakon quoted in Ed. and also in Hkr. (H. Gr. 6, 15; O.T. 16, 18, 26, 28, 50). He was drowned on Einar's-skerry in Broadfirth (Landn.). See the note on him and his work, *C.P.B.* vol. II, pp. 41–3.

14 OSVIF THE WISE. See note 13 above, on Einar Jingle-scale.

15 STAVE. The last couplet has been variously interpreted. I read 'of' instead of 'af', following Ernst A. Kock ("Notationes Norrænæ", *Lunds Universitets Årsskrift*)—

> létk of emblo aske
> elde valbasta kastat.

Kock says (*loc. cit.*) that 'to let cast the fire of [valbasta] over Embla's ash' = 'to let the glittering of a sword stand over a man'. Embla is the first woman, according to Eddic mythology: her 'Ash-tree' is a man. See also the stave on p. 175 and note thereon, p. 297.

16 EARL HAKON SIGURDSON. See special note, p. 250.

17 KING HARALD ERICSON. As to these events, see note on Earl Hakon, p. 251.

18 Stave. One of the finest of Egil's staves.

> Þverra nú þeirs þverþo
> þingbirtingar Ingva
> (hvar skalk manna mildra)
> máreitar dag (leita?)
> þeir es hauks fyr handan
> háfjǫll digolsnjáve
> jarþar gjǫrþ viþ orþom
> eyneglþa mér heglþo.

'Mew-field'—the *sea*. The 'day', or glitter, of that—*silver*. Minishers of silver: people who (like Arinbiorn) are always giving it away. 'Brighteners of Ingvi's [a sea-king] thing', ornaments of battle—*warriors*. 'Hawk's high-fell'—the *hand* (that the hawk sits on). 'Limbeck's snow', snow of the crucible, i.e. *silver*. 'Earth's girdle,' the sea: that 'island-nailed with words'—*poetry*. This seems to be the meaning: that his sea of song which, like a jewelled girdle with gem-like words for islands, encompassed the earth, brought from these bounteous patrons a snow-storm of refined silver, falling in showers on his hand, that lofty seat of falcons. There are few verses where the magnificence of poetic imagery which inspires what may at first appear the cold conceits of skaldic verse, can better be studied. The piling up, in this particular stave, of sublime and gorgeous metaphors, combined with the severity and concentration of the verse-form, has an effect comparable to great chords of music, e.g. those which usher in the tremendous *Maestoso* of Beethoven's Op. 111.

19 Gold-lack. See note on Einar Jingle-scale, p. 304.

20 Stave. 'Ale of Odin' (veig Váfaþar), lit. 'drink of Váfuðr', (a by-name of Odin)—*poesy*. 'Captain' (virþa vǫrþr), lit. 'Warden of the *virðar* or king's men', i.e. *Earl Hakon*. 'That sits o'er earth', i.e. rules the land; cf. the similar phrase in Egil's stave recited before King Eric in York, p. 137, and in *Arinbjarnarkviða*, p. 195.

21 Stave. 'That earl', i.e. *Sigvaldi*. 'Twi-row'd' (borþróenn), with oars on both sides. 'Ring-shielded' (baugskjǫldr), i.e. with a ring painted on his shield. 'Drop hand with me' (drepr viþ mér hendc), i.e. drive me away, cast me off. 'Wound-serpent' (sárlinnr)—*sword*; the 'swayer' (sveiger) of that—a *warrior*; here, *Sigvaldi*. 'Endil's snow-shoe' (Endels ǫndorr)—a *ship* (Endil, a sea-king).

Internal evidence dates this stave shortly before the great sea-fight of Hiorungwick, circ. 986, when the Jomsburg vikings came north with a great fleet to wrest Norway from Earl Hakon, but were defeated by him and his sons. Earl Sigvaldi, who was then captain of the Jomsburgers, fled with all his own ships when the day was in the balance; other lords of Jomsburg, e.g. Bui the Thick, fell in the battle, and others were laid hand on and hewn down in cold blood: see the whole story in Hkr. (O.T. 38–47), and in more detail in the *Jómsvíkinga Saga*, which however is not available in English.

22 DRAWN UPON WITH TALES OF OLD. Cf. Achilles's shield.

23 AND SLAY HIM. Said, of course, not 'with a sad brow', but in jest.

24 STAVE. 'Glittering fence of ships' (ljósgarþ barþa)—*shields* were hung on the gunwale side by side; cf. the Bayeux tapestry. The 'treasure-sender' (hoddsender) is Einar Jingle-scale. 'Gylfi's land'— the *sea* (G. a sea-king); the 'stallion' (glaumr) of that—a *ship*; the ship of the 'Earth-born' (i.e. of the *dwarf*) is *poesy*.

25 WHEY-VAT (sýruker). Such as can be seen at any farmhouse in Iceland to-day. At the burning of Flugumyri nearly 300 years later, Gizur saved his life by hiding in the whey-vat and actually had to put aside gently with his hands, to prevent their piercing his belly, the spears of his enemies who were prodding in the dark to find if anyone was lurking there (*Sturlunga Saga*: this scene is translated by W. P. Ker, *Epic and Romance*, p. 259 ff.).

CHAPTER LXXIX

1 EGIL LOVED HIM LITTLE. Presumably because he thought him a milksop. He seems to have thought better of him after the affair with Steinar (ch. LXXX ff.).

2 HILL OF LAWS (lögberg). "Here, on the highest peak of the rock, on the Lögberg properly so called, formal notices of trials, and proclamations on matters of public interest, were uttered by word of mouth" (Dasent, Nj. vol. I, p. cxxviii). The exact site of the Lögberg is in dispute.

3 STAVE. First couplet seems to mean, 'I had no heir that was any great use to me'. 'Water-horse's bestrider' (vatna viggrípande), seaman, man—*Thorstein*. 'They that own the sea-sleighs' (hafskípa hljótendr'), lit. 'the allottees *or* conquerors of the sea-skis'; i.e. vikings, and so simply—*men*. The piling of stones is, of course, laying in howe.

4 GUNNAR HLIFARSON. For more of him, see Hen-Th. *passim.*

5 OLAF FEILAN. Grandson of Queen Aud, with whom he came to Iceland about 892 and from whom he inherited the family seat of Hvamm. See note on Thord the Yeller, p. 269.

6 THORD THE YELLER. See note, p. 269.

7 ODD-A-TONGUE. A famous lord in the west country, dwelt at Broadlairstead in Reekdale of Burgfirth. He plays a large part in Hen-Th., which says (ch. 1) that "he was not held for a man of fair dealings". For more of him, see ch. LXXXI ff.

8 DIED ASGERD. The power of the saga style is nowhere more surprisingly shown than in the little passages like this. The pathos and beauty of the plain, measured statement ('A little after...that were then alive') touch one as gentians do, seen suddenly on the naked mountain-side; yet there is no rhetoric or appeal to sentiment, simply the succession of relevant facts.

9 TARGE-DRAPA (Berudrápa). The rest of the poem is lost.

10 STAVE. 'King's thane' (þegn konungs), Thorstein Thorason. 'The altar's falling-tresséd Friend' (fallhadds vinr stalla)—*Odin*; His 'force *or* waterfall'—*poesy*. 'Hordland' (trǫþ Hǫrþa), lit. 'that which is trod by Hords'—*Hordaland*. 'Crop of eagle's chaps *or* beak' (arnar kjapta ǫrþ)—*poesy*: from the story (Ed. p. 117) of Odin's stealing of Suttung's mead and flying off with it to Asgard in eagle's-shape, and "spitting it out" into the casks of the Gods, "but Suttung's mead gave Odin to the Aesir and to those men who have wit to use it". The last two lines are corrupt: the 'Raven' is no doubt a ship, and her 'steerer' Thorstein Thorason.

11 HELGA THE FAIR. The heroine of Gunnl.

CHAPTER LXXX

1 SNAEFELLSTRAND. The south coast of the Snaefellsness peninsula. (Cf. the curious New Zealand place-name 'Snufflenose', which is obviously 'Snæfellsnes' corrupted by foreigners who did not understand its meaning.)

2 KORMAK. See his Saga, one of the oldest; Collingwood's translation (the only one in English) has very great merits: the more the pity that it should be unwarrantably free and padded out, so as to give a reader no inkling, with its mask of lady-like smoothness, of the rough old features of its original. Kormak probably had Irish blood in his veins; his life-story hangs mainly on his love for Steingerd and his holmgangs with her successive husbands; of his poems addressed to her *C.P.B.* says, "were they perfect, they would probably be the finest of all Northern classic love-poetry". Steinar plays some part in Kormak's saga.

3 THE CATTLE WOULD GO WHERE IT LIKED. A pretty quarrel: "Cursed be he that removeth his neighbour's landmark".

4 INGS (engjar). The same word, commonly used of meadows to-day in the north country, e.g. in Yorkshire.

5 WALL OF THE HOME-MEAD (túngarðr). *Tún* is used in Iceland to-day, as it was in the saga-time, of the green cultivated field surrounding the home buildings.

6 LITTLE AT STAKE WHERE I AM (lítlu til verja, þar sem ek em). Meaning, it will not be any great loss to Steinar if Thrand should unluckily be slain.

CHAPTER LXXXI

1 HAVE NIGHT-QUARTERS UNDER MINE AXE (eiga náttból undir öxi minni). Cf. *Reykdæla* 12, where Vemund Kogur had set on a foolish fellow, on promise of free winter-quarters, to put a public shame upon Steingrim of Kropp by smiting him with a boiled sheep's head, and Steingrim avenged it by slaying his assailant, 'and gave him winter-quarters there and then, and saved Vemund the trouble'.

2 GOOD LUCK (hamingja). See note, p. 257.

3 A magnificent conversation between Steinar and Thorstein.

4 EINAR OF STAFFHOLT. Also mentioned in Landn.

5 REEKDALE. See note, p. 272.

6 THRALL-GILD. This law is also quoted in Eb. 43: see that and the following chapter for the famous bringing home of the thrall-gild by Steinthor of Ere, which led to the battle of Swanfirth between the men of Ere on the one side and Snorri the Priest and his turbulent foster-brethren on the other.

7 THE NESSES (Nes). I.e. the countryside bordering on the S. and S.E. of Faxa Flow.

8 Egil's hard common-sense and Onund's sentimentality are finely contrasted.

9 IN SADNESS (af alvöru). In the Shakespearean sense: *alvara*, 'earnestness, seriousness'.

10 FIGHTING HORSES (kapalhestar). Horse-fighting was a recognized sport which, even more than the ball-play, was apt to lead to bloodshed. Cf. Nj. 57–8. "Then the horses ran at one another, and bit each other long, so that there was no need for anyone to touch them, and that was the greatest sport" (*ibid.* 58). The good little Iceland horses of to-day are spared such hateful treatment.

11 FROM UNDER THE TONGUE-ROOTS OF ODD (undir tungurótu Odds). Meaning he will not take orders from Odd as to what he (Onund) proposes to say on the subject.

12 IN THY TEETH (í fangi þér). Lit. 'in thy *catch* (sc. of fish)', or 'in thine *arms* (i.e. that with which one clasps or embraces)'; *D.* s.v.

13 FARED THE COURTS OUT (fóru dómar út). I.e. the courts *opened*. The judges went out in a body in procession and took their seats (*D.* p. 101).

CHAPTER LXXXII

1 EGIL'S AWARD. This is one of the key passages for Egil's character. It repays, and will bear, study.

2 SOMETHING ASKEW. Icel. 'heldr skökk'.

3 THE HONOUR THEY DESERVED (skapnaðar-virðing). Said, of course, in irony.

CHAPTER LXXXIII

1 AN OUTLANDER (útlendr). From his name, Irish.

2 WINTER-ROAD (vetrgata). A road through marshes, passable only in winter, when the ground is frozen.

3 WHY MUST HE BE SO SET ON MEETING ME? 'He' is, of course, Olvald, mentioned in the next sentence. Thorstein's purpose is to put his men off the scent, so that he can avoid a meeting with Steinar without appearing to be afraid of him.

CHAPTER LXXXIV

1 THORGEIR. Probably the grandson of Thorgeir Lambi and of Thordis, Yngvar's daughter, from Alptaness.

2 HIS EASTMAN (austmaðr hans). I.e. his Norse guest. Norse chapmen trading to Iceland were commonly called 'eastmen'. Powerful men generally took them in as guests; cf. Eb. 18, Nj. 28, 148.

3 THORSTEIN THE WHITE (Þorsteinn hvíti). Thorstein was 'of all men the fairest to look on, white of hair' (p. 202). But in Steinar's mouth the word carries the alternative meaning of white-livered, milksop, white with fear: 'Thorstein pap-face'. I can find no English counterpart for it.

4 SKRYMIR. Steinar used this sword in his fight with Holmgang-Bersi: it "was never fouled, and no mishap followed it" (Korm. 12); afterwards he gave it to his nephew Kormak, who seems to have wielded it in his last battle (*ibid.* 27).

5 LAMBI. A charming episode, and most unexpectedly bloodless.

6 WIND-SHEATH (vindskeið). From *vinda*, 'to wind'. There was a gabled porch over the door, and the two boards forming the edges were fitted together crosswise at the top and carved into the likeness of serpents' tails intertwined, the heads being at the eaves.

7 STAVE. Last couplet, lit. 'Blund may not (has not the power to) bind himself from bale (i.e. abstain from misbehaving himself); I wonder at such things'.

8 A MAN OF NO FOXISH TRICKS (maðr órefjusamr). 'Refjur', f. pl., 'cheats, tricks'; from *refr*, 'a fox'.

CHAPTER LXXXV

1 STAVE. Lit. 'The tottering have I of a hobbled horse: in woeful peril of a fall am I on my bald pate: soft is for me leg-berg's borer: and hearing is at an end'. *Þorrin*, 'drained, ebbed out, waned, ceased'. F.J. thinks *bergifótar borr* means the 'tongue'; *D.* (s.v. *borr*) interprets it *ad loc.* as "metaphorically the *pipe* of a marrow-bone". The real

meaning is, no doubt, that given by Sveinbjörn Egilsson (*Lex. Poet.*) and by *C.P.B.* vol. II, p. 573 (which quotes a parallel from *Piers Plowman*, Pass. xx, on his old age): an interpretation which is borne out by the context.

2 STAVE. 'Spear-care's goddess': that which takes care of the spear is the whet-stone: hence, a stone in general; the goddess of a *hearth-stone*—a *woman*. 'Words of the captain of Hamdir's spear', i.e. gold. Cf. *Hamðismál* (*C.P.B.* vol. I, p. 53 ff.); Hamdir and Sorli avenged their sister Swanhild's murder on Jormunrek, King of the Goths, by hewing off his hands and feet, but the king's men stoned them to death. The spear that slew Hamdir, therefore, is a *stone*; the 'prince' or 'captain' (gramr) of that—a *giant*; the 'words' of the giant—*gold* (see the story in Ed. pp. 112–13).

3 OVER-DEAFLIKE (ofdaufligt). A tragic echo from his youth; for it can hardly be accidental that the same words are in his mouth here in his grievous old age that were used (p. 80) on the eve of the first violent clash, two generations ago, between his fierce and headstrong youth and the might of Eric and Gunnhild.

4 STAVE. This exquisite little epigram, the last of Egil's verses that survives, reads in the original as follows:

Langt þykke mér,
likk einn saman
karl afgamall
firr konungs vǫrnom;
eigom ekkjor
allkaldar tvær,
en þær konor
þurfo blossa.

The pun in the last half rests on the double meaning of *hæll*, (1) heel, (2) widow. Lit. 'I have two widows (*ekkja*, the ordinary word, suggesting to the hearer the synonym *hæll* which commonly means *heel*) all cold, and those women need warmth'.

CHAPTER LXXXVI

1 MASS-PRIEST (prestr). As distinct from priest (goði), which of course has no christian signification or connexion.

CHAPTER LXXXVII

1 SKULI. Cf. O.T. 114, on the battle of Svold: "So saith Skuli Thorsteinson, who was with Earl Eric that day:

The Frisian's foe I followed,
And Sigvaldi; young gat I
Life-gain, where spears were singing
(Old now do people find me).

Where I bore reddened wound-leek
To the mote against the meeter
Of mail-Thing in the helm-din
Off Svold-mouth in the south-land".

The first lines may mean that that Skuli followed Earl Sigvaldi and
the Jomsburg vikings in their fatal battle against Earl Hakon in
Hiorungwick. Earl Eric, the son of the great Earl Hakon (on whom
see note, p. 250), avenged his father in the great sea-fight off Svold
where he, with the help of the kings of Denmark (Svein Twi-beard)
and Sweden, defeated and slew King Olaf Tryggvison: see the whole
story in Hkr. (O.T. 106–22).

The quiet ending, retrospective, dying away like falling embers,
surveying the line of the Myresmen in their generations dead and gone,
falls with the true saga cadence of 'Tout passe'. Cf. the greatest of
such endings: that of *Njála*, with the reconciliation of Flosi and Kari,
Nj. 158.

INDEX

The Icelandic word, where it differs in spelling from the word used in the translation, is given immediately after it in brackets: e.g. ODIN (Óðinn).

In references to the Introduction, to the Notes, to the Terminal Essay, etc., the printing of a page-number in *italics* indicates that that is the main reference to the matter in question.

HALLSTEIN (Hallsteinn): s. of Earl Atli the Slender 2

HALLVARD HARDFARER (Hallvarðr harðfari): and his brother Sigtrygg Sharp-farer, men of the Wick, instruments of K. Harald Hairfair where hazardous deeds were to be done, such as the taking off of men; sent by the K. to take Thorolf Kveldulfson's cheaping-ship from Thorgils the Yeller 32–3; their house robbed and burned for this by Thorolf 35; obtain the K.'s leave to take Th.'s life for this 37; the K.'s sarcasm on their chances against Th. 38; their slow journey north gives warning and causes a war-rush of the folk of Halogaland in support of Th.; they come too late and are laughed at 41; sent by K. Harald east to the Wick to bring home the sons of Duke Gutthorm 50–1; waylaid and slain by Kveldulf and Skallagrim at the mouth of the Sogn Firth 52; Sk.'s ditty on their slaying 53

HALOGALAND (Hálogaland): the northernmost folkland of Norw., mod. Helgeland 3; 9; 11; 15; 18–21; 25; 29; 31; 42; 43

HÁLS: see the Neck

HAMINGJA: see Luck

HAMRAMMR: see Shape-strong

HARALD GORMSON (Haraldr Gormsson): King of the Danes 90; makes Eyvind Braggart warder of his land against vikings 96. 249, 250, 251, 254, 277

HARALD GREYCLOAK (gráfeldr): King of Norway; s. of K. Eric Bloodaxe and Q. Gunnhild 125; fostered by Arinbiorn the Hersir 134, 163; A. joins him in Denmark 166; takes kingdom 194; betrayed and slain in battle against Earl Hakon at the Neck in the Limfirth 200. 251, 286

HARALD HAIRFAIR (hárfagri): King of Norway; takes heritage after his f., K. Halfdan the Black, and swears not to let cut nor comb his hair till he is sole K. over all Norway; called Harald Shockhead (H. lúfa); conquers the Uplands, Thrandheim, Naumdale, Halogaland, Northmere and Raumsdale 3; Kveldulf thinks he has 'a load of luck' 4; by a great victory off Solskel conquers Southmere; sets Earl Rognvald over Mere and Raums-dale; makes Oliver Hnufa his skald; lays under him the Firths and Fialir 5; his policy and overweening might drives many great men from the land abroad; sends messengers to Kveldulf 6; ill content with his answer, but consents, by Oliver's persuasions, to receive his son 7; Kveldulf's and Thorolf's respective opinions of him 8–9; takes Bard Bryniolfson into his bodyguard; sets great account by his skalds 11; takes Thorolf into his bodyguard 12; fights his last battle within the land at Hafrsfirth, after which he finds none to withstand him 14; makes Thorolf a landed man, and gives him great revenues north in Halogaland; his loving kindness toward Th. 15; guests with Th. at Torgar; vexed at the display of power, but appeased by Th.'s gift of a ship 19; guests with Hildirid's sons and gives ear to their slanders 20–22; receives the Finn-scat from Thorgils the Yeller, and is better disposed towards Thorolf 23–4; Th.'s truth and loyalty to him 26; drinks in fresh slanders from Hildirid's sons; next year sees Th. and receives the scat from him; offers Th. the command of his bodyguard, so that "I may overlook thee night and day" 27–8; on Th.'s refusal, takes away his revenues and gives them to Hildirid's sons 29; blames them next year for the poorness of the scat 30; accepts their ex-planation (fresh slanders against Th.) 31; sends Hallvard and his b. to seize Th.'s ship 32; Th.'s saying, "Good it is...with the King for partner" 33; 34; Kveldulf's saying of him 36; gives Hallvard and Sigtrygg leave to take Th.'s life if they can 37; his scoffing estimate of their chances against Th.; his own swift action with forced marches by sea and land from Hladir to Sandness 38; offers peace to Th. but not to his men; bids fire the house

Index 331

Index

CAMBRIDGE: PRINTED BY W. LEWIS, M.A., AT THE UNIVERSITY PRESS

MAPS

Map of
NORWAY
in the Saga-Time

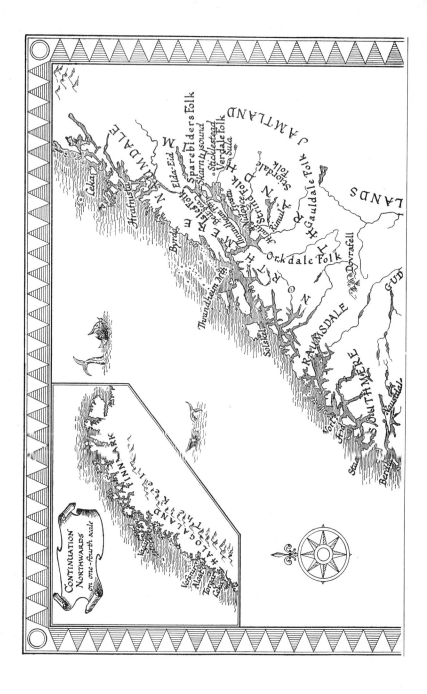

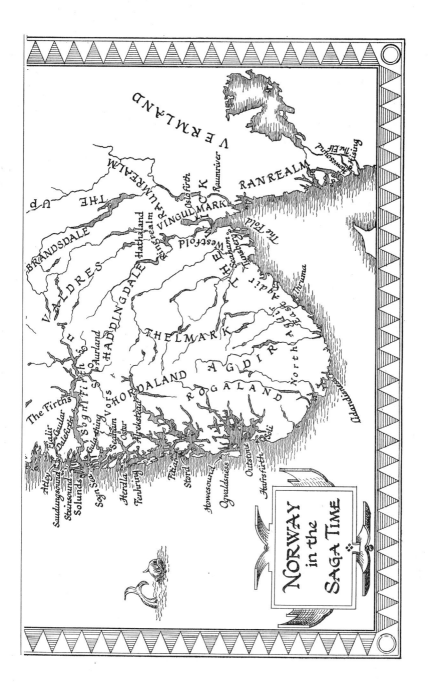

NORWAY in the SAGA TIME

Map of the countryside

of

BURGFIRTH

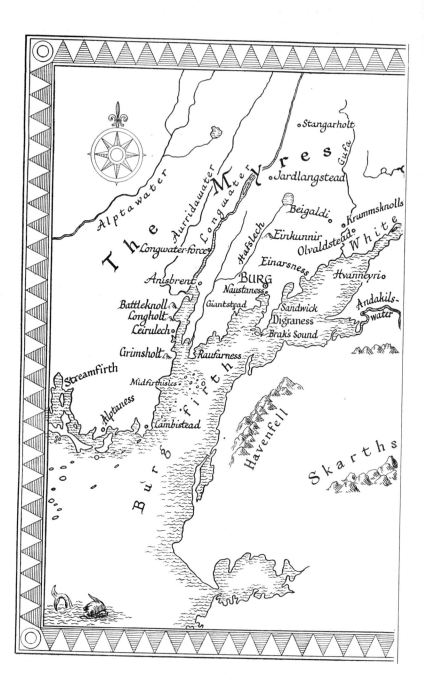

Map of
BURGFIRTH